Merry Christmas, Andrew
Love, Aunt Judy
Christmas 2013

Merry Christmas, Andrew
Love, Aunt Judy
Christmas 2013

INCREDIBLE VISUAL GUIDE TO
EARTH & ANIMALS

**LONDON, NEW YORK,
MELBOURNE, MUNICH, AND DELHI**

For Tall Tree Ltd:
Editors Rob Colson, David John, and Jon Richards
Designers Ben Ruocco, Ed Simkins, and Jonathan Vipond

For Dorling Kindersley:
Senior editors Victoria Heyworth-Dunne, Cécile Landau
US editor Margaret Parrish
Senior designer Smiljka Surla
Managing editor Linda Esposito
Managing art editor Diane Thistlethwaite
Creative retouching Steve Willis
DTP Designer Kavita Varma
Producer Verity Powell

Picture research Claire Bowers, Nic Dean, and Emma Shepherd

First published in the United States in 2013
by DK Publishing
345 Hudson Street, New York,
New York 10014

Material in this publication was previously published in
One Million Things: Planet Earth (2009), and *One Million Things: Animal Life* (2009)

Copyright © 2009, 2013 Dorling Kindersley Limited

001 – 195831 – Jul/13

A catalog record for this book
is available from the Library of Congress

ISBN: 978-1-4654-1510-3

Hi-res workflow proofed by Altaimage, UK
Design and digital artworking by Stefan Podhorodecki
Printed and bound in China by Leo Paper Products Ltd.

**Discover more at
www.dk.com**

INCREDIBLE VISUAL GUIDE TO
EARTH & ANIMALS

Written by:

John Woodward and Richard Walker

Consultant:

Kim Bryan

EARTH

ANIMALS

Contents

EARTH

VOLCANIC LIGHTNING
Lightning crackles through a plume of volcanic ash erupted from the Chaiten volcano in Chile during a storm. Such spectacular events are dramatic evidence of the titanic forces that have shaped our planet.

Planet Earth

OUR GALAXY

The universe contains at least 100 billion galaxies, each with billions of stars—most of which probably have orbiting planets. Our own galaxy, the Milky Way, consists of about 500 billion stars, including all the ones that we can see in the night sky, as well as large clouds of gas and dust, some of which form new stars. The Milky Way is a flat disk with a central bulge and bright spiral arms. Our Sun is a medium-sized star in one of the spiral arms, about two-thirds of the way out from the center. From Earth, we look out across the galaxy's disk, so the densely packed stars at its center look like a milky band of light across the night sky.

❶ GAS AND DUST

The galaxy contains masses of gas and dust particles that are thrown out by the explosions of giant stars. During their lives, these stars generate energy by nuclear fusion, turning lighter elements into heavier ones. The biggest stars contain many of the elements that form new stars, planets, and even life on Earth. These elements are scattered into space when dying stars explode.

❷ SPIRAL ARMS

The Milky Way galaxy has a pattern of spiral arms swirling out from its central bulge. These arms are made up of young, bright blue stars and slightly older, whiter stars, as well as clouds of dust and gas. Other stars lie between the arms, but they are not as bright. All these stars are slowly orbiting the central bulge. Each follows its own route, and takes several hundred million years to complete its orbit.

❸ STAR NURSERY

The pink patches on this image mark regions where stars are created within clouds of hydrogen gas. Part of a cloud comes together to form a dense ball of gas. This attracts more gas by gravity, squeezing the ball into a tighter, hotter mass. Eventually, this triggers a nuclear fusion reaction that turns hydrogen into helium gas and radiates energy as brilliant starlight.

Scutum-Centaurus Arm

Sagittarius Arm

Far 3kpc Arm

Near 3kpc Arm

Outer Arm

Perseus Arm

YOU ARE HERE

❹ HOT BLUE STAR

Stars glow with color, just like hot steel. Some glow red-hot, while hotter ones like our Sun glow yellow. Many even hotter stars glow white-hot, but the hottest, brightest stars are an intense blue. As stars get older they cool down and change color. Most eventually swell up to form "red giants" of dispersing gas. Some of the very biggest stars end their lives in vast explosions called supernovas.

❺ SOLAR SYSTEM

The Sun is a ball of hot gas that acts as a nuclear fusion reactor. It squeezes together hydrogen atoms to form helium atoms, and this releases massive amounts of energy, which we experience as light and heat. Gas and dust left over from the Sun's creation 4.6 billion years ago have clumped together to form the planets, asteroids, and comets that make up the solar system.

❻ CENTRAL BULGE

The hub of the galaxy is packed with stars that radiate yellow or red light. This shows that they are cooler and older than the blue, white, or pale yellow stars found in the spiral arms. These older stars form the vast central bulge of the galactic disk, which we see from Earth as the brightest part of the Milky Way. The bulge also contains a huge amount of gas that forms a ring around the center.

❼ BLACK HOLE

At the heart of the central bulge lies a supermassive black hole. Black holes have such colossal gravity that even light cannot escape from them. Most are formed by the collapse of giant stars, but a supermassive black hole is created by the collapse of many stars, which are sucked into the hole like water swirling down a drain. The violence of this process generates intense energy that makes the region glow white-hot.

❽ DARK MATTER

Galaxies glow with the light generated by stars, but they also contain a lot of gas and dust that does not emit light. Something also exists in the apparent voids between galaxies, because galaxies interact in ways that can be explained only by the gravity of material that we cannot see. Astronomers call this material dark matter and are unsure about what it is exactly. However, dark matter may account for about 23 percent of the universe.

THE MILKY WAY

This artist's impression shows the Milky Way galaxy as it would appear to a space traveler approaching from above the huge swirling disk of stars. Although we cannot see our galaxy's shape from Earth, we know that it has this form—partly because powerful telescopes reveal many similar spiral galaxies in deep space.

Norma Arm

THE SOLAR SYSTEM

The Sun is a vast ball of hot gas that formed from a spinning cloud of gas and dust about 4.6 billion years ago. Some of this material spread out as a spinning disk, and clumped together to create the orbiting planets of the solar system.

The four small inner planets are balls of rock. The much bigger outer planets are mainly gas and ice, although they have many rocky moons. There are also a few dwarf planets and billions of small rocky asteroids.

Near vertical ring around Uranus shows that the planet spins on its side

Surface features hidden by atmosphere are revealed by radar

Great Red Spot is a huge storm, wider than the Earth

Surface of Mercury is pitted with impact craters

❶ URANUS
A distant, cold world, Uranus is made mainly of water-ice and frozen gases, such as methane and ammonia. However, it does have a rocky core and a hydrogen-rich atmosphere. It also has 27 moons and a ring of dust particles that orbit the planet from top to bottom. This is because the planet is spinning on its side, on an almost horizontal axis.

❷ JUPITER
The fifth planet from the Sun is more than twice the size of all the other planets put together. Its rocky core is surrounded by thick layers of hydrogen and helium gas that are continually rising and falling in currents that form colorful swirling bands. This gas giant has 63 moons, although only four are easily visible from Earth through telescopes.

❸ VENUS
Similar in size to Earth, but orbiting nearer the Sun, Venus is a rocky planet peppered with giant, extinct volcanoes. Its surface is hidden by a thick cloudy atmosphere rich in carbon dioxide. This traps heat, making Venus the hottest of the planets, with a surface temperature of 867°F (464°C)—hot enough to melt lead.

❹ MERCURY
Mercury is the smallest of the inner planets, and the closest to the Sun. Its rocky surface is covered with craters, and it has a thin atmosphere. This allows the Sun to build up scorching surface temperatures of up to 806°F (430°C) by day. At night the heat escapes and temperatures plunge as low as -292°F (-180°C).

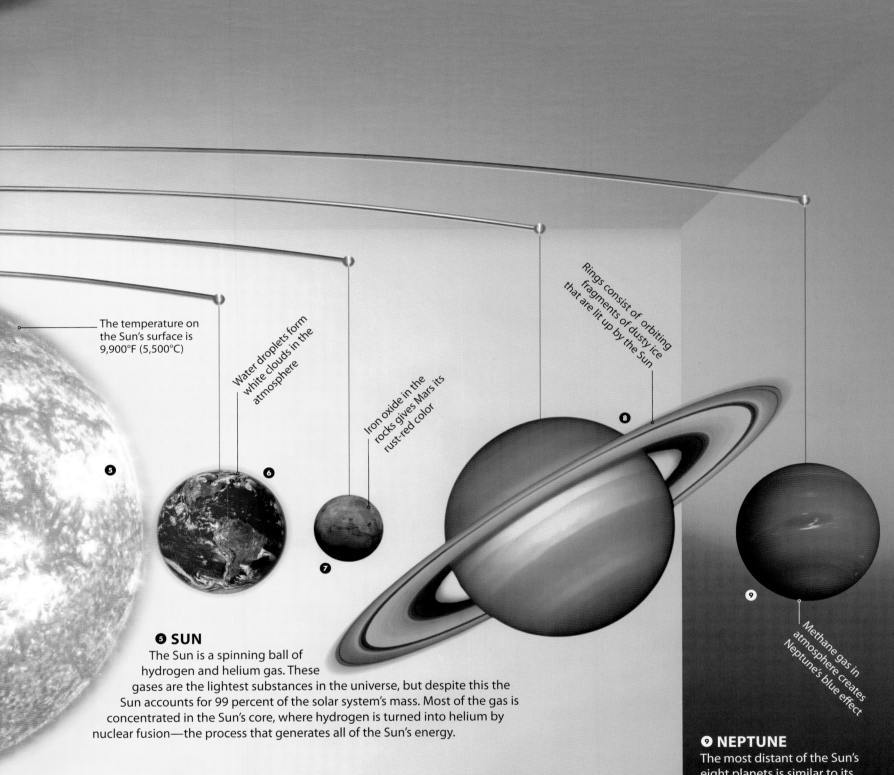

The temperature on the Sun's surface is 9,900°F (5,500°C)

Water droplets form white clouds in the atmosphere

Iron oxide in the rocks gives Mars its rust-red color

Rings consist of orbiting fragments of dusty ice that are lit up by the Sun

Methane gas in atmosphere creates Neptune's blue effect

❺ SUN

The Sun is a spinning ball of hydrogen and helium gas. These gases are the lightest substances in the universe, but despite this the Sun accounts for 99 percent of the solar system's mass. Most of the gas is concentrated in the Sun's core, where hydrogen is turned into helium by nuclear fusion—the process that generates all of the Sun's energy.

❻ EARTH

The largest of the rocky inner planets, Earth is the only one with large amounts of liquid water, and this allows life to flourish. One reason for this is that Earth's atmosphere acts like a blanket, keeping the planet warm enough to stop the water from freezing solid. Most of the water forms broad oceans that cover nearly two-thirds of the planet.

❼ MARS

Half the width of Earth and farther from the Sun, Mars is a cold, dry world of reddish rock. Its thin atmosphere is mostly carbon dioxide, as on Venus. Three billion years ago, the atmosphere was thicker and it kept the planet warm enough for rivers of water to flow on the surface. Nearly all the water on Mars has now turned to ice.

❽ SATURN

Surrounded by its rings, Saturn is a gas giant with a core of rock and ice, second only in size to Jupiter and with at least 60 small moons. Like Jupiter, Saturn is made mainly of hydrogen and helium. However, both planets are too small for their gravity to trigger the nuclear reactions that would turn them into stars.

❾ NEPTUNE

The most distant of the Sun's eight planets is similar to its neighbor, Uranus—a giant ball of frozen water, methane, and ammonia with a rocky core. Neptune is so far from the Sun that its surface temperature is roughly -320°F (-200°C), and it takes 165 years to complete one orbit. It has one large moon, Triton, and 12 much smaller ones.

ASTEROIDS, METEORITES, AND COMETS

In addition to the big planets, the solar system contains many billions of smaller orbiting objects. Many of these are lumps of rock, iron, and nickel left over from the formation of the planets. These include the asteroids that mainly orbit the Sun between Mars and Jupiter. There are also comets—big chunks of ice and dust that loop around the Sun before vanishing into the far reaches of the solar system. Smaller pieces of rock and ice shoot through Earth's sky as meteors. Some of these pieces may even fall to Earth as meteorites.

▶ IMPACT CRATERS

This crater in Arizona is one of about 170 that have been found on Earth. Formed by an asteroid strike about 50,000 years ago, it is ¾ miles (1.2 km) across. The impact would have caused a colossal explosion, killing everything in the region. Luckily, these large impacts are very rare. The last occurred in 1908, when an asteroid exploded high above a remote region of Siberia called Tunguska.

▲ COMETS

There are billions of comets in the Oort Cloud, a region of the solar system beyond the orbit of Neptune. A few of these icy bodies travel close to the Sun. As they approach, they are blasted by solar radiation that makes them trail long tails of glowing dust and gas. After several weeks, the comets vanish, but some reappear many years later. This is Halley's Comet, which orbits the Sun every 76 years.

▼ ASTEROIDS

The Asteroid Belt between the orbits of Mars and Jupiter contains vast numbers of asteroids. Most are too small to have names, but a few, such as Gaspra and Ida, are big enough to have been photographed by passing space probes. Some asteroids orbit outside the main belt, including Eros, which passes within 14 million miles (22 million km) of Earth.

GASPRA

Discovery date	1916
Length	11 miles (18 km)
Orbital period	1,200 days
Orbital speed	12 miles (20 km) per sec

EROS

Discovery date	1898
Length	20 miles (33 km)
Orbital period	643 days
Orbital speed	15 miles (24 km) per sec

IDA

Discovery date	1884
Length	33 miles (53 km)
Orbital period	1,768 days
Orbital speed	11 miles (18 km) per sec

▼ METEOR SHOWER

Particles attracted by Earth's gravity streak through the atmosphere and are heated by friction until they glow white-hot. Most of these meteors burn up high above the surface, but a few reach the ground as meteorites. Showers of meteors occur very year when Earth passes through trails of space dust left by comets.

▲ PROTECTIVE JUPITER

Many of the asteroids and comets that might hit Earth are dragged off course by the intense gravity of Jupiter. This has probably saved us from many catastrophic impacts in the past. In 1994, scientists watched as parts of the comet Shoemaker-Levy 9 plunged into the giant planet, creating a series of huge dark scars in its thick atmosphere—some as big as Earth itself.

Meteorite fragment

► METEORITES

Thousands of meteorites hit Earth every year, although few are big enough to be dangerous. Most are stony, but others are largely made of iron or—rarely—a mixture of the two. Many are fragments of asteroids, and some are made of the material that formed the planets. A few, like the Nakhla meteorite, have been blasted from the surface of Mars by other impacts, and others have come from the Moon.

Nakhla meteorite

Shargottite Sayh al Uhaymir 008 meteorite

15

Our Moon was created when an object the size of Mars crashed into Earth some 4.5 billion years ago. The impact melted part of Earth's rocky mantle, and the molten rock burst out and clumped together to form the Moon. Unlike Earth, the Moon does not have a big, heavy core of iron, which is why it does not have enough gravity to have an atmosphere. However, it does attract asteroids, and their impacts have left it pockmarked with craters. It is a dry, sterile world, not at all like its closest neighbor.

▼ SPINNING PARTNERS

The Moon is trapped in Earth orbit by Earth's gravity, which stops it from spinning away into space. But the Moon also has gravity, and this pulls on the water in Earth's oceans, creating the rising and falling tides.

▲ LUNAR LANDSCAPES

The Moon's surface is covered with dust and rocks blasted from asteroid impact craters during the first 750 million years of its history. The biggest craters are more than 90 miles (150 km) across, and their rims form the Moon's pale uplands. The darker "seas" are big craters that have flooded with dark volcanic rock.

Solar panels collected sunlight to generate power for the probe

Antenna sent and received data

Antenna beamed images to Earth

◄ UNMANNED PROBES

The first spacecraft sent to the Moon were robots, which analyzed the surface conditions, gathered images, and beamed the data back to Earth. The information they collected was vital to the safety of the first astronauts to visit the Moon in the late 1960s. Since then, further unmanned missions have provided scientists with a steady stream of information about the Moon.

American *Surveyor 1* (landed in June 1966)

Russian *Lunokhod 2* (landed in January 1973)

Eight wheels carried probe over lunar terrain

Spring-loaded legs cushioned landing

▼ MOON ROCK

The boulders that litter the Moon are made of rock that is very old by Earth standards. Pale moon rock is 4.5 billion years old—as old as the Moon itself—and the dark lava that fills some of the larger craters is at least 3.2 billion years old. This is because, aside from a few asteroid impacts, all geological activity on the Moon stopped long ago.

Boulder lies where it fell after being blasted from a crater

Apollo 11: The first humans to step on the Moon were Neil Armstrong and Buzz Aldrin on July 20, 1969. They spent 2.5 hours on the surface.

MOON MISSIONS

In 1969, as part of the Apollo project, the United States sent the first manned mission to land on the Moon. Six similar missions followed, only one of which was unsuccessful, and a total of 12 Apollo astronauts explored the lunar surface.

There is no air on the Moon, and no atmosphere of any kind to create a pale sky and soften the harsh sunlight. The temperature can rise to 240°F (120°C) in the sunlight, but plummets to -240°F (-150°C) in the dark because there is no atmosphere to stop the heat from escaping into space. Since the Moon takes 27.3 Earth days to complete one spin, more than 320 hours of daylight are followed by the same period of darkness.

Apollo astronaut's suit gave protection against intense solar radiation

New Moon

Waxing crescent

Waning crescent

Lunar cycle
The Moon takes nearly four weeks to orbit Earth. It spins at the same rate, so the same side always faces Earth. During this time, the Sun lights up different amounts of the side we see, creating the lunar phases.

Last quarter

First quarter

Waning gibbous

Waxing gibbous

Full Moon

Apollo 12: This was the first mission to carry scientific equipment to the Moon. Earthquake and magnetism detectors were left on the surface.

Apollo 13: An explosion on the spacecraft prevented a Moon landing, but the crew managed to return to Earth.

Apollo 14: This mission landed in a hilly region of the Moon in February 1971. It was led by Alan Shepard, who had also been the first American in space.

Apollo 15: Landing in July 1971, the crew took a lunar rover vehicle that allowed them to explore much more of the surface.

Apollo 16: In April 1972 this mission used another lunar rover to explore the Descartes Highlands region and conduct experiments.

Apollo 17: The last Apollo mission in December 1972 included the only scientist to visit the Moon—geologist Harrison Schmitt.

EARLY EARTH

Earth was created from pieces of dust and rubble orbiting the young star that became the Sun. These gradually clumped together to form a planet in a process called accretion. The process began slowly but, as the planet grew, its increasing gravity attracted more fragments of space rock. Eventually, the whole mass melted, and the heavier iron and nickel in the molten rock sank toward the center of the planet to form its core. The rest formed the thick, hot mantle and the relatively thin, cool, brittle crust.

▶ ACCRETION

Made by nuclear fusion in giant exploding stars, heavy elements such as silicon and iron formed clouds of space dust and rock in the region of the galaxy where the Sun was born. As the pieces of dust and rock orbited the star, they were pulled together by their own gravity, and the energy of these collisions was transformed into heat. This heat welded the rocks together, forming larger and larger chunks and eventually creating the "proto-planet" that became Earth.

Colliding at colossal speed, two rock fragments melt into each other

◀ BOMBARDMENT

While the young Earth was surrounded by rocky debris, the planet was bombarded by all kinds of objects. The energy of each impact was converted into heat that ultimately melted the entire planet and created its layered structure. As the bombardment slowed down, Earth cooled, but radioactivity near the core still generates heat that causes volcanoes and earthquakes.

Big impacts created vast craters, later erased by geological events

Earth's core is a mass of molten iron, nickel, and sulfur, with a ball of solid metal at its heart. Intense heat causes swirling currents in the molten outer core, which interact with the planet's spin to generate an electromagnetic field. This makes the planet act as a giant magnet, and is why a compass can be used to find magnetic north.

▲ **MASSIVE VOLCANISM**

As the early Earth became hotter and hotter, and its metallic core started to form, chemical reactions released vast amounts of carbon dioxide, sulfur dioxide, and water vapor. These gases boiled to the surface and erupted from colossal volcanoes, along with masses of molten rock. The gases formed the first atmosphere, and the water vapor turned into torrential rain that filled the first oceans.

Rivers of red-hot lava pour from the craters of giant volcanoes

EARTH'S STRUCTURE

If we could cut down through Earth to its center and take out a slice, it would reveal that the planet is made up of distinct layers. At its heart lies the solid inner core, surrounded by a liquid outer core. Both are made mainly of heavy iron. The outer core is enclosed by a deep layer of heavy, very hot, yet solid rock called the mantle. The cool shell of the mantle forms the oceanic crust beneath the ocean floors, while vast slabs of lighter rock form thicker continental crust. Scientists have deduced much of this from the way shock waves generated by earthquakes travel through the planet.

❶ CORE

Earth's metallic heart consists of a solid inner core about 1,515 miles (2,440 km) across and a liquid outer core some 1,400 miles (2,250 km) thick. The inner core is about 80 percent iron and 20 percent nickel. It has a temperature of about 12,600°F (7,000°C), but intense pressure stops it from melting. The outer core is 88 percent molten iron and 12 percent sulfur.

❷ MANTLE

At 1,800 miles (2,900 km) thick, the mantle makes up most of the planet. It is mostly made of heavy, dark rock called peridotite, and although its temperature ranges from 1,800°F (1,000°C) to 6,300°F (3,500°C), colossal pressure keeps it solid. Despite this, heat currents rising through the mantle keep the rock moving very slowly, and this movement is the root cause of earthquakes.

❸ OCEAN FLOORS

At the top of the mantle, movement in the rock creates cracks that reduce pressure, allowing the peridotite rock to melt. It erupts through the cracks and solidifies as basalt, a slightly lighter rock that forms the ocean floors. This oceanic crust is roughly 5 miles (8 km) thick. It is constantly being recycled and renewed, so no part of the ocean floor is more than 200 million years old.

Basalt

Peridotite

Granite

Mountains form as crust is squeezed and folded

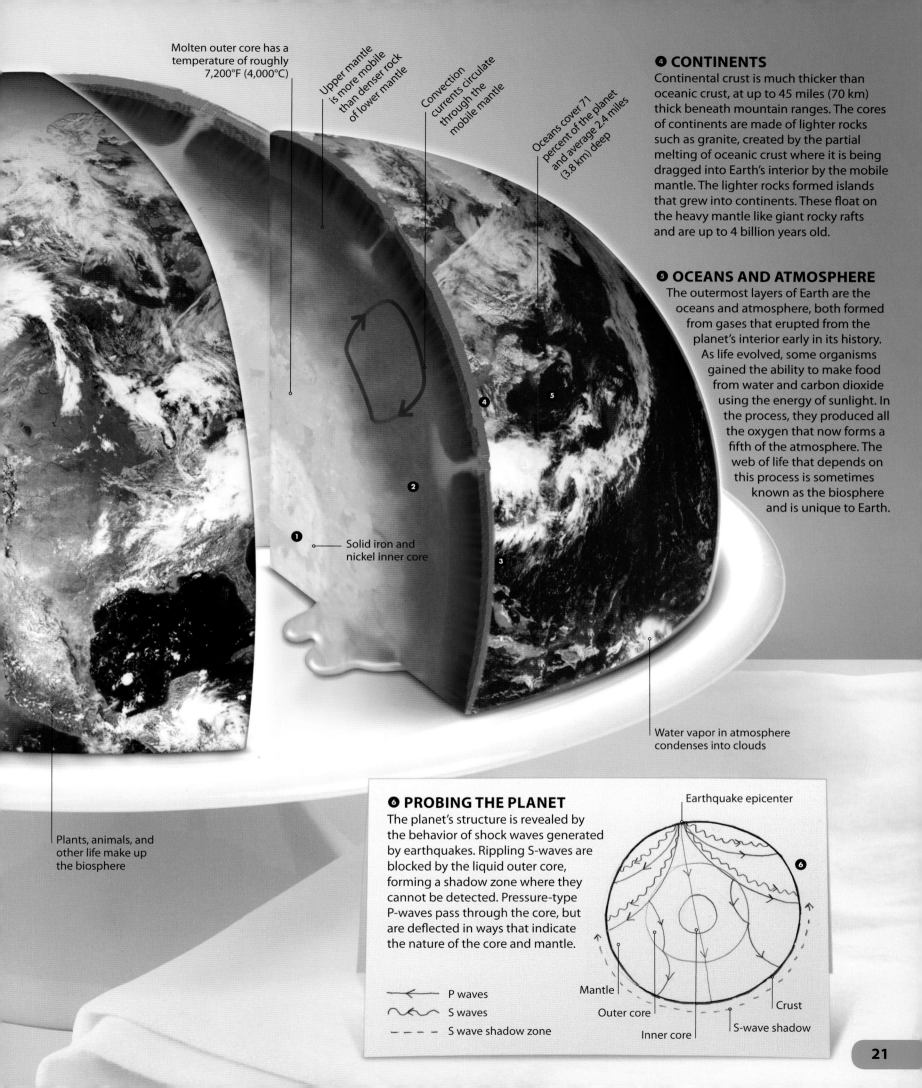

Molten outer core has a temperature of roughly 7,200°F (4,000°C)

Upper mantle is more mobile than denser rock of lower mantle

Convection currents circulate through the mobile mantle

Oceans cover 71 percent of the planet and average 2.4 miles (3.8 km) deep

❹ CONTINENTS

Continental crust is much thicker than oceanic crust, at up to 45 miles (70 km) thick beneath mountain ranges. The cores of continents are made of lighter rocks such as granite, created by the partial melting of oceanic crust where it is being dragged into Earth's interior by the mobile mantle. The lighter rocks formed islands that grew into continents. These float on the heavy mantle like giant rocky rafts and are up to 4 billion years old.

❺ OCEANS AND ATMOSPHERE

The outermost layers of Earth are the oceans and atmosphere, both formed from gases that erupted from the planet's interior early in its history. As life evolved, some organisms gained the ability to make food from water and carbon dioxide using the energy of sunlight. In the process, they produced all the oxygen that now forms a fifth of the atmosphere. The web of life that depends on this process is sometimes known as the biosphere and is unique to Earth.

Solid iron and nickel inner core

Water vapor in atmosphere condenses into clouds

Plants, animals, and other life make up the biosphere

❻ PROBING THE PLANET

The planet's structure is revealed by the behavior of shock waves generated by earthquakes. Rippling S-waves are blocked by the liquid outer core, forming a shadow zone where they cannot be detected. Pressure-type P-waves pass through the core, but are deflected in ways that indicate the nature of the core and mantle.

Earthquake epicenter

⟵⟵ P waves
〰〰 S waves
– – – S wave shadow zone

Mantle

Outer core

Inner core

Crust

S-wave shadow

21

PLATE TECTONICS

Radioactive rocks deep inside the planet generate heat, which rises through the mantle. This creates convection currents that make the hot rock flow at roughly the rate your fingernails grow. It flows sideways near the surface, dragging sections of the crust with it and splitting the crust into curved plates. Where two plates pull apart, they form a rift. Where they push together, one plate slips beneath another, causing earthquakes and volcanic eruptions. This process is known as plate tectonics.

❶ SUBDUCTION ZONES

The plate boundaries where one plate of the crust is diving beneath another are known as subduction zones. As the crust is dragged down, often creating a deep ocean trench, part of it melts and erupts, forming chains of volcanoes. The movement also triggers earthquakes. In some subduction zones, one plate of ocean floor is slipping beneath another. In others, oceanic crust is grinding beneath continents and pushing up mountains.

❷ SPREADING RIFTS

Where plates are being pulled apart at oceanic spreading rifts, the pressure beneath the crust is reduced, allowing the hot mantle rock to melt and erupt as basalt lava. As the rift widens, more lava erupts and hardens, adding new rock to the ocean floor. These boundaries are marked by a network of midocean ridges. Similar spreading rifts can divide continents, forming seas, such as the Red Sea, that may eventually grow into oceans.

❹ San Andreas Fault

This notorious earthquake zone in California is a transform fault that marks the boundary where the Pacific plate is moving northwest against the North American plate. The movement is frequent and gentle on some sections of the fault line, but rare and violent on others.

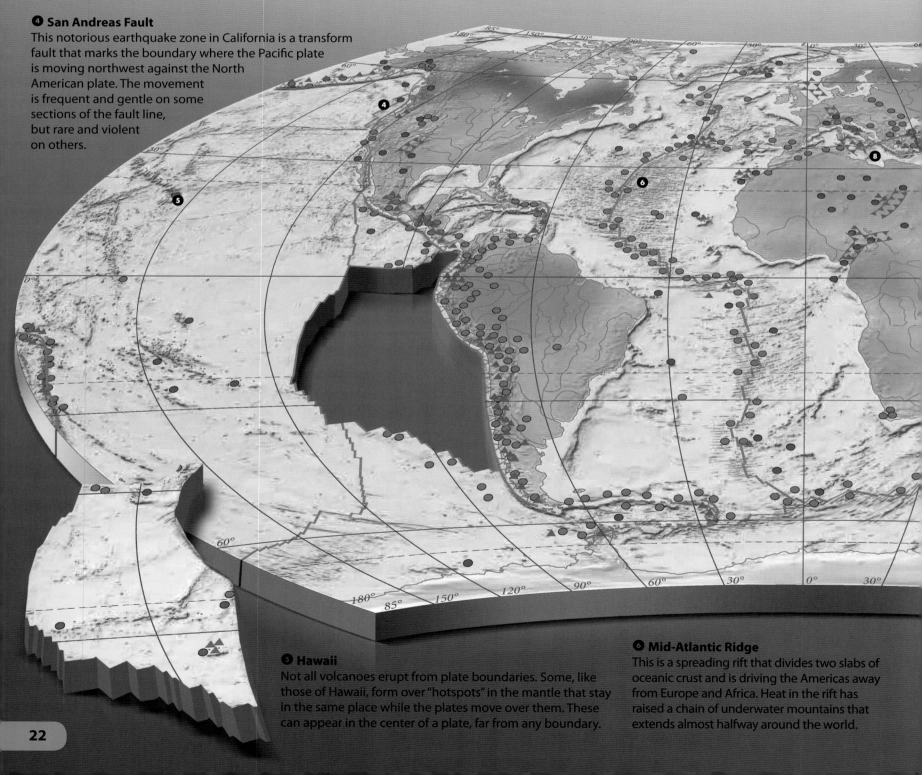

❺ Hawaii

Not all volcanoes erupt from plate boundaries. Some, like those of Hawaii, form over "hotspots" in the mantle that stay in the same place while the plates move over them. These can appear in the center of a plate, far from any boundary.

❻ Mid-Atlantic Ridge

This is a spreading rift that divides two slabs of oceanic crust and is driving the Americas away from Europe and Africa. Heat in the rift has raised a chain of underwater mountains that extends almost halfway around the world.

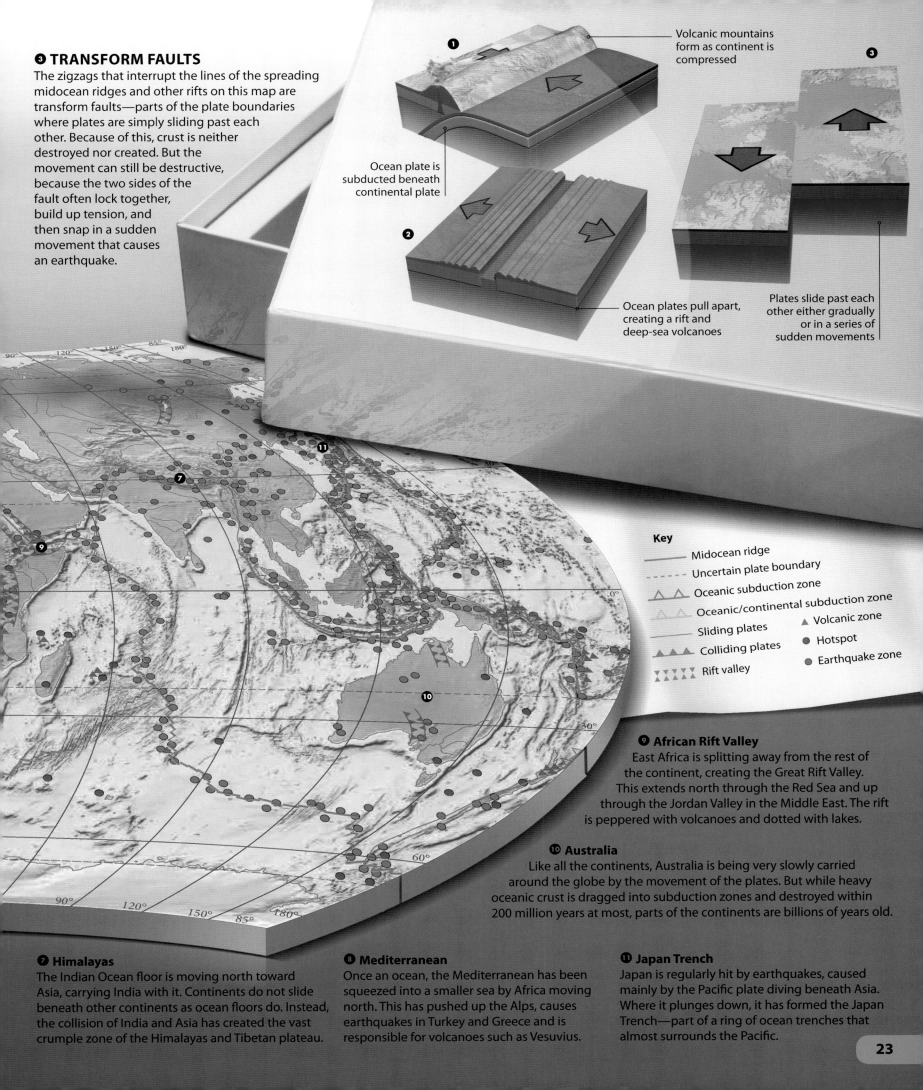

❸ TRANSFORM FAULTS

The zigzags that interrupt the lines of the spreading midocean ridges and other rifts on this map are transform faults—parts of the plate boundaries where plates are simply sliding past each other. Because of this, crust is neither destroyed nor created. But the movement can still be destructive, because the two sides of the fault often lock together, build up tension, and then snap in a sudden movement that causes an earthquake.

Volcanic mountains form as continent is compressed

❶

Ocean plate is subducted beneath continental plate

❷

Ocean plates pull apart, creating a rift and deep-sea volcanoes

❸

Plates slide past each other either gradually or in a series of sudden movements

Key

— Midocean ridge

--- Uncertain plate boundary

△△△ Oceanic subduction zone

△△△ Oceanic/continental subduction zone

— Sliding plates

▲▲▲ Colliding plates

∨∨∨∨ Rift valley

▲ Volcanic zone

● Hotspot

● Earthquake zone

❾ African Rift Valley

East Africa is splitting away from the rest of the continent, creating the Great Rift Valley. This extends north through the Red Sea and up through the Jordan Valley in the Middle East. The rift is peppered with volcanoes and dotted with lakes.

❿ Australia

Like all the continents, Australia is being very slowly carried around the globe by the movement of the plates. But while heavy oceanic crust is dragged into subduction zones and destroyed within 200 million years at most, parts of the continents are billions of years old.

❼ Himalayas

The Indian Ocean floor is moving north toward Asia, carrying India with it. Continents do not slide beneath other continents as ocean floors do. Instead, the collision of India and Asia has created the vast crumple zone of the Himalayas and Tibetan plateau.

❽ Mediterranean

Once an ocean, the Mediterranean has been squeezed into a smaller sea by Africa moving north. This has pushed up the Alps, causes earthquakes in Turkey and Greece and is responsible for volcanoes such as Vesuvius.

⓫ Japan Trench

Japan is regularly hit by earthquakes, caused mainly by the Pacific plate diving beneath Asia. Where it plunges down, it has formed the Japan Trench—part of a ring of ocean trenches that almost surrounds the Pacific.

CONTINENTAL DRIFT

As early as the 1600s, people noticed that the shapes of South America and Africa fit together like two sections of a jigsaw puzzle. It looked as if they might have split apart to create the Atlantic Ocean, but such "continental drift" seemed impossible. In the 1960s, however, the development of plate tectonic theory showed that it was true. Ever since the continents started to grow from rock erupting from ocean floors, they have been carried around the globe by the mobile plates of Earth's crust. They have joined up, split apart, and crashed together again several times, forming many different arrangements—and they are still moving.

Huge ocean will become the Pacific

North America has drifted northwest

Tethys Ocean will shrink to form the Mediterranean

Rift between Africa and South America widens

▲ 170 MILLION YEARS AGO

In the Jurassic period, now famous for its dinosaurs, all the southern continents were joined together in a supercontinent known to geologists as Gondwanaland. We know this partly from the way they fit together along the edges of their submerged continental shelves. But the various rocks and rock layers on the coasts also match, and so do the fossils preserved in them. The fossils also give the supercontinent a date.

▲ 95 MILLION YEARS AGO

By the later age of the dinosaurs, giant rift valleys had split Gondwanaland into the continents we know today, although they were still quite close together. South America parted from Africa, and the mid-Atlantic opened up as North America drifted away toward the northwest. The split isolated animals and plants on their own continents, so they began to evolve in different ways.

▼ 45 MILLION YEARS AGO

By the early age of mammals, North America and Greenland had split from northern Europe and were moving west, so the Atlantic was getting steadily wider while the Pacific was shrinking. Meanwhile, India was drifting north toward Asia. Australia was isolated, along with the pouched mammals that evolved into the kangaroos, koalas, and other marsupials of today.

▼ PRESENT DAY

About 20 million years ago, India collided with Asia and is still plowing slowly north, pushing up the Himalayas. Some 3.5 million years ago, volcanoes erupting in the Caribbean region created a narrow neck of land linking the Americas, completely altering the pattern of ocean currents. Meanwhile, the northward movement of Africa has almost isolated the Mediterranean.

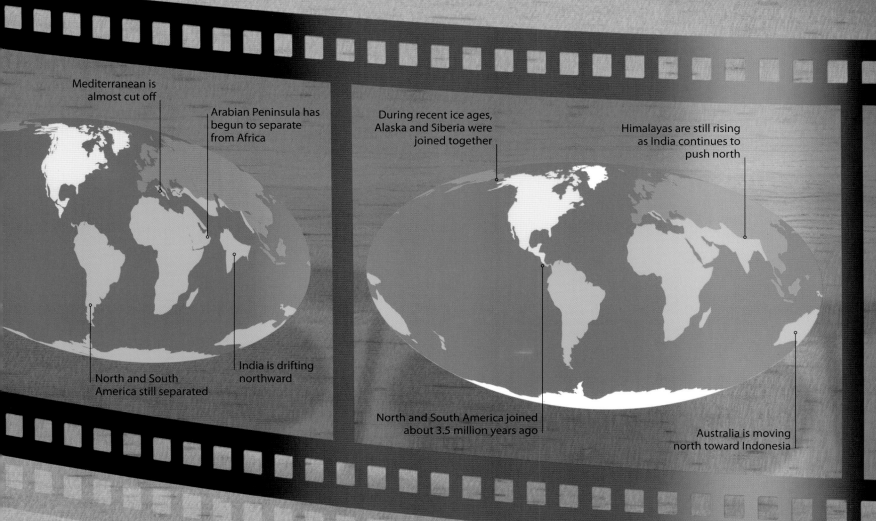

Mediterranean is almost cut off

Arabian Peninsula has begun to separate from Africa

North and South America still separated

India is drifting northward

During recent ice ages, Alaska and Siberia were joined together

Himalayas are still rising as India continues to push north

North and South America joined about 3.5 million years ago

Australia is moving north toward Indonesia

MOUNTAINS

Built up by the titanic forces of plate tectonics folding or fracturing Earth's crust, mountains are spectacular evidence of our dynamic planet. The highest, most dramatic mountain ranges, such as the Himalayas, Alps, and Andes, are the youngest, and they are still in the process of being formed. But as fast as mountains are raised up, the forces of erosion start to grind them down, and all mountains are eventually worn away to nothing.

❶ RUGGED PEAKS

The spectacular peaks of the Andes are less than 50 million years old, which is young by geological standards. Extending all the way down the western edge of South America, a distance of 4,500 miles (7,200 km), they form the longest mountain range on land. They are still being pushed up, but here in icy Patagonia they have been eroded by glaciers that have carved deep valleys between the peaks.

MOUNTAIN BUILDING

Most mountains are pushed up along the margins of continents, where one tectonic plate is colliding with another. Some, such as the Andes in South America, are forced up by a plate of oceanic crust plowing beneath the continental fringe. Others, like the Himalayas, are crumple zones created by the collisions of continents. But mountains can also be formed by more complex forces, such as rifting (cracking apart) or molten rock pushing up from below.

Fold mountains This satellite image of the snow-capped Alps shows the crumple zone created by Italy being pushed by the African plate into the rest of Europe. The process causes massive folding of layered sedimentary rocks that can turn the layers on end or even upside down. It may also raise ancient sea floors into the air, so marine fossils occur on mountain peaks.

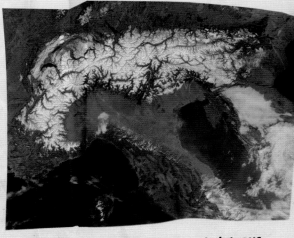

Cliffs and plateaus The steep slopes of the Drakensburg mountains in South Africa were created when a whole landscape was uplifted by molten rock pushing up beneath it. The rock also erupted from volcanoes to create thick lava flows that now form a high plateau, fringed to the east by dramatic cliffs.

❷ ANCIENT RANGES

Many ancient mountain ranges mark geological events in the distant past. The Caledonian mountains of Scotland were formed by a collision of continents more than 400 million years ago, along a tectonic plate boundary that no longer exists. The mountains were once as high as the Himalayas, but they have been worn down to form the heavily eroded landscape that now makes up the Scottish Highlands.

❸ ERODED STUMPS

Eventually all mountains are reduced to rounded stumps by the relentless forces of erosion. The Bungle Bungle range in northwestern Australia was once a high plateau formed from horizontal layers of sandstone. Over some 350 million years, the edge of the plateau has crumbled under the assault of torrential rain, blistering summer heat, and winter frosts to create these layered domes.

❹ MOUNTAIN WILDLIFE

The higher you go, the colder it gets, so being near the top of a high mountain on the equator is almost like being in the Arctic. The plants that live there have to be tough to survive, and at really high altitudes nothing can grow at all. Mountain animals like the snow leopard have thick fur coats to keep out the cold, and must be surefooted to move confidently through the rugged and often frozen terrain.

❺ THIN AIR

For climbers, every mountain is a challenge. Climbing can involve not only the dangers of ascending steep, icy rock faces, but also the problem of surviving at high altitudes. It can be freezing cold, and the air on the highest peaks is so thin that there is barely enough oxygen to breathe. This makes climbing almost impossible, so many mountaineers are forced to wear breathing equipment.

Barren granite peaks are separated by steep valleys gouged out by ice

The Torres del Paine rise above the steppe in southern Chile

Iron oxide makes the layered sandstone glow rust-red

Suilven in northwest Scotland is the remains of a much bigger peak

FAULTS AND RIFTS

As plate tectonics squeeze and stretch Earth's crust, the rocks may snap. This causes the fracture lines known as faults. Vertical faults can form where one side of a fault plane has slipped down. Where plate boundaries are diverging, great blocks of crust drop between pairs of vertical faults to create rift valleys. Converging plates can heave one side of a fault upward, or rock can be pushed sideways along a horizontal fault. Many visible faults are now inactive, but others are moving and causing earthquakes.

❶ VERTICAL FAULTS

Faults that incline vertically are caused by rocks being pulled apart or pushed together. Where layers of sedimentary rock are disrupted in this way, the displacement can be obvious. These sandstones near Canberra, Australia, have been drawn apart, allowing the rocks on the left of each fault to slip down the fault plane. The "bar code" pattern of the layers allows the displacement to be measured precisely.

❷ FAULT PLANES

Most faults are visible only within rocks, but sometimes a fault plane is exposed like a cliff. This sheer precipice near Arkitsa in central Greece has been created by the rock on the far side of the fault being thrust vertically upward over thousands of years, dwarfing the man at the bottom of the photo. The fault plane itself has vertical grooves etched into it by the relentless movement. These grooves are known as slickensides.

Fault plane cuts right through the various layers of rock

❸ SIDESLIP

If two slabs of Earth's crust slide past each other horizontally, they create faults that can be seen from the air as long lines across the landscape. The paler rock in this aerial view of a fault in Nevada, US, was once a continuous ridge, but it has been pushed to the left at the bottom of the image. The San Andreas Fault in California is another example of this fault type.

❹ RIFT VALLEYS

These steep cliffs are fault planes along one side of the African Rift Valley, a vast feature created by East Africa moving east away from the rest of the continent. This has allowed the central part of the valley—on the left of the picture—to sink into the Earth. On average the valley is 30 miles (50 km) wide, with cliffs marking the fault planes on each side.

Lake Baikal is 395 miles (636 km) long and 30 miles (50 km) wide

❺ RIFT VALLEY LAKES

Many rift valleys are filled with long, very deep lakes. They include Lake Baikal in Russia, which is the deepest lake on Earth and contains a fifth of the world's fresh water. The floor of the rift valley is as much as 5,716 ft (1,741 m) below the lake surface. It is peppered with hot springs that erupt volcanically heated water into the black depths near the lake bed.

❻ MIDOCEAN RIDGES

Immensely long rift valleys have formed where the plates of the Earth's crust are pulling apart on the ocean floors. This is a false-color sonar image of the East Pacific Rise, showing showing two ridges of mountains (in red) with the rift valley in between. The ridges are created by lava erupting from fissures in the rift valley and heat, making the rock of the ocean floor expand upward.

EARTHQUAKES AND TSUNAMIS

Earthquakes are caused by faults giving way under pressure from the movement of the Earth's crust. If a fault slips easily, the earthquakes are fairly small tremors. But if the rocks on each side of a fault lock together, pressure builds up, distorting the rocks until something snaps, releasing the energy suddenly and causing an earthquake. If this happens underwater, it generates a submarine shock wave that causes a tsunami.

Big deflection indicates a powerful earthquake

Slender stylus responds to the slightest tremor

MEASURING ▶

An earthquake is measured using the Richter scale. This is based on the degree of ground movement recorded by an instrument known as a seismograph. As the ground shakes, the machine moves a pen that records the event on a scroll of paper wound onto a rotating cylinder. The bigger the earthquake, the more the pen moves.

As plates grind past each other, energy is released

Plates separate and move along fault line

Shockwaves radiate from the earthquake's epicenter

▲ GRADUAL SLIP

Many faults slip gently all the time. These include the central part of the San Andreas Fault in California, where the rocks creep past each other at up to 1½ in (37 mm) a year without causing serious earthquakes. Other parts of the fault are locked, building up the tension that eventually makes something snap.

▲ SHOCK WAVE

The point where a locked fault snaps is called the epicenter. In this case, the rupture point is below ground on a laterally sliding fault, such as the San Andreas Fault in California. Shock waves radiate from the epicenter in the same way as the shock of an explosion radiates through the air, and can be just as destructive. The farther the waves travel, the weaker they get, but they can often be detected on the other side of the world.

◄ GROUNDSHIFT

The fault movement that causes an earthquake is often deep underground, but sometimes it is very obviously on the surface. Here one side of a fault has moved up by well over 1 yd (1 m). The strain would have been building up for decades, but when the fault finally gave way, all the movement would have occurred in a few seconds.

EARTHQUAKE CITY ►

The city of San Francisco lies at the northern end of the San Andreas Fault, and suffers regular earth tremors. The last earthquake struck in 1989, destroying part of the elevated Nimitz Freeway and leading to the deaths of 63 people. But this was relatively mild compared to the massive earthquake that devastated San Francisco in 1906, and it is only a matter of time before another "big one" hits the city.

▲ CATASTROPHE

Earthquakes can have catastrophic effects on cities, especially those built of traditional materials such as bricks. As the ground shakes beneath it, a brick building collapses into a heap of rubble, burying anyone inside. Steel-framed buildings are much stronger, and often remain standing, as seen here in Japan after the Kobe earthquake of 1995.

▲ TSUNAMI

The Asian tsunami of late 2004 was caused by movement of a fault deep in the ocean off Sumatra, where the Indian Ocean floor is grinding beneath Indonesia. The movement built up immense tension that was released in the second most powerful earthquake ever recorded, generating huge waves that devastated this nearby coastline.

31

VOLCANOES

Volcanoes erupt in places where very hot rock deep below the surface has melted to form liquid magma. This happens where there are rising currents of heat beneath the crust, known as hotspots, and in places where the brittle crust is being pulled apart, reducing the intense pressure that keeps the hot rock solid. It also happens where one slab of crust is being dragged beneath another, along with water that lowers the melting point of the rock. The way the magma is formed affects its nature and how it erupts from volcanoes.

◄ ASH CONES

Most volcanoes erupt above the subduction zones where one plate of crust is plunging beneath another. The magma formed in these zones is thick, sticky, and full of gas. It erupts explosively, blasting huge ash clouds high into the sky. The molten rock that erupts from the vent as lava is too viscous to flow far, so it builds up in layers, along with ash falling from the air, to form cone-shaped volcanoes.

MOLTEN RIVERS ►

The magma that forms above hotspots or beneath rifts in the crust is very liquid, almost like water. Any gas can escape easily, so although it can erupt in spectacular "fire fountains" it does not build up enough pressure to cause explosive eruptions. The molten rock that boils to the surface flows in rivers of liquid lava, like this one on Hawaii, that form very broad shield volcanoes.

Aleutian Trench is part of the Pacific Ring of Fire

Ring of Fire runs around edge of Pacific Ocean

Hawaii is a volcanic hotspot

Magma chamber fills with molten rock from the base of the crust

▲ RING OF FIRE

The Pacific Ocean is surrounded by a ring of more than 450 active volcanoes that have erupted from near deep ocean trenches. The ocean floor in the trenches is being destroyed as plates push together. The volcanoes of this "Ring of Fire" are explosive, erupting sticky lava and clouds of ash. But Hawaii in the middle of the ocean has been formed by hotspot volcanoes that erupt very liquid lava.

▲ ANATOMY OF A VOLCANO

A typical volcano has a central crater fed by a magma chamber deep in the crust. The magma chamber forms first, in a place where rock has melted, and the magma melts a path though the rock above until it erupts as lava, gas, and ash. It can also push up through cracks to form secondary vents. The lava and rock debris that erupt from the crater build up to form the cone of the volcano.

▶ VOLCANIC EXPLOSIONS

Thick, viscous lava can block the vent of a volcano, and if gas pressure then builds up, the volcano may explode. A big eruption can also empty the magma chamber, so it collapses to form a vast super-crater, or caldera. In 1650 BCE this happened in Santorini, Greece, seen here from space. Sea water pouring into the caldera then caused a cataclysmic explosion that destroyed the civilization on nearby Crete.

Modern volcano has erupted in the center of the huge caldera

▲ PYROCLASTIC FLOWS

Some eruptions produce deadly avalanches of red-hot rock and dust known as pyroclastic flows. They surge over the landscape at high speed, and may travel much farther than liquid lava. This is a small one, on Arenal in Costa Rica. In 1902, on Martinique in the Caribbean, a pyroclastic flow from Mont Pelée overwhelmed the city of St. Pierre, killing 30,000 people in just two minutes.

Liquid lava

Wrinkled surface of pahoehoe lava shows it was very fluid

◀ LAVA

The very liquid lava that flows from hotspot volcanoes like those on Hawaii spreads out and solidifies as sheets of dark basalt. As it cools, movement often wrinkles the skin on the surface to create a ropelike effect known as pahoehoe—a Hawaiian word. More viscous lava tends to break up as it cools, forming blocks that resemble lumps of coal. The stickier the lava, the blockier it is, and the blocks often contain gas bubbles.

Less fluid lava forms tumbled blocks as it cools and solidifies

Blocky lava

VOLCANIC ERUPTIONS

Volcanoes are among the most powerful forces on the planet, and their eruptions can cause almost unimaginable destruction. Strangely, the most active volcanoes are often the least destructive, since they release their energy little by little, in a spectacular but often predictable way. The really dangerous volcanoes are the ones that appear to lie dormant for many years, but are really building up to something big. These are the volcanic eruptions that make history.

➋ KILAUEA

The most active volcano on Earth is Kilauea on Hawaii. It has been erupting continuously since 1983, ejecting huge quantities of gas and molten rock in spectacular fire fountains and rivers of liquid basalt lava. These pour down the flanks of the volcano toward the coast, where they spill into the ocean amid vast clouds of steam. In places the lava has solidified on top to form rocky tubes containing fast-flowing torrents of molten rock.

➊ MOUNT ETNA

Mount Etna on Sicily is Europe's biggest and most active volcano. It has a history of frequent eruptions dating back 2,500 years. It produces fast-flowing rivers of basalt lava that have destroyed villages and towns, notably in 1669 and 1928. It has also been the site of catastrophic explosions in the distant past.

❸ KRAKATAU

One of hundreds of volcanoes that form the islands of Indonesia, Krakatau is notorious for a cataclysmic eruption in 1883 that killed more than 36,000 people. The volcano exploded and then collapsed into a huge oceanic crater or caldera, generating tsunamis that engulfed the coasts of Java and Sumatra. The explosion was heard 3,000 miles (4,800 km) away, and is the loudest sound ever recorded.

❹ MOUNT ST. HELENS

In May 1980, a colossal explosion blew the top off Mount St. Helens in North America's Cascade mountains. The blast sent a plume of hot ash 15 miles (24 km) high into the sky and flattened 10 million trees. Fortunately, the volcano was being monitored by scientists who could see its flank visibly bulging as the pressure built up. Most of the area was evacuated before the explosion, and only 60 people died.

❺ SURTSEY

Iceland is a part of the Mid-Atlantic Ridge—the spreading volcanic rift that is making the Atlantic Ocean wider each year. Iceland has at least eight active volcanoes, and in 1963 a new volcano erupted from the rift to the south of the island, boiling out of the sea in a cloud of ash and steam. Named Surtsey, it continued erupting until 1967. It has been dormant ever since, and is being gradually eroded away by the waves.

❻ VESUVIUS

In Roman times, Mount Vesuvius in Italy was thought to be extinct, but in the year 79 CE the volcano erupted violently, spilling deep layers of red-hot ash and debris over the nearby town of Pompeii. Many of the citizens managed to escape before the main eruption, but many more—including this dog—were overwhelmed and killed. The hollow casts left by their bodies were discovered as the city was being excavated in the 1860s.

❼ OLYMPUS MONS

Volcanoes are not just found on planet Earth. Olympus Mons is a colossal volcano on Mars. It is 16¾ miles (27 km) high, which is more than twice the height of Mauna Kea, Earth's biggest volcano. It has the same shape as Mauna Kea and seems to have formed in the same way, from a hotspot beneath the crust.

GEYSERS AND HOT SPRINGS

In some volcanic regions, water seeps down through the ground and comes into contact with very hot rock. It usually boils back up to the surface, but in some places the weight of the water increases the pressure and stops the hot water from turning to steam. Eventually some of the water is pushed up a flue and
the pressure drops. This allows all the superheated water to turn to steam at once, blowing the remaining water out

Mineral terraces retain pools of hot water

▶FLY GEYSER
In 1916, a drilling operation in the Nevada desert struck a source of boiling water, creating an artificial geyser. Decades later, the superheated water found another route to the surface to form a natural geyser, which now has several vents. Unlike most geysers it spouts hot water continuously, building up rocky pinnacles of mineral deposits.

▼OLD FAITHFUL
The most famous of about 200 geysers in the Yellowstone region of the United States, Old Faithful gets its name from the way it erupts, on average, every 67 minutes. Each eruption sends a jet of steam and hot water to heights of up to 180 ft (55 m). This exhausts its store of water, which takes another 67 minutes to refill and get hot enough to erupt again.

Superheated water bursts up and turns to steam

▼BOILING MUD
The hot water that creates geysers can also form hot pools of bubbling liquid mud. The mud pools shown here are at Rotorua in New Zealand, one of the world's most active geyser zones which, like Yellowstone in the United States, is part of a much larger area of simmering volcanic activity. Some 800 years ago Rotorua was the site of a colossal volcanic eruption, but it is now a flourishing tourist resort.

The hot water that fuels geysers and hot springs can be harnessed as a source of energy. In Iceland and many other parts of the world the superheated water is used to drive electrical power plants. Reykjavik, the capital of Iceland, is heated by this hot water, and the city even has geothermally heated open-air swimming pools.

▲ EVAPORITE MINERALS
When water is superheated under pressure deep within the Earth, it often dissolves a lot of minerals from the rocks. If the water erupts from geysers or hot springs, evaporation and cooling turn the minerals solid again, and they form evaporites like these at Mammoth Hot Springs in Yellowstone. Every day the water adds some 4,400 lb (2,000 kg) of minerals to these terraces.

Terraces are built up from soluble calcite

Up to 250 macaques use the hot pools

▼ HOT SPRINGS
At Yamanouchi near Nagano in central Japan, steaming hot springs feed a series of pools high in the snowy mountains. The water stays at about 122°F (50°C), and in the 1960s local Japanese macaques—or snow monkeys—discovered that bathing in the pools was an ideal way of keeping warm in a climate where the winter temperature can drop to a bone-chilling 5°F (-15°C).

▶ BLACK SMOKER
Seawater seeping down through the rifted crust of midocean ridges is superheated by contact with volcanic rock and blasted out of hydrothermal vents. The hot water dissolves minerals from the rock of the ocean floor, but as the hot solution mixes with the very cold seawater the chemicals form dense, sooty clouds that look like billowing smoke.

ROCKY WAVE
At Vermilion Cliffs in Arizona, ancient desert dunes that hardened into solid rock have been carved into fantastic shapes by the erosive power of the wind. The rocks are at least 165 million years old.

Rocks and minerals

MINERALS AND GEMSTONES

Minerals are the natural solid substances that form rocks. A few consist of just one element, in which all the atoms are the same. They include diamond, a form of pure carbon. But most of the 4,000 or more known minerals are compounds of two or more elements. Quartz, for example, is a compound of silicon and oxygen. Most minerals can form crystals—natural geometric shapes that reflect the way their atoms are bonded together. The crystals of some minerals are cut and polished into valuable gems.

Halite can be tinted by impurities

Quartz can form big, six-sided, pyramidal crystals

❶

❸

❷

Graphite

Olivine is named for its olive color

Rough diamond looks like glass

❹

Diamond

❺

❻

Sulfur crystals form as sulfurous water evaporates

Calcite crystals may be transparent or opaque

❶ HALITE
Often known as rock salt, halite is the same mineral as the salt used in cooking—a compound of sodium and chlorine. Halite deposits found deep underground were created by the evaporation of salt water in ancient oceans. It forms cubic crystals that can often be found in coarse-ground table salt, and is colorless when pure.

❷ QUARTZ
The most abundant mineral on Earth's surface, quartz is one of the main ingredients of granite and similar hard rocks that have formed from molten magma. When these rocks are broken down by erosion, the tough quartz crystals tend to survive as sand grains, and these are used to make glass. Various colored forms of quartz, such as purple amethyst, are valuable gemstones.

❸ OLIVINE
Like quartz, olivine is a mineral based on silica—the compound of silicon and oxygen that is the basis of most rocks—but it also contains iron and magnesium. It is more abundant than quartz, but mostly below the crust because it is the main ingredient of the peridotite rock that forms much of the planet's deep mantle. Olivine crystals are usually green, as seen here.

❹ DIAMOND AND GRAPHITE
Although they are both pure carbon, diamond and graphite are physically very different. Diamond is the hardest of all minerals and a valuable gemstone, while graphite is the soft, streaky mineral used to make pencils. The difference is due to the way diamond has a very strong atomic structure, while the atoms of graphite are arranged in layers.

❺ SULFUR
Most frequently found as deposits around volcanic craters and hot springs, pure sulfur is a soft, usually bright yellow mineral. It consists of just one type of atom, but it combines with other elements such as iron and oxygen to form compounds such as pyrite and sulfur dioxide. It is an important ingredient of many artificial chemicals.

❻ CALCITE
Another of the most common minerals, calcite is the main ingredient of limestones. These are usually formed from the shells or skeletons of marine organisms, which absorb the mineral from seawater. Calcite is easily dissolved by slightly acidic rainwater, but recrystallizes in a variety of forms.

❼ BERYL

The main source of beryllium, one of the lightest metals, beryl is better known for its big prismatic crystals. These are cut into gemstones that have different names depending on their color, such as deep green emerald and pale blue-green aquamarine. Some beryl crystals are very big—an aquamarine found in Brazil in 1910 weighed 243 lb (110.5 kg).

❿ FELDSPAR

Big, colorful feldspar crystals are a conspicuous part of many types of granite, and can often be seen in the polished granite slabs used in architecture. The crystals often show a feature called twinning, where the crystal structure is symmetrical with a clear centerline. Feldspar can contain a variety of elements depending on how it formed, but it always contains aluminum and silicon.

Beryl forms long hexagonal crystals

Mica crystals can be split into thinner sheets

❽ ZIRCON

Similar to diamonds and often used as gemstones, zircon crystals are extremely hard and resistant to erosion. As a result, they survive when other minerals are destroyed. Some Australian zircon crystals have been radiometrically dated to 4.2 billion years ago, which is almost as old as Earth and older than any other known substance on the planet.

Zircon is is often purplish brown

⓫ MICA

A major ingredient of granite and similar rocks, mica has an unusually complex chemical makeup and forms strange flat, flaky crystals with six sides. These can be astonishingly big—one crystal found in eastern Russia had an area of 54 sq ft (5 sq m). Mica has a high melting point, and thin, transparent sheets of it are sometimes used as furnace windows.

Pink feldspar is also called orthoclase

Pyroxene often occurs in massive form, without obvious crystals

Talc is usually noncrystalline

❾ PYROXENE

One of the most important rock-forming minerals, pyroxene is a major ingredient of ocean-floor rocks such as basalt. It can contain a variety of metallic elements such as iron, magnesium, or titanium, but always in combination with silicon and oxygen. One form, jadeite, is very strong and was once used to make polished ax blades.

⓬ TALC

The softest mineral, easily scratched by a fingernail, talc is sometimes known as soapstone because of its soapy feel. It is used for decorative carvings and ground into talcum powder, but its main use is in the manufacture of heat-resistant ceramics such as cookware, and in papermaking.

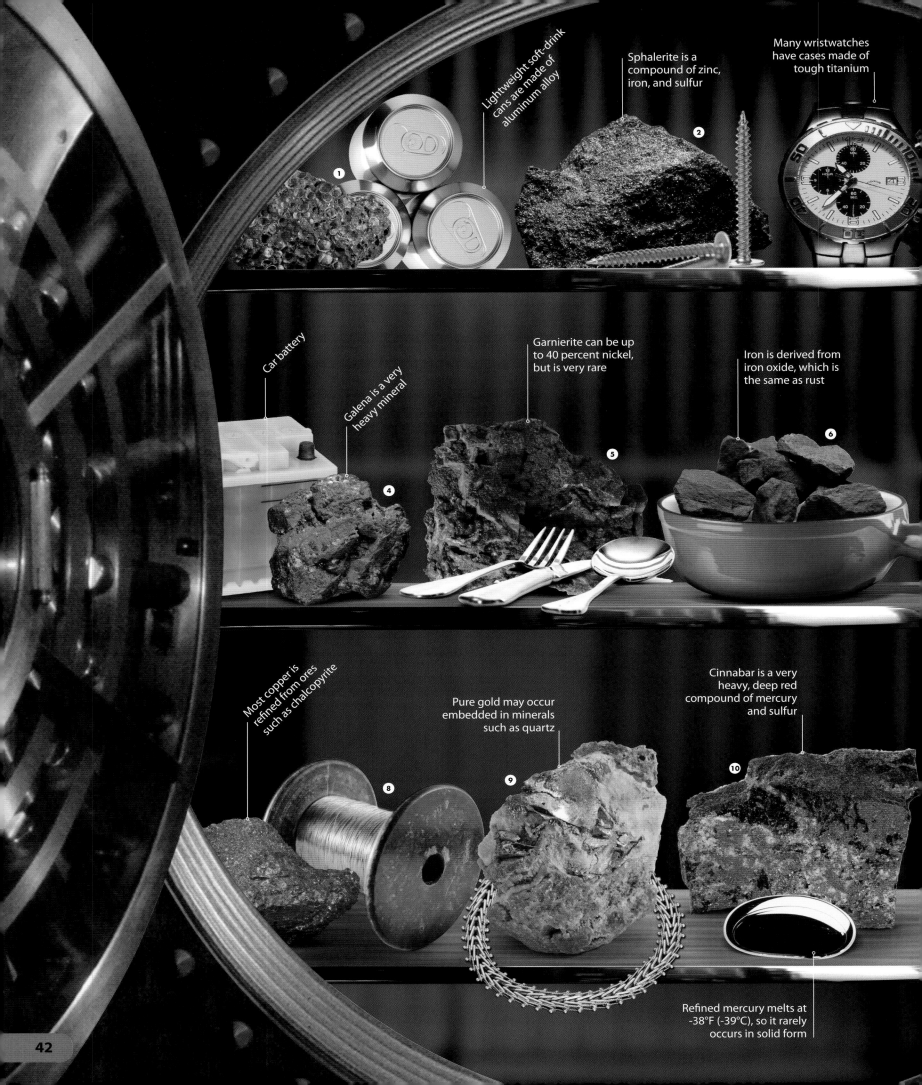

Lightweight soft-drink cans are made of aluminum alloy

Sphalerite is a compound of zinc, iron, and sulfur

Many wristwatches have cases made of tough titanium

① ②

Car battery

Galena is a very heavy mineral

Garnierite can be up to 40 percent nickel, but is very rare

Iron is derived from iron oxide, which is the same as rust

④ ⑤ ⑥

Most copper is refined from ores such as chalcopyrite

Pure gold may occur embedded in minerals such as quartz

Cinnabar is a very heavy, deep red compound of mercury and sulfur

⑧ ⑨ ⑩

Refined mercury melts at -38°F (-39°C), so it rarely occurs in solid form

METALS

Aside from artificial alloys, all metals are elements—substances that contain just one type of atom. Some, such as gold and silver, are naturally found in this pure "native" form, but most metals occur as more complex minerals known as ores. Iron, for example, is usually obtained from compounds of iron and oxygen called iron oxides. Once purified, metals have the tough, workable nature that makes them such useful materials. They also conduct heat and electricity well, making them vital to modern technology.

Tin is alloyed with lead to make solder—vital to all electric circuits

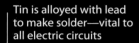

Native silver occurs in branching or wiry form in mineral veins

1 Aluminum Very light, aluminum conducts electricity well and does not corrode easily. It is fairly soft in pure form, so it is combined with other metals to make tougher alloys for use where light weight is vital, as in aircraft. Aluminum is obtained from a complex but abundant ore called bauxite.

2 Zinc Usually obtained from an ore called sphalerite, this white metal is widely used as a rust-proof coating for steel—a plating process known as galvanizing. It is also alloyed with copper to make brass, the shiny yellow metal that is widely used to make door handles and decorative metalwork.

3 Titanium Like aluminum, this is a very lightweight metal—but it is harder and much stronger. It is also much rarer, so it is usually combined with other metals to make the tough, yet light alloys used in aircraft and spacecraft. Its main ore is a compound of oxygen and titanium called rutile.

4 Lead Very heavy, and with a low melting point, lead is also very soft and easy to work. It has been used to make all kinds of things, from Roman water pipes to modern lead-acid car batteries. The main ore is a compound of lead and sulfur called galena.

5 Nickel This metal probably forms about a fifth of Earth's inner core, the rest being iron. At the surface, it occurs in the form of complex ores such as garnierite. Iron and nickel are combined to make strong, corrosion-proof stainless steel, one of the most useful alloys.

6 Iron Forming most of Earth's core and very common in rocks and soils, iron is the most abundant metal on the planet. It is a very important material because of its hardness, even though it is brittle and corrodes badly. Iron is refined into steel, which is springy and easier to work.

7 Tin About 4,000 years ago, early metal-workers discovered that mixing a small amount of molten tin with molten copper made a much stronger alloy, bronze. They obtained the tin by heating ores such as greenish cassiterite to about 1,800°F (1,000°C) in a charcoal furnace.

8 Copper This was one of the first metals to be used by humankind, from about 7,000 years ago. This is because, like gold, it can be found in its native form. An excellent conductor of electricity, it is widely used in the form of copper wire.

9 Gold Since gold does not easily combine with any other element, it is usually found as gleaming nuggets or grains. This also means that it does not tarnish, a fact that—combined with its rarity—has always made it valuable. Although very heavy, it can be beaten into very thin sheets.

10 Mercury The only metal that is liquid at room temperature, mercury is obtained from a colorful ore called cinnabar. The metal is best known for its use in medical thermometers, but it is also used to make batteries, electronic components, and the silvery backing of glass mirrors.

11 Silver Like gold, silver is a rare metal that is soft, easy to work, and found in its native form—all qualities that have made it highly valued for thousands of years. Unlike gold, it tarnishes, but it is very attractive when polished.

IGNEOUS ROCKS

Igneous rocks form from molten mixtures of minerals that erupt from deep within the Earth as magma or volcanic lava. As the minerals cool, they form interlocking crystals, giving the resulting rocks their strength. Some minerals are heavier than others, or melt at higher temperatures, so they tend to get left behind when the molten rock wells up. This means that an igneous rock is rarely the same as its parent rock, and usually lighter. The process has created a wide variety of rocks from the same raw material.

❶ PERIDOTITE

This is the rock that forms much of the deep mantle beneath the crust, and therefore 80 percent of the planet. It is rare on the surface, occurring in places where major earth movements have squeezed it up from beneath the ocean floor. It is very heavy and mainly consists of dark green olivine, rich in magnesium and iron.

❷ BASALT

Dark, dense basalt forms the bedrock of the ocean floors. It erupts from the spreading rifts of midocean ridges, and also from hotspot volcanoes like those on Hawaii. It is created by partial melting of peridotite in the mantle, to form a very fluid lava that contains far less of the heavy, greenish olivine that is such an important ingredient of peridotite. This makes basalt lighter, too.

❸ ANDESITE

Named after the Andes of South America, where it is abundant, andesite is solidified volcanic lava that has erupted from deep below the mountains. Here, basalt ocean floor is being dragged beneath the continent and is melting. The molten rock that rises to the surface contains fewer heavy minerals than basalt, so andesite is a lighter rock. It is one of the main rocks that form continents.

❹ GRANITE
All rocks contain silica—the substance that we use to make glass. This can form relatively light minerals that melt at much lower temperatures than the heavy minerals in rocks like basalt. As the rocks beneath continents are heated, the silicate minerals may form sticky magma that rises and then cools, turning into relatively light but very hard granite. It is mostly pale feldspar and quartz, with very little dark, heavy material.

❺ RHYOLITE
The magma that becomes granite usually cools deep in the crust. This takes a very long time, allowing big crystals to grow and form the granite. But if the magma reaches the surface it erupts as very viscous lava that cools quickly into fine-grained rhyolite. The only difference between the two rocks is their crystal size. In the same way, basalt that cools deep in the crust forms a coarse-grained rock called gabbro.

❼ PUMICE
The lava erupted from volcanoes often contains a lot of gas. The gas usually boils out of very liquid basalt lava easily, but has more difficulty escaping from much stickier silica-rich lava such as rhyolite. If the rock then solidifies with the gas bubbles still inside, it forms pumice. This has much the same structure as plastic foam, and is so light that it floats on water.

❻ OBSIDIAN
Obsidian is volcanic lava that has cooled too fast for crystals to form. It can be created from any type of lava, but usually has the same mineral composition as rhyolite or granite. When it breaks it has a rippling fracture pattern like that of flint or glass, and equally sharp edges, so like flint it was used to make stone tools in the past. Always very dark, it has also been used as a gemstone.

Rhyolite crystals are too small to be seen with the naked eye

Bubbles of volcanic gas form a frothy lava that turns into pumice

IGNEOUS INTRUSIONS

As molten rock forms deep in the crust, it forces its way up through cracks or as big molten masses. The viscous magma that forms granite usually starts solidifying deep below the surface to create massive igneous intrusions called batholiths. Over millions of years, the rock above may wear away to expose these as granite mountains. More fluid types of lava tend to harden in cracks to form dykes, or force their way between rock layers to create sills. Lava can also harden in the core of an extinct volcano, to be exposed by erosion as a volcanic plug.

▼ GRANITE BATHOLITHS

The rounded mass of Sugar Loaf Mountain in Rio de Janeiro, Brazil, is just part of a huge granite batholith that lies beneath the city. Originally formed deep in the crust, the granite is much harder than the surrounding rocks, which is why it has survived the erosion that has worn those other rocks away. A similar batholith forms the mountains of the Sierra Nevada in California.

Granite of Sugar Loaf Mountain is 800 million years old

Hard igneous intrusion forms a rocky wall

◄ DYKES

If molten rock forces its way up through vertical cracks, it forms slabs of igneous rock called dykes. Since they cool much more quickly than big igneous intrusions, the rock has much smaller crystals and is very fine-grained. In places, such dykes form rings around ancient volcanic craters, having formed in circular cracks created by the collapse of the volcano.

Long cooling cracks form
many-sided columns

▼ FLOOD BASALTS

The Deccan Traps are sheets of
basalt more than 1¼ miles (2 km)
thick that cover 190,000 sq miles
(500,000 sq km) of central India.
They are igneous extrusions
rather than intrusions, because
they were formed by enormous
outpourings of molten basalt that
solidified in the layers visible in
these cliffs. They erupted some
65 million years ago, at exactly
the same time as the dinosaurs
became extinct, and the two
events may be connected.

Cliffs expose
layers of basalt

▶ VOLCANIC PLUGS

The magma chambers that lie beneath
volcanoes can harden in the same
way as granite batholiths when the
volcanoes are extinct. If the softer
rock above then wears away, the
hardened magma is revealed as
a volcanic plug. The Devil's Tower
in Wyoming formed like this.
As it cooled, the rock shrank
and fractured into the vertical
columns that give it such a
dramatic appearance.

SILLS ▶

If molten rock intrudes between two layers
of sedimentary rock, the result is a sill. It may form at
any angle, depending on the slope of the rock layers. The
Whin Sill in Britain is a sheet of coarse basalt some 100 ft (30 m) thick
that lies at a slight angle. This exposes its edge, which has vertical
joints like those of the Devil's Tower. The Romans used it as the basis
for Hadrian's Wall, marking the northern frontier of their empire.

◄ DISSOLVING LIMESTONE

Rainwater dissolves carbon dioxide from the air to become weak carbonic acid. This attacks most rocks, but particularly limestones. The water enlarges cracks to create flat, fissured (grooved) limestone pavements and caves. In the Chinese Guilin Hills, vast amounts of limestone have been dissolved completely, leaving these isolated pinnacles.

WEATHERING AND EROSION

As soon as solid rock is exposed to the air, it starts being attacked by the weather. It is baked by the sun, shattered by frost, and dissolved by rainwater, which is naturally slightly acid. Meanwhile it may be scoured by wind-blown sand, and by rock fragments carried by flowing water and ice. By degrees, the weathered rock is worn away—a process known as erosion. This affects all exposed rock, however it was formed, although hard rock is more resistant and often survives when softer rock has been eroded away.

▼ PLANT POWER

Living things play a big part in breaking down rocks. The roots of trees like these can penetrate cracks in rocks and force them apart. The lichens that grow on rocks produce acids that help dissolve the minerals. Microorganisms living in the soil and even within some rocks also contribute to rock decay, turning their minerals into other forms.

WADIS AND CANYONS ▼

Rare but violent rainstorms in deserts cause flash floods that pour over the bare rock in torrents, carving gullies known as wadis, arroyos, or slot canyons. The water is loaded with sand, stones, and boulders that, over thousands of years, erode the rock into fantastic shapes like these at Antelope Canyon in the United States.

▲ EXFOLIATION

Rocks such as granite are formed deep underground under extreme heat and pressure. When they are exposed to the air, they cool and shrink as the pressure is released. This can make layers of rock split away like onion skin—a process called exfoliation that is accelerated by hot days and cold nights.

◄ FROST-SHATTERING

In cold climates and at high altitudes, water seeping into cracks and crevices freezes at night, expanding as it turns to ice. This exerts enormous pressure on the rock, pushing it apart. Repeated freezing and thawing can shatter the rock, creating drifts of rubble known as scree that build steep slopes at the foot of the frost-shattered cliffs.

MESAS AND BUTTES ▼

Monument Valley in the western United States is a landscape of isolated plateaus and pinnacles called mesas and buttes. They were created over millions of years by desert flash floods pouring over barren land that was being pushed up by ground movements. Most of the surface was eroded away, leaving these towering "monuments."

Sheer cliffs of this mesa (plateau) reveal horizontal rock layers

▲ SAND-BLASTING

In desert zones, where there are few plants to bind the soil together, the wind picks up sand grains and hurls them at exposed rocks. The sand enlarges any fissures, but may also smooth the rock surface into swooping curves like these at Coyote Buttes in the United States. The curved lines mark ancient rock layers.

◄ BREAKING WAVES

On exposed coasts, big waves smash into the rock and penetrate any cracks, exerting tremendous hydraulic pressure that can blow the rock apart. Rocky debris picked up by the waves completes the demolition job. As these mushroom-shaped Pacific islands show, all the active erosion happens at wave level, undercutting the rock and eventually causing it to collapse into the sea.

TRANSPORTATION AND DEPOSITION

▲ BOULDERS

It takes a lot of energy to move a big boulder, so on coasts they are not carried far from exposed cliffs. In rivers they are shifted only by the torrents that pour down steep valleys after heavy rain or snow melt. Stray boulders found in the lowlands have usually been transported by glaciers during past ice ages.

Boulders

The debris eroded from exposed rock is swept away by flowing water and wind, either by rolling and bumping it along or, if the particles are small enough, carrying them along in suspension. As the flow of water in a river slows down, it drops the heavier particles but keeps moving the lighter ones. This usually means that the particles are deposited in order of size. The lightest grains of silt and mud end up in sheltered places where the flow is slowest.

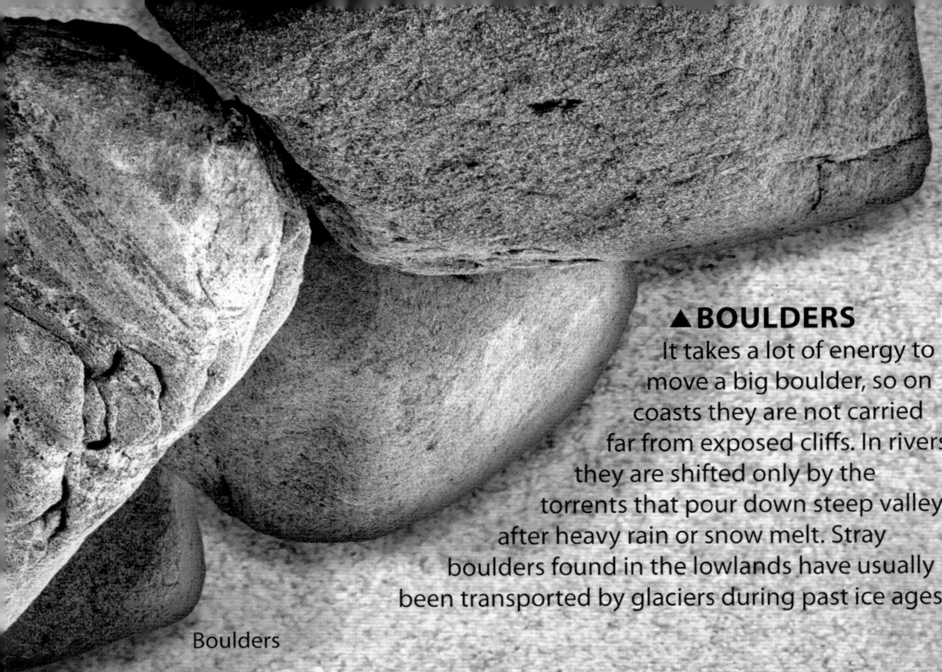

Cobbles

Rounded form caused by water transportation

▲ COBBLES

Over the years, boulders break up into smaller, lighter stones that can be bounced around by water currents and carried much farther. The rolling and tumbling caused by the flowing water knocks the corners off the stones to create rounded cobbles and even smaller pieces of shingle.

▶ GRAVEL BEDS

Many upland rivers swell to torrents when the snow melts in spring. The rushing water transports masses of small stones, then drops them in quieter stretches as gravel beds. These are also found in lowland areas that experienced torrents of meltwater during ice ages.

▲ SANDY BEACHES

Exposed rocky headlands on coasts are often interspersed with bays containing sandy beaches. The sand is all that is left of solid rock that has been shattered by the waves. Currents sweep the sand into the sheltered bays and then drop it because the water is not moving so vigorously.

Gravel

◀ WIND-BLOWN DUST

Strong winds can pick up fine dust and carry it over great distances before dumping it to form beds of fine-grained sediment called loess. The most famous are in northern China, where thick deposits of yellow loess form the basis of fertile farmland. But it erodes easily, and the Yellow River is named for the heavy load of loess that it carries into the Yellow Sea.

▲ SAND DUNES

The wind can build dry sand into immense dunes, both on coasts and in deserts. It bounces the sand grains up the windward slope of each dune so they roll over the crest, and by degrees the dune creeps downwind. On coasts, dunes stabilize as they move inland, but new ones keep forming. Desert dunes may keep moving for thousands of years, forming vast "sand seas" in regions such as Arabia.

Clouds of sediment swept out to sea

◀ DELTAS AND FANS

A fast-flowing river can carry huge quantities of sediment down to the sea. Here the river loses its energy, so the sediment falls to the seabed and creates a deep submarine fan, so heavy that its weight can distort Earth's crust. Meanwhile the river mouth migrates seaward over the top of the fan to form a low-lying delta with many channels, as seen in this satellite view of the Ganges Delta in Bangladesh.

◀ MUDDY ESTUARIES

When slow-flowing rivers approach the coast, any fine particles suspended in the water settle to form thick layers of mud in the tidal lower reaches. This is partly because rising tides stop the river flow, but salt water also makes the mud particles clump together and become heavier, making them sink. The mudflats are exposed at low tide, when the sea water drains away.

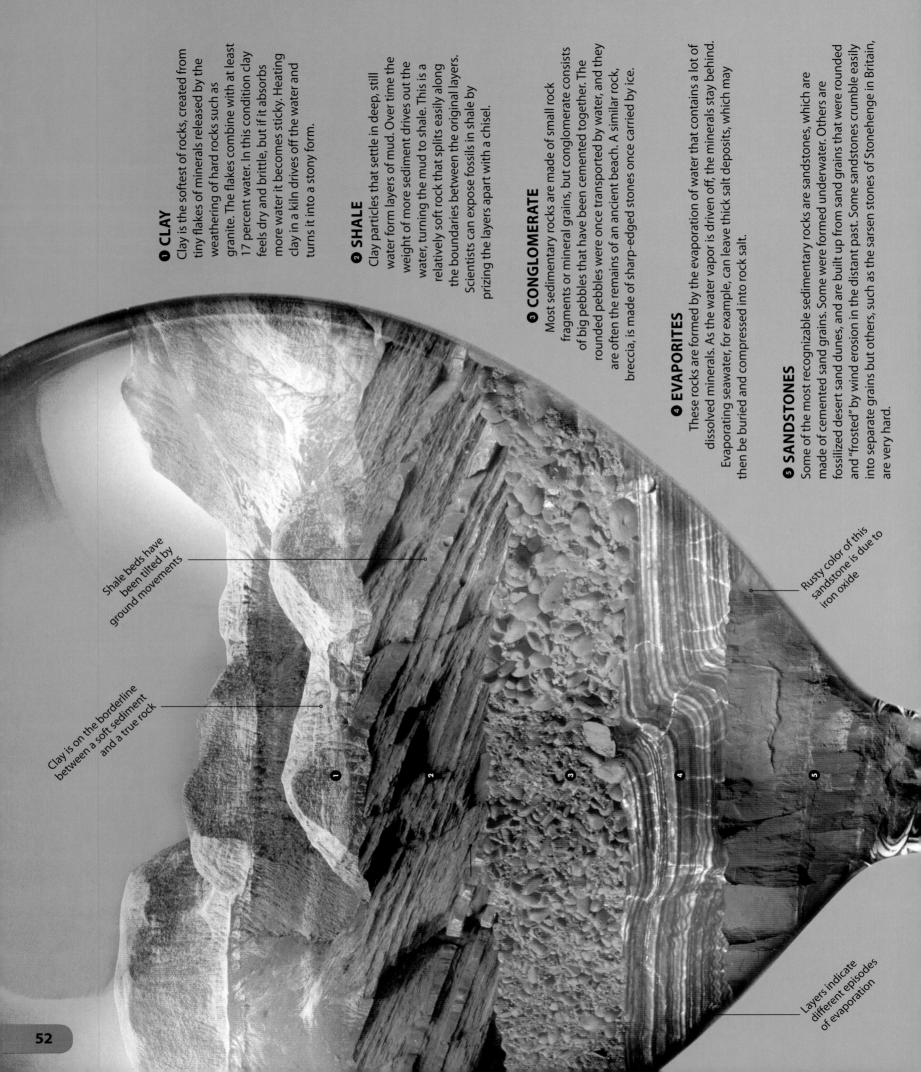

❶ CLAY

Clay is the softest of rocks, created from tiny flakes of minerals released by the weathering of hard rocks such as granite. The flakes combine with at least 17 percent water. In this condition clay feels dry and brittle, but if it absorbs more water it becomes sticky. Heating clay in a kiln drives off the water and turns it into a stony form.

❷ SHALE

Clay particles that settle in deep, still water form layers of mud. Over time the weight of more sediment drives out the water, turning the mud to shale. This is a relatively soft rock that splits easily along the boundaries between the original layers. Scientists can expose fossils in shale by prizing the layers apart with a chisel.

❸ CONGLOMERATE

Most sedimentary rocks are made of small rock fragments or mineral grains, but conglomerate consists of big pebbles that have been cemented together. The rounded pebbles were once transported by water, and they are often the remains of an ancient beach. A similar rock, breccia, is made of sharp-edged stones once carried by ice.

❹ EVAPORITES

These rocks are formed by the evaporation of water that contains a lot of dissolved minerals. As the water vapor is driven off, the minerals stay behind. Evaporating seawater, for example, can leave thick salt deposits, which may then be buried and compressed into rock salt.

❺ SANDSTONES

Some of the most recognizable sedimentary rocks are sandstones, which are made of cemented sand grains. Some were formed underwater. Others are fossilized desert sand dunes, and are built up from sand grains that were rounded and "frosted" by wind erosion in the distant past. Some sandstones crumble easily into separate grains but others, such as the sarsen stones of Stonehenge in Britain, are very very hard.

Shale beds have been tilted by ground movements

Clay is on the borderline between a soft sediment and a true rock

Rusty color of this sandstone is due to iron oxide

Layers indicate different episodes of evaporation

SEDIMENTARY ROCKS

Sediments carried by water or wind may build up in deep layers, either on land or more commonly on the seabed. As more material is added, its weight compresses the lower layers. Over millions of years minerals dissolved in seawater or groundwater cement the compressed grains of sediment together to form sedimentary rocks. Most of these are made of rock debris, but typical limestones consist of the skeletons and shells of marine organisms, while coal is made of the remains of long-dead plants.

❻ LIMESTONE

Marine organisms absorb dissolved chalky minerals from seawater and use them to build their skeletons and shells. When they die the chalky, calcareous material survives decay and builds up in layers on the seabed. Over time, the layers may be compressed into chalk or limestone, which often contains visible shell fragments.

❼ FLINT

Chalk is a soft white limestone made of the calcareous skeletons of countless microscopic marine organisms that lived roughly 100 million years ago in a shallow tropical sea. It often contains nodules of hard black flint, which probably formed from the glassy skeletons of other organisms such as sponges. Flint is a lot like glass, fracturing to produce razor-sharp edges, and was widely used by early humans to make stone tools.

❽ COAL

If plant remains accumulate in waterlogged, airless conditions, they turn into peat. If the peat is buried deep beneath more sediments, it can be compacted and heated to form coal—a black, shiny rock that can be burnt as fuel. The oldest, hardest coal, formed from plants that lived some 300 million years ago, is almost pure carbon.

Limestone often has a jointed, blocky look

Sandstone is made up of grains of hard quartz

FOSSILS

If the remains of living organisms are buried by sediments that turn into rock, they can be preserved as fossils. A fossil may be any once-living thing, or even its impression, that survives the normal processes of decay. But most fossils are formed by minerals seeping into the organic material and turning it to stone. This usually happens to hard shells or bones, but sometimes even soft tissues are preserved, giving us vital information about life in the distant past.

❷ DISCOVERY
The finest fossils have been buried for millions of years, and are discovered only when they are partly exposed by erosion of the surrounding rock. They may be revealed by coastal cliff falls or heavy rain. Experts return frequently to good sites. Once they find a fossil, they start removing the rock around it.

❶ FOSSILIZATION
Most living things are destroyed after they die, but a very few may be smothered by something that preserves them. Insects and spiders drowned in sticky tree sap millions of years ago are perfectly preserved in the hardened sap, known as amber. Sea shells and dinosaur bones may be soaked in water containing minerals that slowly fossilize them. Even a footprint in mud may be preserved if it is buried and the mud turns to rock.

Only the hard shell of this ancient sea creature is preserved as stony fossil

Spider in amber is perfectly preserved down to every tiny detail of its body

Leaf impression

Ammonite

❸ EXTRACTION
Small fossils are often easy to remove, especially if the surrounding rock is soft. Bigger fossils such as dinosaur bones are more awkward, because they are heavy and often fragile. Excavators cover them with protective plaster before digging them out. They then add more plaster so that the fossils can be transported safely to a laboratory.

❹ PRESERVATION
Fossils rarely come out of the ground in perfect condition. They are usually surrounded by a rocky "matrix," which has to be chipped away using tools ranging from rock chisels to dentist's drills. When the bones are exposed, they are preserved, often with a varnish, to stop them falling apart. Scientists can then work out how they once fit together.

❻FOSSILS AND EVOLUTION
Fossils show that, although extinct animals are not exactly like those that live today, they are similar. This provided the first evidence that living things evolve into new forms. The course of evolution can often be traced through fossils—but since many organisms, such as birds, are rarely found as fossils, we still have a lot to learn.

Trilobite

❺ INTERPRETATION
Most fossils are just bones, or even fragments of bones. Scientists can use medical scanners to probe the fossils for fine details, but it is very hard to know what the animals really looked like, or how they lived. Some clues may survive, such as imprints of feathers or scales, and experts can use these to create reconstructions of the living animals.

Dinosaur claw

ROCK STRATA

Sedimentary rocks are usually laid down as layers of soft sediment, such as mud on a lake bed. The oldest layers lie at the bottom, so if they are compressed into rock, the oldest rock layers, or strata, are also the lowest. However, movements in the Earth can fold and even overturn the strata, so geologists need other ways of figuring out the ages of rocks. The nature and sequence of the strata can also reveal a great deal about climates and events in the distant past.

▼ HORIZONTAL STRATA
When soft sediments are turned into rock without being disturbed, they become horizontal strata. The lowest strata are the oldest. All these rocks date from the Cretaceous period of the age of dinosaurs. The older brown and red strata are described as lower Cretaceous, while the younger white chalk is upper Cretaceous.

▼ FOSSIL EVIDENCE
Rocks can now be dated using a technique known as radiometric dating. Before radiometric dating was developed, rocks were dated relatively by their position in layers of strata. Rocks can also be dated by any fossils they contain, since living things keep changing over time. Some of these fossils are big bones, but most are sea shells and other remains of sea creatures.

▼ DUNE BEDDING
Sediments that settle in water nearly always form horizontal layers. But a sand dune builds up as a series of inclined layers as wind-blown sand settles on the lee, or sheltered, side of the dune. If the dune becomes sandstone, the "dune bedding" is preserved in the rock. This reveals that the rock formed in a desert, even though its current location may have a wet climate.

Sand laid down on the slope of an ancient dune

▼ BENDING AND FOLDING

If rock strata are bent rapidly by a dramatic earthquake, they snap. But steady pressure over long periods, or at high temperatures, can bend and fold the rock. The strata may seem to be simply tilted. This is because you can see only part of a very big fold. Sometimes the folding is tight enough to create visible ridges and troughs, known as anticlines and synclines, or even complete overfolds that turn the strata upside down.

▼ FAULT PLANES

If rock strata snap, the result is a fault plane, like the one this climber has her feet on. Strata can snap due to extreme or sudden pressure, but more frequently they snap due to tension pulling the rocks apart. One side of the fault drops relative to the other—or is pushed up by pressure—and the rock strata become offset. By matching the layers, you can often see how they used to join up, and how far they have moved.

▼ UNCONFORMITIES

Ancient, distorted strata are often ground flat by erosion. If more rock layers are then laid down on the smooth, horizontal surface, this creates an effect known to geologists as an unconformity. It becomes visible only if both groups of strata are revealed on a cliff face. Unconformity is evidence of dramatic change, such as a mountain range being eroded away and submerged beneath the sea.

Rocks above this unconformity are much younger than those below it

Folded strata are evidence of massive Earth movement

Climbers often use fault planes to secure a firm footing

SCHIST

Relatively soft metamorphic rocks such as slate are created by modest pressure and heat. If these forces are more intense, they create rocks called schists. Schists contain bigger crystals, such as glittering mica and deep red garnet. All the crystals are aligned in sheets, as they are in slate.

GNEISS

Very high temperatures and pressures form the hardest metamorphic rocks, known as gneisses. These granite-like rocks have clear pale and dark bands, which show how they formed. Gneisses include the oldest rocks on Earth, found in Greenland and Canada. These formed some 4 billion years ago—although the rocks that they were created from must have been even older.

MARBLE

One of the most familiar metamorphic rocks, marble is an altered form of limestone. Some types of marble have been baked, and contain intact fossils of sea shells. Others, like these, have been created by intense pressure, which has squeezed the minerals into layers. Marble is mostly relatively soft calcite, so it is easy to carve and highly valued for sculpture.

Marble can be scratched by steel

Minerals form colored bands

Loupe

Magnifying glass

Rock hammer

SLATE

If mudrock or shale is heated and squeezed by the forces that build mountains, new minerals form in layers that are flattened by the pressure. The result is slate, a rock that can be easily split into thin sheets, and is often used for roofing. Slate is an example of regional metamorphism—a change in rock type that affects very large areas.

METAMORPHIC ROCKS

The forces that distort, snap, or melt rocks can also change their physical nature. Extreme pressure can make the rock harder and align its crystals in distinct bands, as when shale is turned into slate. Heat can cause partial melting followed by recrystallization into new minerals. These may include gemstones, such as the garnet in some schists, or veins of precious metals. Metamorphic processes are often triggered by intrusions of molten magma that distort and bake the surrounding rock.

QUARTZITE

If sandstone is heated enough, the quartz crystals that form the sand grains become welded together by more quartz. This creates a very hard, brittle rock called quartzite. Many mountain peaks survive erosion because they are capped with a pale, glittering layer of tough quartzite.

ECLOGITE

Most metamorphic rock is formed from sedimentary rocks, but under extreme conditions of heat and pressure even very hard igneous rocks can be turned into new forms. Deep in the crust, granite may be transformed into a type of gneiss, while darker, heavier gabbro may become eclogite. The very heavy rock that forms much of Earth's mantle, peridotite, may be baked and squeezed into greenish serpentinite.

HORNFELS

A rock that is baked by a nearby intrusion of molten magma such as granite becomes harder and is often spotted with the crystals of new minerals. Known as a hornfels, the rock loses all its original features. These features survive in rock that is farther from the heat source.

VOLCANIC
LAVA

VOLCANIC LAVA

Much of the rock that erupts from continental volcanoes forms broad deposits of lava and ash. The deposits build up the continents and may survive for many millions of years, but some of the rock is broken down by erosion and carried into the oceans. Vast amounts of volcanic ash billow up into the air and fall in the sea.

rocks
lifted up

magma
rises

exposed rock
eroded and
carried away

IGNEOUS INTRUSIONS

Sticky, silica-rich magma forms deep in continental crust and pushes slowly upward to solidify underground as granite intrusions. Eventually these may be exposed as the rock above is worn away. The granite is attacked by rainwater and reduced to sand and clay, which are carried to the ocean.

IGNEOUS
INTRUSIONS

pressure
transforms rock

magma
solidifies

rock buried
deeper

MAGMA

MAGMA

Although the rock beneath Earth's crust is very hot, it is normally kept in a solid state by intense pressure. However, rifting of the crust can reduce the pressure, and water carried down by sinking oceanic crust lowers the rock's melting point. This turns some of it into the magma that fuels volcanoes or bubbles up as granite intrusions.

melting
metamorphic
rock

solid
metamorphic
rock

ROCK CYCLE

Over millions of years, rocks are transformed from one form to another. Mountains are worn down by erosion, and the debris is carried into the sea to form sedimentary rocks. These may be pushed up into more mountains by the movement of tectonic plates, or carried deep into Earth, where they are transformed into metamorphic rocks or melted. The molten rock pushes up and cools to form igneous rocks that are eroded to create more sediments.

SEDIMENTARY ROCK

pressure transforms rock

rock lifted up

METAMORPHIC ROCK

rock buried deeper

SEDIMENTARY ROCK

Much of the debris created by the erosion of rocks on land is swept into shallow seas. Here it sinks to the bottom, where it forms thick beds of sediment. Over time the sediment is compressed and cemented into layered sedimentary rocks such as sandstone and shale, which are buried deeper and deeper by more sediment.

METAMORPHIC ROCK

As sedimentary rocks are buried and squeezed by the forces of plate tectonics, they heat up and are put under intense pressure. The increased pressure makes them more dense and recrystallizes their ingredients into new minerals, forming metamorphic rocks. These may then partially melt to produce magma that becomes granite.

SOILS

Soils are essential to most plants, because they supply the substances that plants use as nutrients. They consist of rock that has broken up into mineral fragments and become mixed with humus—a "compost" created from decaying plant and animal remains by countless soil organisms. The activity of these soil organisms is affected by the rock type, climate, and vegetation, and this in turn creates many different types of soil with varying degrees of fertility.

Dark, fertile topsoil forms a deep layer above mineral subsoil

Soil is shallow, and is mainly clay and rock fragments

❸ GRASSLAND SOIL
Centuries of grass growth and decay on prairies and steppes creates a deep, brown, fertile soil containing a lot of organic matter. It is neither acid nor alkaline, which is ideal for the microbes that break down organic matter into plant nutrients. It also suits the earthworms that churn up the soil, keeping it well mixed. Most grassland soils are now used for growing crops because they are very fertile.

Dark plant material lies on a pale, washed-out layer of sand

❶ YOUNG SOILS
Many soils develop from solid rock that is being broken down by weathering. This clay soil is being created from a soft mudstone, which is also being split and crumbled by plant roots pushing down through cracks to find water. The soil above the rock is too young to have distinct layers, but over time a fertile topsoil will form near the surface.

❷ TEMPERATE ACID SOIL
Rain washing through sand or gravel dissolves alkaline plant nutrients and carries them to a lower level. This creates distinct layers of soil, with those near the top being too acidic and infertile for most plants. Those that can thrive, such as pine and heather, take over and create conifer woodlands, heaths, and moorlands.

Woodland soil has distinct layers, but is more fertile than acid soil

❺ PEATY SOILS

These soils begin life as waterlogged masses of half-decayed vegetation on peat bogs and fens. Bog peat is fed by rainwater and is very acidic, mainly due to the growth of sphagnum moss, which acidifies the water. Fen peat is waterlogged by neutral groundwater, and if it is drained it dries out to create very fertile soil. It has little mineral content, which means that it is light and easily blown away by the wind.

Plant remains build up and gradually turn into dark peat

Volcanic soil on Hawaii is red with iron

❹ WOODLAND SOIL

The soils that form under deciduous trees, such as oak or maple, get a regular input of organic matter from the leaves that fall each year with the approach of winter. The leaves contain acids that dissolve some of the minerals in the upper layers, carrying them down to lower levels. However, microbes and worms still flourish, and the soil is naturally fertile.

❻ VOLCANIC SOILS

The rock that erupts from volcanoes is rich in the minerals that plants need, so soils that develop from cooled volcanic ash are often very fertile. The basalt that erupts from some volcanoes also contains a lot of iron. A volcanic soil may include big lumps of solidified lava that have been blown from the crater, and sometimes there are layers of pale ash marking recent eruptions.

BRAIDED STREAMS
Fed by meltwater pouring off the glaciers of Iceland, the Þjórsá River forms a braided network of streams flowing over sand and gravel. Much of the landscape is shaped by the power of running water.

Water and weather

WATER AND ICE

The feature of planet Earth that makes it so special is liquid water—the substance that is vital to life as we know it. As a simple compound of hydrogen and oxygen, water is probably common throughout the universe, but mainly in the form of solid ice or gaseous water vapor. Both occur throughout the solar system, but liquid water is rare, mainly because the other planets are either too hot or too cold. Earth is unique in the solar system in having temperatures that allow all three forms of water to exist, sometimes in the same place at the same time.

▼ ATOMS AND MOLECULES

Water is a mass of molecules, each with two hydrogen atoms and one oxygen atom. This explains its chemical formula, H_2O. The molecules of liquid water are loosely bound by electronic forces, enabling them to move in relation to each other. When water freezes, the molecules become locked together, and when it evaporates they burst apart.

Ice If water freezes, the water molecules lock together in a "crystal lattice" to form the solid structure of ice.

Water In liquid form, the water molecules cling together, but are able to move around each other and flow.

Water vapor Heat energy breaks the bonds holding water molecules together, so they move apart to create a gas.

Ice has a regular geometrical structure of water molecules

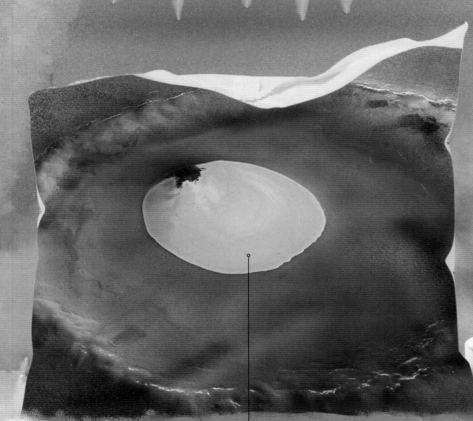

◄ WATER IN SPACE

Water is constantly careening around the solar system in the form of comets—"dirty snowballs" of ice, dust, and rock fragments. It also occurs on other planets, but mainly as water vapor or, as in this crater near the north pole of Mars, as ice. However, liquid water may exist beneath the icy surface of Europa, one of the moons of Jupiter—and where there is water, there may be life.

Ice forms a thin crust on the sand dunes of this crater floor on Mars

▼ LATENT HEAT

When water evaporates, its molecules absorb energy. This makes them moves faster, so they burst apart to form water vapor. This energy is called latent heat. If the vapor condenses into clouds, latent heat is released, warming the air and making it rise, building the clouds higher. This helps fuel thunderstorms and hurricanes, and, in fact, the whole weather machine of our planet.

▼ WATER ON EARTH

Most of the water on Earth is salty seawater. Only 3 percent is fresh water, and most of that is either frozen or lying deep underground. Of the rest, two-thirds is contained in freshwater lakes and wetlands, with far less in rivers. Almost 10 percent of the fresh water that is neither frozen nor buried is in the form of atmospheric water vapor or clouds.

▼ FLOATING ICE

When water freezes, the molecules become locked into a structure in which they are farther apart than they are in cold water. This means that ice is less dense than liquid water, so it floats. Water is the only substance that behaves like this. This is vitally important to life on Earth, for if water sank when it froze, the ocean depths would probably freeze solid.

▼ WATER AND LIFE

The electronic forces that make water molecules cling together also make them cling to the atoms of other substances such as salts, pulling them apart so they dissolve. This makes water an ideal medium for the chemical reactions that are the basis of life. Living cells like these bacteria are basically envelopes of water, containing dissolved chemicals which the organisms use to fuel their activities and build their tissues.

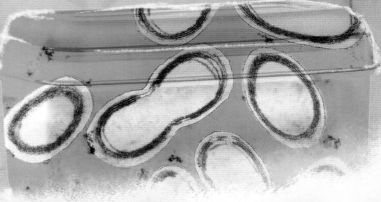

WATER CYCLE

Water vapor evaporating from the oceans forms clouds that are carried over the land by wind. More clouds build up from water vapor rising off the land. Eventually, rain and snow fall, and the water that seeps into the ground drains into streams and rivers that flow back to the ocean. The process turns salty seawater into fresh water, which then picks up minerals from the land and carries them back to the sea. Some parts of this cycle take just a few days or weeks, while others take hundreds or even thousands of years to run their course.

Clouds are blown on the wind, so they form in one place and spill rain in another

❶ WATER VAPOR

As the ocean surface is warmed by the Sun, water molecules absorb energy. This makes them break free from the liquid water and rise into the air as pure water vapor, leaving any impurities, such as salt, behind. The same thing happens to the water in lakes, rivers, and vegetation. Water vapor is an invisible gas, but as it rises it expands and cools, losing energy and turning into the tiny droplets of liquid water that form clouds.

❷ RAIN AND SNOW

Air currents within clouds make the tiny cloud droplets join together to form bigger, heavier drops. When these get too heavy to stay airborne, they fall as rain. The same process makes the microscopic ice crystals in colder clouds link together as snowflakes. Both rain and snow fall most heavily over high ground, which forces moist, moving air to rise to cooler altitudes and form more clouds.

Plants pump water vapor into the air as the Sun warms their leaves

❸ SURFACE WATER

Some of the water that falls as rain flows straight off the land and back to the sea, especially in coastal regions where the terrain consists of hard rock with steep slopes. This type of fast runoff is also common in urban areas, where concrete stops rainwater soaking into the ground and channels it into storm drains. Deforestation can have a similar effect, by removing the vegetation that traps water and stops it from spilling straight into rivers.

Most of the water vapor in the air rises off the surface of oceans

Nearly all the water that flows back to the sea is carried by rivers or coastal glaciers

Deep-flowing groundwater seeps directly into the ocean from water-bearing rocks

Water that spills rapidly off the land often contains a lot of mud and debris

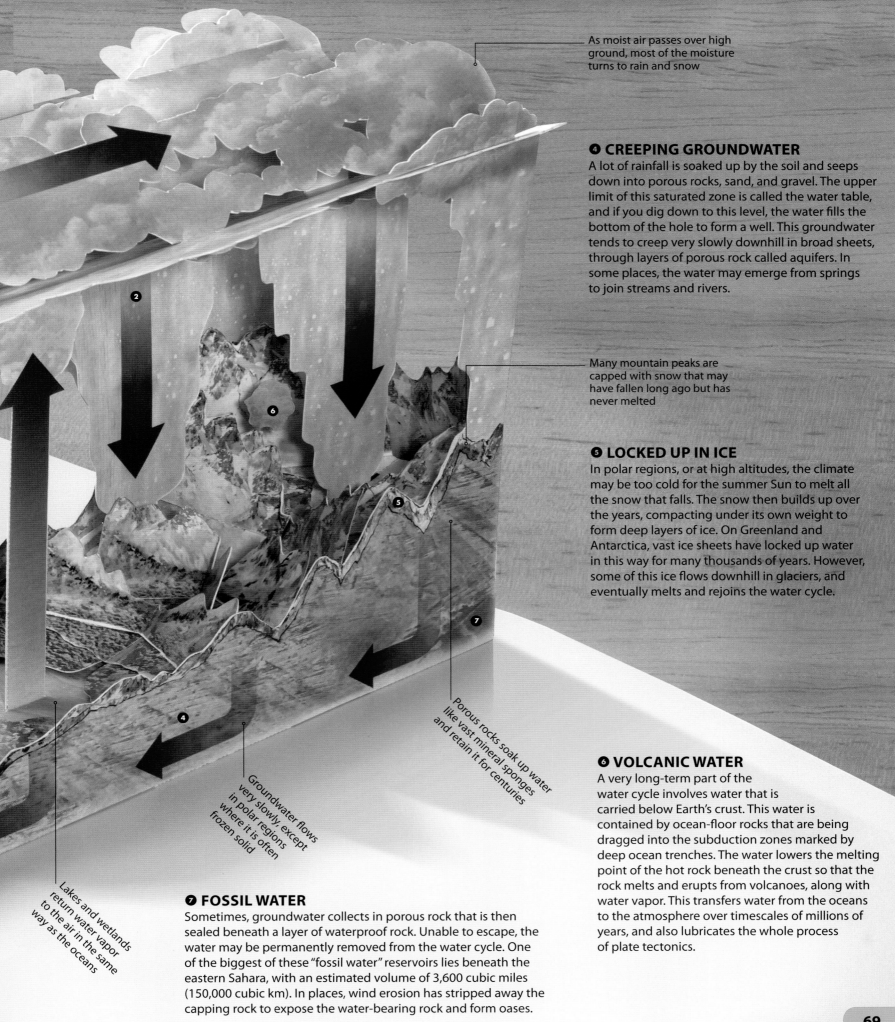

As moist air passes over high ground, most of the moisture turns to rain and snow

❹ CREEPING GROUNDWATER

A lot of rainfall is soaked up by the soil and seeps down into porous rocks, sand, and gravel. The upper limit of this saturated zone is called the water table, and if you dig down to this level, the water fills the bottom of the hole to form a well. This groundwater tends to creep very slowly downhill in broad sheets, through layers of porous rock called aquifers. In some places, the water may emerge from springs to join streams and rivers.

Many mountain peaks are capped with snow that may have fallen long ago but has never melted

❺ LOCKED UP IN ICE

In polar regions, or at high altitudes, the climate may be too cold for the summer Sun to melt all the snow that falls. The snow then builds up over the years, compacting under its own weight to form deep layers of ice. On Greenland and Antarctica, vast ice sheets have locked up water in this way for many thousands of years. However, some of this ice flows downhill in glaciers, and eventually melts and rejoins the water cycle.

Groundwater flows very slowly, except in polar regions where it is often frozen solid

Porous rocks soak up water like vast mineral sponges and retain it for centuries

Lakes and wetlands return water vapor to the air in the same way as the oceans

❻ VOLCANIC WATER

A very long-term part of the water cycle involves water that is carried below Earth's crust. This water is contained by ocean-floor rocks that are being dragged into the subduction zones marked by deep ocean trenches. The water lowers the melting point of the hot rock beneath the crust so that the rock melts and erupts from volcanoes, along with water vapor. This transfers water from the oceans to the atmosphere over timescales of millions of years, and also lubricates the whole process of plate tectonics.

❼ FOSSIL WATER

Sometimes, groundwater collects in porous rock that is then sealed beneath a layer of waterproof rock. Unable to escape, the water may be permanently removed from the water cycle. One of the biggest of these "fossil water" reservoirs lies beneath the eastern Sahara, with an estimated volume of 3,600 cubic miles (150,000 cubic km). In places, wind erosion has stripped away the capping rock to expose the water-bearing rock and form oases.

Many rivers can be traced back to a source that bursts out of the ground as a spring. The spring is fed by groundwater that seeps downward until it reaches a layer of waterproof rock. The water flows over the top of this layer. If the rock outcrops on the slope of a hill, the water spills out above it as a spring. It is usually crystal clear, but may contain dissolved minerals.

▶ MOUNTAIN STREAMS

As it tumbles down the steep slopes, a mountain stream flows very fast, with many waterfalls and rapids. Seasonal torrents caused by heavy rain or snow melt can shift big boulders, as well as great volumes of gravel and sand eroded from the mountain. The water is clear, cold, and rich in dissolved oxygen.

RIVERS

As water drains off the land it flows into a network of streams that join together to form bigger and bigger rivers. Rivers shape the landscape by eroding valleys and, by degrees, wearing down mountain ranges. They carry the eroded debris from the uplands to the lowlands, and so tend to level out the land. They also transport plant nutrients that make most lowlands so fertile. In general rivers have a fast, turbulent upper course in the uplands, a tranquil middle course in the lowlands, and a tidal lower course as they flow across coastal plains into the sea.

▶ YOUNG RIVERS

As it flows down through the uplands, a young river lays down a bed of gravel. Most of the gravel is bounced downstream by fast-flowing water during times of spate (heavy flow) such as the spring thaw. The river often follows several channels across the gravel to create a complex "braided stream." Eventually, all the channels join up to create one broad, shallow river flanked by gravel banks.

▶ MEANDERS

A river often winds across its floodplain in a series of loops called meanders. The river flows more strongly around the outside of the bend, cutting away the bank. It flows more slowly on the inside of the bend, where it deposits sediment. This exaggerates the meanders, making them wider. Some meanders become so extreme that the river takes a short cut, leaving an isolated oxbow lake.

◀ FLOODPLAINS

Rivers slow down as they reach the lowlands, and this makes them drop lighter particles of sand and mud. If they are not artificially confined, they tend to overflow their banks in winter or during the wet season and flood the surrounding landscape. The floodwaters drop fine sediment to create broad floodplains of nutrient-rich silt and organic material, and over the centuries this develops into a fertile soil.

▶ ESTUARIES AND DELTAS

Most rivers flow to the sea. When the fresh water encounters salty seawater in the tidal lower course, the salt makes fine mud particles in the water settle to form the broad tidal mudflats of an estuary. Where the flow is faster, it carries coarser sediment out to sea to build up a delta with many radiating channels, as shown in this satellite image of the Lena River in Siberia.

RIVER VALLEYS AND GORGES

The fast-flowing water of upland rivers carries rocks, stones, and sand that erode watercourses into V-shaped valleys. These join up to create patterns of tributaries that form a drainage basin, or river catchment. Most river valleys get broader as the river gets bigger, but rivers flowing through limestone may disappear into underground systems that then collapse, creating limestone gorges. Earth movements can also push the land up slowly as the river keeps cutting down, and this can carve even deeper gorges.

❶ BRANCHING PATTERNS

This satellite view of the snow-capped western Himalayas shows how the valleys of small rivers join up to create bigger rivers that flow into the lowlands. Eventually these join up, too, forming vast rivers like the Indus and Ganges. The pattern of valleys resembles the trunk, branches, and slender twigs of a tree.

❷ UPLAND VALLEY

Torrents of debris-laden water pouring off mountains after heavy rain or snow-melt cut deep, steep-sided valleys into the mountain slopes. The water flows too fast to drop any fine sediment, so the valley is etched right down to the bedrock in a narrow V-shape. Its course zigzags between ridges of harder rock.

❸ MATURE VALLEY

As a river flows out of mountains and hills across flatter land, it flows more slowly. This makes it drop a lot of the rocky debris that it carries out of the uplands, filling up the bottom of its valley. So instead of being confined by a deep V-shaped valley, a mature river flows over a broad plain built up from deep layers of sediment. It may change its course regularly, and the valley often has traces of old river channels.

❹ WATERFALLS

Mountain streams often tumble over precipices to create waterfalls, but they are less common on mature rivers. In places, however, a rift in a capping layer of hard rock allows a big river to plunge into a gorge that has been eroded in the softer rock below. In Zambia, southern Africa, the mighty Zambezi River plunges 355 ft (108 m) over Victoria Falls, known locally as Mosi-oa-Tuya, or "the smoke that thunders."

❺ UPLIFT CANYON

The titanic forces that push up mountains can raise the beds of rivers, forcing them to erode deeper valleys. In Arizona, massive uplift of the landscape has made the Colorado River cut down through more than 1 mile (1.8 km) of rock to create a gorge 220 miles (350 km) long and up to 18 miles (29 km) wide—the Grand Canyon. In the process it has revealed rock strata dating back nearly 2 billion years.

❻ LIMESTONE GORGE

Limestone is mostly calcite, a mineral that is dissolved by naturally slightly acid rainwater. This encourages the water to seep down through joints and fissures in the rock and flow through underground cave systems. The caves may eventually get so large that their ceilings collapse, and the river ends up flowing through a spectacular steep-sided gorge, like this one in Provence, southern France.

GLACIERS AND ICEBERGS

In the polar regions and on high mountains, freezing temperatures stop snow from melting away. As more snow falls on top, it builds up in deep layers that, over centuries, are compressed into solid ice. This tends to creep downhill as glaciers, and where these reach the sea the ice breaks away to form floating icebergs. In the coldest regions, the same process creates immensely thick ice sheets. The East Antarctic ice sheet forms a huge dome up to 3 miles (4.5 km) thick, and its weight has depressed the continent more than half a mile (1 km) into the Earth's crust.

❶ CIRQUE GLACIER

High in the mountains, snow collects in rocky basins and is compacted into ice. Eventually, this overflows each basin and heads downhill as a glacier. Meanwhile, the moving ice freezes onto the mountain, plucking rock away to form vertical rock walls and deepen the basin. The result is a bowl-shaped cirque, which typically acts as the source of a valley glacier.

❷ VALLEY GLACIER

Ice flows down valleys extremely slowly—too slowly to be seen as movement. In the process, it deforms to flow around bends, and may even flow uphill over a hump of hard rock. But mostly the ice grinds the rock away. This often forms dark lines of shattered rock on the glacier surface, like these on the Kennicott Glacier in the Wrangell Mountains of Alaska.

❸ GLACIER SNOUT

Most mountain glaciers terminate on the lower slopes of the mountains, at the point where the warmer climate makes the ice melt as quickly as it is moving downhill. This is the snout of the glacier, which stays in the same place unless the climate changes. Meltwater pouring from tunnels and caves in the ice flows away in outwash streams or rivers.

❹ MORAINE

A glacier moves a lot of rock downhill, both embedded within the ice and in long piles, called moraines, that are carried on its surface. It acts like a conveyor belt, dumping all the debris near its snout as a terminal moraine—a pile of angular rock fragments mixed with fine "rock flour" created by the grinding action of the ice. A lot of the finer rocky material is swept away by water from outwash streams.

❺ TIDEWATER GLACIER

In the polar regions, southeastern Alaska and southern New Zealand, glaciers flow all the way to the coast and out to sea. Here, the floating snout of the Hubbard Glacier flows into the Gulf of Alaska. Great chunks of ice break away from these glaciers and float away as icebergs, while much of the rubble carried by the ice is dumped on the sea floor.

❻ ICEBERG

The icebergs that break away from tidewater glaciers float with at least 90 percent of their mass underwater, depending on the weight of rock they carry. Many drift long distances before melting, and those that drift south from Greenland into the North Atlantic are very dangerous to shipping—notoriously causing the sinking of the *Titanic* in 1912.

❼ ADVANCE AND RETREAT

Climate change is making glaciers behave in strange ways. Many are retreating as higher temperatures make them melt back to higher altitudes, leaving empty valleys and fjords. But melting can also make a glacier flow faster and advance, because extra meltwater beneath the ice stops it sticking to the rock. This increases the number of icebergs that spill into the ocean, raising sea levels.

ICE AGES

Earth has gone through several phases when the climate has cooled, mainly because of regular variations in its orbit around the Sun. Each of these phases, known as ice ages, has included warm and cold periods. We are now living in the warm period of an ice age. During the last cold period, which ended about 12,000 years ago, glaciers and permafrost extended across much of northern Eurasia and North America, reshaping the landscape. The Southern Hemisphere was less affected because it has little land in cooler latitudes—except for Antarctica, which is still frozen.

❶ GLACIATED VALLEYS

The deep U-shaped valleys found in many mountain landscapes in the north were gouged out by ice-age glaciers. The ice ground away the rock to create the steep valley walls, and scooped hollows in the valley floors, which now contain lakes. Many mountain peaks were reduced to narrow ridges and pinnacles by ice ripping away their flanks to form rounded cirques.

❷ FJORDS

During the last ice age, so much water was locked up as continental ice that the sea level fell by more than 330 ft (100 m). Glaciers eroded deep valleys as they flowed to the coast. When the ice melted, the seas filled up again, reaching their present level about 6,000 years ago. Water flooded coastal valleys to create the steep-sided fjords of regions such as Scandinavia and southern New Zealand.

Glacial valley, Norway

❶

Moving ice once filled this valley

Groove shows direction of ice flow

Ice-scoured rock, Canada

❸

❷ Fjord is 1,300 ft (400 m) deep

Milford Sound, New Zealand

❸ ICE-SCOURED ROCKS

Sheets of moving ice grinding across northern regions such as Canada and Scandinavia scraped away soil and soft rock to reveal ancient, hard rocks below. Some rocks show graphic evidence of this, with long grooves scored into their surface by boulders embedded in the ice. These landscapes are dotted with hundreds of lakes, which fill hollows gouged out by the ice.

❹ GLACIAL DEBRIS

As the ice melted and retreated, it left heaps of rubble known as moraines, and broad expanses of soft clay mixed with rock fragments, known as boulder clay or till. It also dumped any big rocks that it was carrying. The most striking of these "glacial erratics" are very different from the surrounding bedrock, because the ice has carried them from areas with different geology.

❺ ANCIENT TUNDRA

In the tundra that surrounds ice sheets, groundwater freezes solid to form permafrost. During the ice ages, permafrost covered vast areas not buried beneath ice. The freezing soil created strange patterns in the ground. Where big lumps of underground ice have melted away, the ground has subsided to form "kettle holes" that are now filled with water.

❻ GLACIAL REBOUND

The colossal weight of the ice-age ice sheets distorted Earth's crust downward. In the 12,000 years since they melted, the crust has been steadily rising at the rate of up to ½ in (1 cm) a year. This "glacial rebound" effect has raised many former beaches well above the waves. Some 1,000-year-old Viking harbors in Scandinavia are now 33 ft (10 m) above sea level.

Glacial erratic, UK

Sandstone rock sits on limestone

Rhossili Bay, UK

Raised beach was once at sea level

Tundra is frozen but not glaciated

Ellesmere Island, Canada

77

LAKES

Lakes are large pools of standing water that form on land. The water may collect in hollows left by melting glaciers, in the folds and rifts created by ground movements, or even in volcanic craters. Most contain fresh water, which flows into the lake at one end and out at the other. In hot climates the water may evaporate from the surface rather than flow out, and this causes a buildup of dissolved minerals that makes the lake very salty. Lakes are slowly silted up by sediment, which is carried into them by rivers and settles on the lake floors. Over time, this can turn a lake into a swamp, and eventually make it vanish altogether.

❶ UPLAND LAKE

Lakes in upland regions with hard rocks usually contain pure, cold water with few of the mineral nutrients needed to support aquatic life. As a result, there are relatively few drifting organisms—plankton—and the water is extremely clear. Lake Tahoe, which has formed in a rift in the mountains of the western United States, has so little plankton that its deep blue waters are as clear as glass.

❷ LOWLAND LAKE

The water that flows into lowland lakes is usually rich in plant nutrients dissolved from the surrounding soil and soft rocks. These support a lot of plankton, making the water relatively cloudy. Such lakes teem with life of all kinds, including aquatic plants, but these grow so fast that the lake becomes choked with vegetation and eventually turns into a swamp.

❸ SALT LAKE

Nearly all "fresh water" contains salts of some kind, dissolved from rocks and soils. As water evaporates from lakes it leaves these salts behind, and in a hot desert climate this can create a salt lake. The waters of the Great Salt Lake in Utah are five times as salty as the sea, and the margins of the lake, seen here, are encrusted with glittering white salt crystals.

❹ SODA LAKE

Typical salt lakes are rich in sodium chloride, or table salt. But some lakes contain other salts. Many lakes in Africa's Rift Valley, such as Lake Nakuru, contain strong solutions of sodium carbonate, or soda. Despite this, the lake water supports a dense population of specialized life, including microscopic algae and shrimplike copepods, which are eaten by vast flocks of flamingos.

❺ GLACIAL LAKE

Most of the world's lakes were formed by ice-age glaciers. The moving ice scooped hollows in the rock, or dumped thick moraines of rocky debris in valleys that now act as natural dams, holding back the lake water. Similar lakes are being formed today by active glaciers like this one in southern Norway. Meltwater flowing from the glacier in the background is rich in mineral sediment, which gives the lake its greenish blue color.

❻ CRATER LAKE

The craters of extinct or dormant volcanoes often contain near-circular crater lakes. They fill with pure rainwater, but, if there is any volcanic activity, the water may become acidified by gases such as sulfur dioxide and carbon dioxide. The water of this crater lake in eastern Siberia is unusually acidic, enabling it to dissolve the minerals that have turned it a milky blue.

79

▲SINKHOLES

Much of the water that forms cave systems seeps into narrow cracks in the rock and apparently vanishes underground. In places, however, a concentrated flow of water enlarges a joint into a vertical shaft, forming a waterfall that plunges into a black void. These sinkholes may be hundreds of yards deep, and often open out into caverns containing underground rivers and lakes.

▲POTHOLES

The narrow passages that link bigger caves are known in some limestone regions as potholes. Their walls are often visibly scoured and polished by the torrents of water that flow through them after heavy rain, and many are full of water all the time. This does not stop determined cavers, who use specially modified diving equipment to pass through flooded passages that may lead to unexplored cave networks.

▲CAVERNS

As caves get broader, their roofs may collapse through lack of support. This may turn a cave near the surface into a rocky gorge open to the sky, but deeper underground the rock falls away, leaving the natural arch of a cavern. Some of these caverns are colossal—the Sarawak chamber in the Gunung Mulu caves of Borneo is at least 2,300 ft (700 m) long, more than 1,000 ft (300 m) wide, and 330 ft (100 m) high.

CAVES AND UNDERGROUND RIVERS

The power of the sea can carve caves into many kinds of coastal rock, but underground cave systems are nearly always the result of groundwater seeping down through limestone. The alkaline limestone is slowly dissolved by acids that are naturally present in rainwater and soils. As the rock dissolves, joints and fissures become enlarged into vertical sinkholes and narrow, winding passages that lead to underground streams and rivers. Some of these cave networks extend for great distances underground, and may carry away all the water so that there are no streams or rivers on the rocky, often half-barren surface.

▲ MEXICAN CENOTES

The Yucatan peninsula in Mexico is an ancient, uplifted coral reef. Since coral rock is a form of limestone it is affected by rainwater in the same way as other limestone landscapes. Tropical rain has eroded a complex cave network that swallows up all the surface water, but it is accessible through sinkholes and collapsed caverns called cenotes. Many of these contain beautiful, yet eerie underground lakes, which were sacred water sources for the ancient Mayan civilization.

▲ STALACTITES AND STALAGMITES

As slightly acidic water seeps through limestone, it dissolves the rock and becomes a weak solution of the mineral calcite. If this then drips into a cave system, exposure to air changes its chemistry and makes the calcite crystallize. Over many years, the crystals build up to form hanging stalactites, or rise from the cave floor as stalagmites. The same process can create other features, such as the curtains of calcite known as flowstones.

▼ UNDERGROUND RIVERS

The water that pours into limestone cave systems tends to keep draining downward through joints in the rock. It may abandon one string of caves to flow through another lower down, leaving the older caves high and dry. But sometimes it reaches a layer of impermeable rock and cannot sink any farther. Here, it forms a broad underground river that flows through a passage until it emerges from a hillside like a gigantic spring—a fully formed river flowing straight out of the ground.

OCEANS AND SEAS

Oceans and shallow seas cover more than two-thirds of the planet, to an average depth of 2½ miles (3.8 km). The Pacific Ocean alone covers nearly half the globe. The oceans contain about 320 million cubic miles (1,330 million cubic km) of salty seawater, which accounts for 97 percent of the water on Earth. Most of this water forms a dark, cold realm deep below the surface, where life is scarce, but the shallow, sunlit waters of coastal seas are some of the world's richest wildlife habitats.

❶ VOLCANIC ORIGINS

Most of the water in the oceans probably erupted as water vapor from massive volcanoes some 4 billion years ago. The vapor formed part of the early atmosphere, but, as the planet's surface cooled, it condensed into rain that poured down for millions of years to fill the oceans. Some water may also have arrived from space in the form of icy comets, which crashed into Earth and vaporized on impact.

❷ SALT WATER

Seawater became salty very slowly, as continents built up from volcanic islands erupting from the ocean floor. As fast as these appeared, they were eroded by heavy rain, which carried mineral salts into the ocean. The main salt is sodium chloride, or table salt, which can be obtained from seawater by evaporating it in coastal salt pans like these.

❸ BLUE TWILIGHT

Sunlight consists of all the colors of the rainbow, but where it shines into deep water the various colors are progressively filtered out, starting with red and yellow. Soon only blue light is left. Below 660 ft (200 m) there is just dim blue twilight, and by 3,300 ft (1,000 m), this fades into darkness. Since the oceans are on average 12,500 ft (3,800 m) deep, most ocean water is pitch black.

❹ HEAT SINK

Water can soak up a lot of heat energy without getting noticeably warmer, which is why the sea is cooler than the land in summer. It cools down as slowly as it warms up, so the sea lapping this snowy beach in winter is warmer than the land. This effect gives coastal regions relatively mild climates, with fewer summer heatwaves or winter frosts.

❺ OCEAN LAYERS

The dark ocean depths are uniformly cold, even in the tropics. This is because the sun-warmed water at the surface expands and becomes less dense, so it floats on top of the colder water like oil on a puddle. These layers are permanent in open tropical oceans, but in cooler regions the layers tend to become mixed in winter.

Only blue light penetrates far below the ocean surface

The salt content of the oceans has now stabilized

Vocanoes like these on Java still erupt a lot of water vapor

❻ CRYSTAL DESERT

The permanent layer of warm surface water in open tropical oceans is usually crystal clear. This is because the layering effect stops nutrients from reaching the sunlit surface and fueling the growth of plankton that makes the water cloudy. As plankton is the basis of the oceanic food chain, there is very little food to support ocean life. So these clear blue oceans are little more than marine deserts.

Surface waters are much warmer than the ocean depths

WAVES, CURRENTS, AND TIDES

Oceanic winds whip up waves and drive surface currents that swirl around oceans in vast circulating "gyres." Surface currents are linked to deepwater currents driven by the sinking of cool, salty water toward the ocean floor, especially in the North Atlantic and around Antarctica. Between them, these currents carry ocean water all around the world, redistributing heat and the dissolved nutrients that support oceanic life. Meanwhile, the gravity of the Moon causes the tides that rise and fall daily, shifting large volumes of water in tidal streams that flow much faster than ocean currents.

❶ SURFACE CURRENTS

Oceanic winds tend to blow toward the west in the tropics, and toward the east in the midlatitudes farther north and south. They drag the surface waters of the oceans with them, creating huge clockwise current gyres in the northern hemisphere, and counterclockwise gyres in the southern hemisphere. As they swirl around the oceans, these currents carry warm water toward the poles and cold water into the tropics.

❷ CALM ZONES

Oceanic winds and surface currents swirl around regions where the seas are calm and the winds are very light. The calm zone at the heart of the North Atlantic is known as the Sargasso Sea, famous for its floating seaweed, which is concentrated in the area by the circulating currents. These also heap up the water slightly, so the sea level at the centre of the Sargasso Sea is roughly 39 in (1 meter) higher than the level of the surrounding ocean.

❸ THE GULF STREAM

One of the fastest-flowing ocean currents, the Gulf Stream carries warm tropical water across the Atlantic Ocean from the Gulf of Mexico toward northern Europe. This helps keep Europe relatively warm, and the climate of the Atlantic coast of Scotland is mild enough for tropical palm trees to grow. Conversely, the Humboldt Current that flows up the western coast of South America from the fringes of Antarctica carries cold water to the tropics, allowing penguins to live on the equatorial Galápagos Islands.

❹ WAVES

Winds blowing over the oceans create ripples that grow into waves. These get bigger the longer the wind acts upon them, so the highest waves are those that have been blown by strong, steady winds across broad oceans. The largest reliably recorded wave was 100 ft (30 m) high, seen in the North Atlantic in 1995. Such huge waves transfer vast amounts of energy, but the water within each wave does not move forward with it until the wave breaks, and its crest topples onto the shore.

➎ TIDAL RISE AND FALL

Ocean water around the globe is dragged into a slight oval by the gravity of the Moon, creating two "tidal bulges." As Earth spins, most coastal regions move in and out of these tidal bulges so the water level rises and falls, usually twice a day. These tides vary with the nature of the coast. Some places such as the Mediterranean are almost tideless, while the Bay of Fundy in eastern Canada, seen here, has a huge tidal range of up to 52 ft (16 m) between low and high tide.

➏ WHIRLPOOLS AND RACES

As the tide rises, it pushes seawater up river estuaries and along coasts. When the tide falls again, the water ebbs away and the flow reverses. Normally these tidal streams are not very obvious. But where they flow around headlands or through narrow straits, they can be concentrated into fast-moving, turbulent tidal races and even giant whirlpools, like this one in the Gulf of Corryvreckan off the west coast of Scotland. These build up to their full fury at midtide, then die away altogether as the tide turns.

➐ LUNAR CYCLES

The tides vary with the phases of the Moon. Twice a month, at full Moon and new Moon, the difference between high and low tide is much greater than at half Moon. This is because the Moon is aligned with the Sun, and their gravities combine to create extra-large tidal effects known as spring tides. At half Moon, the gravity of the Sun offsets that of the Moon, reducing its influence and causing far smaller tides, called neap tides. As a result, the tidal range at any point on the coast changes from day to day.

ATMOSPHERE

Earth is covered by a mantle of air that is roughly 78 percent nitrogen and 21 percent oxygen. The rest consists of small amounts of carbon dioxide, methane, ozone, and water vapor, plus other gases including argon, helium, and neon. Eighty percent of the air is concentrated in the troposphere, the lowest layer of the atmosphere. It acts as a sunscreen by day and retains heat at night. A layer of ozone, a form of oxygen, in the stratosphere also protects all life from dangerous ultraviolet radiation.

▼ FRAGILE ENVELOPE

Seen from space, the atmosphere forms a shallow, glowing blue halo around the planet. The outer atmospheric layers are invisible, because the air in them is so thin. Clouds rise to the top of the troposphere, but no farther, so all the water vapor in the atmosphere—and all the weather—is concentrated in its lowest layer.

▼ THIN AIR

Air density decreases with altitude, so just 6 miles (10 km) above sea level, there is not enough air to breathe. The thin air at high altitudes reduces atmospheric pressure, allowing water to evaporate more easily and boil at a lower temperature. People living on the high plateau of Tibet can drink tea while it is still boiling.

▶ LAYERS

The atmosphere is not just a single thick blanket of air. It has four distinct layers, from the troposphere, up through the stratosphere and mesosphere, to the thermosphere, which fades into space. These layers are defined by their temperature rather than the nature of the air they contain, which gets thinner with altitude until there is no air at all.

Thermosphere
beyond 54 miles (87 km)

Mesosphere
31–54 miles (50–87 km)

Stratosphere
11–31 miles (18–50 km)

Troposphere
0–11 miles (0–18 km)

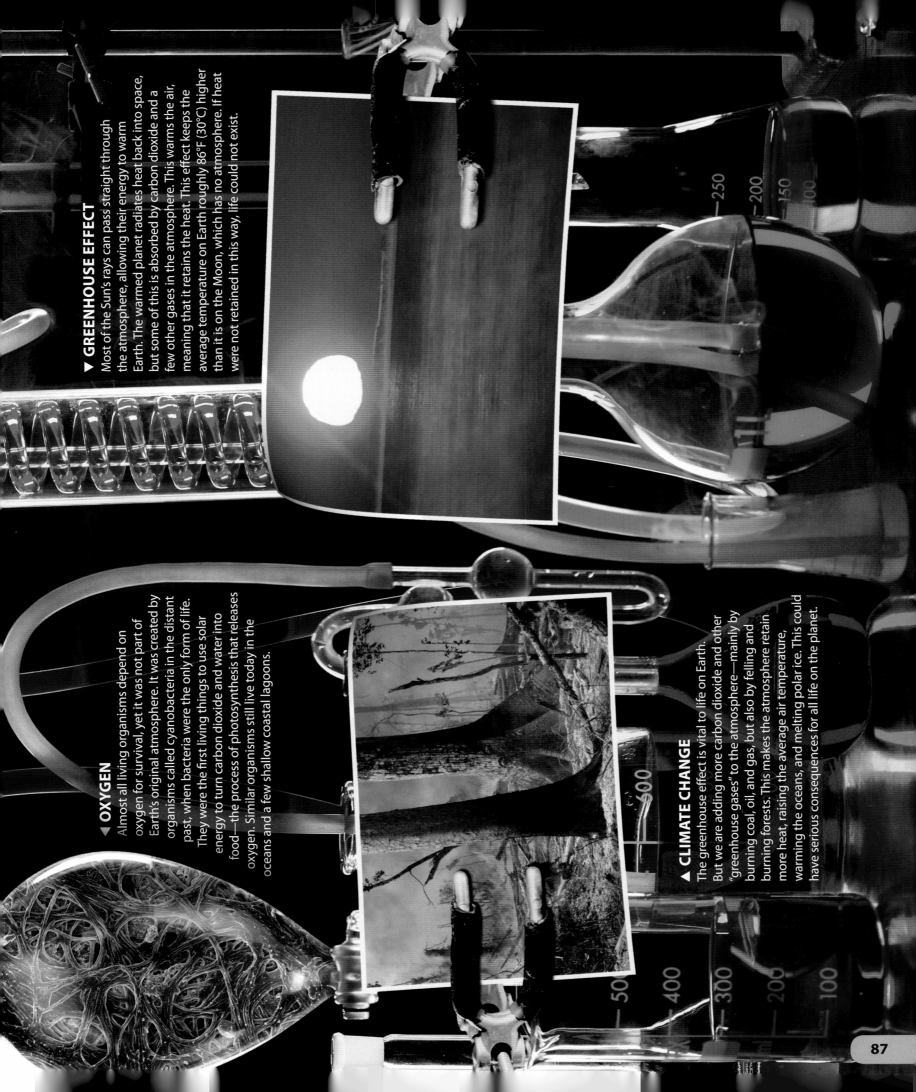

▶ GREENHOUSE EFFECT

Most of the Sun's rays can pass straight through the atmosphere, allowing their energy to warm Earth. The warmed planet radiates heat back into space, but some of this is absorbed by carbon dioxide and a few other gases in the atmosphere. This warms the air, meaning that it retains the heat. This effect keeps the average temperature on Earth roughly 86°F (30°C) higher than it is on the Moon, which has no atmosphere. If heat were not retained in this way, life could not exist.

▶ OXYGEN

Almost all living organisms depend on oxygen for survival, yet it was not part of Earth's original atmosphere. It was created by organisms called cyanobacteria in the distant past, when bacteria were the only form of life. They were the first living things to use solar energy to turn carbon dioxide and water into food—the process of photosynthesis that releases oxygen. Similar organisms still live today in the oceans and a few shallow coastal lagoons.

▲ CLIMATE CHANGE

The greenhouse effect is vital to life on Earth. But we are adding more carbon dioxide and other "greenhouse gases" to the atmosphere—mainly by burning coal, oil, and gas, but also by felling and burning forests. This makes the atmosphere retain more heat, raising the average air temperature, warming the oceans, and melting polar ice. This could have serious consequences for all life on the planet.

Earth's spin deflects airflow

① PREVAILING WINDS

Intense heat in the tropics makes air rise near the equator. The air then sinks in the subtropics and flows back toward the equator as surface winds. This air circulation is known as a convection cell. The winds are deflected by Earth's spin (the Coriolis effect) and swerve toward the west as the trade winds. In regions midway between the poles and the equator, winds are deflected to the east. Since these blow from the west they are called westerlies and include the "Roaring Forties" of the Southern Ocean.

Tropical trade winds swerve west so they blow from the east and are called easterlies

Midlatitude prevailing winds are known as westerlies

② HIGHS AND LOWS

As warm air rises, the upward movement reduces the weight of air to create a low-pressure zone. The rising air draws in more air, which swirls inward and upward in a spiral known as a cyclone, shown in the circling clouds that form as moist air rises and cools. South of the equator the air spirals clockwise, as shown here, while in the north it spirals counterclockwise. Cool, descending air creates cloudless high-pressure anticyclones that spiral in the opposite direction.

Satellite view of a southern tropical cyclone reveals clouds spiraling clockwise

Rain falls in a broad column over Montana

❸ CLOUD FORMATION

When air rises, it expands and cools. Any invisible water vapor that it contains cools, too, and condenses into the countless tiny water droplets—or ice crystals—that form clouds. The condensation process releases energy as heat, making the air warmer. This makes it rise even farther, building up more cloud. The cloud may keep building until there is no water vapor left.

❹ RAIN

Warm air rising inside clouds pushes cooler air aside. This cooler air sinks and swirls in to replace the rising air. The air currents hurl the cloud droplets around so they collide and form bigger droplets. When these get too heavy to be supported by the rising air, they fall as rain. The strong rising air currents in big clouds can support a greater weight of water, so the rain is heavier when it finally falls.

Thermometers record variations in daily temperatures

❺ SNOW

At high altitude or in winter, the air can be cold enough for rising water vapor to freeze into microscopic airborne ice crystals. These form as six-sided plates or prisms, but if they are tossed around by air currents inside big clouds they stick together to form snowflakes. Every snowflake has a different arrangement of crystals, so each one is unique.

❻ WEATHER FORECASTING

Weather forecasters gather data on atmospheric pressure, temperature, and rainfall using satellites, weather balloons, automatic weather stations, and simple instruments such as these thermometers. Forecasters feed all the figures into a computer program, and this works out how the weather is likely to change.

WEATHER

The weather is powered by the energy radiated by the Sun. Its heat generates convection currents in the lower atmosphere that cause global prevailing winds, and carry moisture and heat around the world. Rising warm, moist air forms low-pressure systems that bring clouds, rain, and snow. These are separated by areas of cooler, sinking air, creating high-pressure conditions that suppress cloud formation, bringing clear skies and sunshine. Air flows from high to low pressure as local winds, often in different directions from prevailing winds, and sometimes with the violence of storms.

CLOUDS

There are ten basic types of clouds. Their names are combinations of the Latin words cirrus (curl), stratus (layer), cumulus (heap), and nimbus (rain). Low-level clouds have bases that lie below 6,500 ft (2,000 m). Medium-level clouds, which normally have names beginning with the word alto-, occur at 6,500–20,000 ft (2,000–6,000 m). High-level clouds, with names that begin with cirro-, occur above this. Colossal cumulonimbus storm clouds rise through all the levels, and may be up to 10 miles (16 km) high.

◀ ALTOSTRATUS

Midlevel cloud that blends into broad sheets, as in the distance here, is called altostratus. The highest parts are made of ice crystals, but the lower parts are composed of water droplets. Altostratus often starts as a thin layer that allows the sun to shine through, as here. It then becomes gradually thicker, marking the arrival of a cyclone or depression that will bring wet or snowy weather.

▲ CIRRUS

This basic high-level cloud is formed from tiny ice crystals. Winds sweep the crystals into wispy, curling shapes, so cirrus cloud usually shows the wind direction at high altitude. Although cirrus usually forms in blue skies, it often indicates the approach of rain or snow. It can also be created artificially from the condensation trails of aircraft.

◀ NIMBOSTRATUS

Dark, threatening nimbostratus is a thick layer of midlevel or low-level raincloud that blocks out the sun. It often follows after thinner, mid-level altostratus clouds as a cyclone or depression moves overhead and the weather gets steadily worse. It usually produces persistent rain or snow, which can be heavy but is rarely as torrential as the rain produced during thunderstorms.

▶ ALTOCUMULUS

Fleets of small, puffy clouds that drift across the sky at midlevel are called altocumulus. This type of cloud usually develops in a layer of moist air where the air currents are moving in shallow waves. The clouds form at the cooler wave peaks. They can also form patterns of long, parallel cloud bands that either cover the sky or have clear blue sky between them.

▲ CIRROSTRATUS

A continuous sheet of high-altitude cloud, as at the top of this picture, is described as cirrostratus. It can turn the sky white by day and red at sunset, but is so thin that the Sun, or even the Moon, is clearly visible through it. If cirrostratus is forming from wispy cirrus clouds, it usually means that bad weather is on the way. But if the cloud is breaking up, it generally means that the weather is going to improve.

◀ STRATUS

Any cloud that forms a continuous sheet or layer is known as stratus. It usually forms at low level, turning the whole sky a dreary gray, but may form a little higher, as in this photograph taken at sunset. Stratus often forms when moist air is carried over a cold surface such as the sea, cooling the water vapor so it condenses into cloud. The same process also causes fog.

◀ CUMULONIMBUS

The biggest clouds are those that produce torrential rain, lightning, and hail. Seen in the background here, a cumulonimbus cloud has its base near the ground but builds up to the highest level where it often spreads out like a mushroom because it cannot rise any higher. These clouds contain violent upcurrents that toss raindrops and ice crystals up and down until they finally fall as heavy rain and hail.

▶ CUMULUS

The fluffy clouds that form in blue summer skies are known as cumulus clouds. They form when warm, moist air rises to a height where the temperature is low enough for water vapor to condense into droplets. As the air rises, cooler air descends around each cloud, and this stops it from spreading sideways. Cumulus can grow into more threatening forms, but the type shown here never leads to rain.

EXTREME WEATHER

Intense solar heating can cause very high evaporation rates that make warm, moist air rise unusually fast. This builds up huge cumulonimbus clouds that cause thunderstorms and hail, and creates conditions of extremely low pressure. Air swirls into the low-pressure zone, creating a deep depression with very strong winds. In tropical oceans, intense heating generates hurricanes. In extreme cases the updrafts can give rise to the destructive vortex of a tornado.

▶HAILSTORMS

The giant cumulonimbus clouds that cause thunderstorms are built up by powerful air currents with vertical speeds of 100 mph (160 kph) or more. Ice crystals hurled around by the turbulent air pick up water that freezes onto them, and if they are tossed up and down enough this builds up layer after layer of ice to form hailstones. If the air currents are strong enough, they can create huge—and very dangerous—hailstones like these.

◀LIGHTNING

As the air currents inside a storm cloud throw ice crystals around, friction between the crystals generates static electricity. It charges up the cloud like a giant battery, with the positive charge at the top and the negative charge at the bottom. If the voltage reaches about one million volts, it is discharged as a giant spark of lightning. This heats the air along its path to such a high temperature that it expands explosively, causing the shockwave that we call thunder.

▶TORNADOES

These terrifying events are caused by air swirling into the base of a very vigorous storm cloud and spiraling upward. The updrafts are powerful enough to rip houses apart, and the winds around such tornadoes are the most powerful ever recorded, reaching at least 318 mph (512 kph) on one occasion.

▼ HURRICANES

In tropical oceans, summer warmth makes vast quantities of water turn to water vapor. This rises to form extremely big storm clouds, which circulate around an area of very low air pressure. The clouds spiral inward, with the windspeed building up to 185 mph (300 kph) or more as the spiral tightens—yet the eye of the storm is calm and clear.

▲ WATERSPOUTS

Tornadoes can develop over seas and large lakes, especially in the tropics and subtropics. The powerful upcurrents spiraling up into the cloud draw water up with them, so they are known as waterspouts. They are usually less violent than tornadoes, but a waterspout is strong enough to easily capsize a boat. It is most destructive when it collapses and dumps its heavy load of water.

Updraft can reach 150 mph (240 kph)

Narrow funnel cloud extends down to ground level

▲ STORM SURGE

During a hurricane, the converging winds and extremely low air pressure over the ocean build up a hump of water or "storm surge." This can sweep over the land like a tsunami and causes massive devastation. A storm surge almost destroyed New Orleans in 2005, and killed at least 150,000 people in Burma (Myanmar) in 2008.

CLIMATES

The climate of any region is basically its average weather—its temperatures, rainfall, and winds—and how this varies from season to season. It is defined by a combination of a region's distance from the equator, its altitude above sea level, and how near it is to an ocean. The climate is one of the key influences on the character of the landscape—whether it is green and lush, barren and dusty, or frozen for part or all of the year.

So, although the climate itself is defined by statistics, its effects are usually very obvious.

❶ SOLAR ENERGY
Sunlight is most intense in the tropics, where it strikes Earth directly, and least intense in the polar regions, where it is dispersed. Earth spins on a tilted axis, so the regions facing the Sun most directly change throughout the year, creating the seasons. These become more extreme toward the polar regions, where there is almost constant daylight in summer and constant darkness and extreme cold in winter.

❷ TROPICAL
In the tropics, the intense heat during the day makes vast amounts of water evaporate from the oceans, building up a virtually permanent belt of storm clouds around the world. These spill torrential rain on the land, often almost every day. The rain supports the tropical rain forests, which help make their own climate by pumping more moisture into the air.

❸ SUBTROPICAL
The moist air that rises in the tropics flows away to north and south at high altitude. By the time it reaches the subtropics it has cooled and lost all its water vapor. It starts to sink, creating broad high-pressure zones, but as it sinks it heats up, absorbs any moisture in the land below, and carries it away, creating subtropical deserts such as the Sahara or the arid interior of Australia.

❹ MONSOONS
Northern Asia gets very cold in winter, so it cools the air above and makes it sink. The air flows south toward the Indian Ocean, where it rises again. So in winter India is swept by dry continental air, and there are months of drought. But in summer the continent heats up. This warms the air so it rises and draws moist air from the ocean, causing torrential rain. The seasonal reversal is called a monsoon.

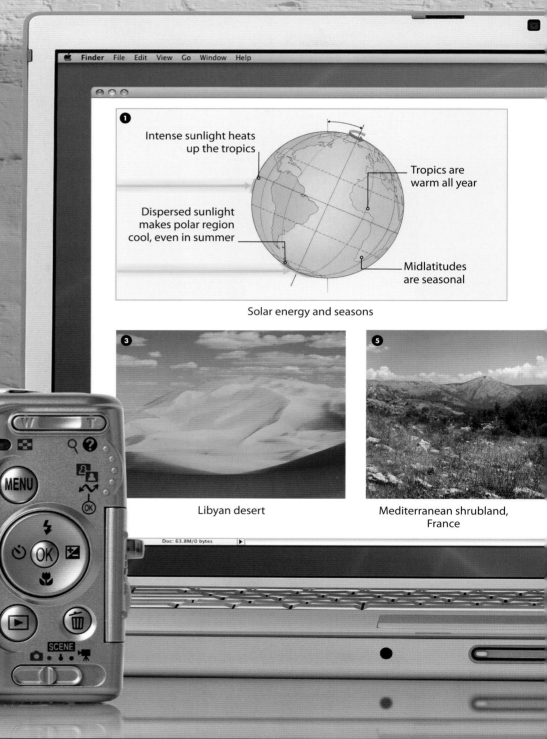

Intense sunlight heats up the tropics

Tropics are warm all year

Dispersed sunlight makes polar region cool, even in summer

Midlatitudes are seasonal

Solar energy and seasons

Libyan desert

Mediterranean shrubland, France

❺ DRY SHRUBLANDS

Around the Mediterranean, and in similar regions such as parts of California and Australia, hot dry summers are followed by mild wet winters. This suits evergreen shrubs with small, leathery leaves, such as wild olive and sagebrush, which lie dormant in summer and grow in the winter. Many are adapted to survive frequent fires, and some even need a fire to make them release their seeds.

❻ MARITIME

In the temperate regions, weather systems move east from the oceans over the land. This means that the western fringes of the continents— places such as Ireland—have mild, often damp maritime climates, with forests and lush grass. By the time the air reaches the continental heartlands it has lost most of its moisture, so the forests are replaced by dry grassland and even deserts.

❼ POLAR FRINGES

The Arctic ice is surrounded by treeless, barren-looking tundra that eventually gives way to a vast belt of evergreen forest. The winters are extremely cold, especially in continental regions that are a long way from oceans. In the tundra this creates permanently frozen ground, or permafrost. The summers are cool, but warm enough to melt the winter snow and allow tough, cold-adapted plants to grow.

❽ POLAR DESERTS

Very little snow falls over polar regions, because of the cold air that sinks over the poles and prevents cloud formation. These regions are, in fact, cold deserts. Over most of Greenland and Antarctica the summers are not warm enough to melt the snow, which builds up over centuries to create permanent ice sheets. Plants cannot grow in such conditions, and there is very little life at all.

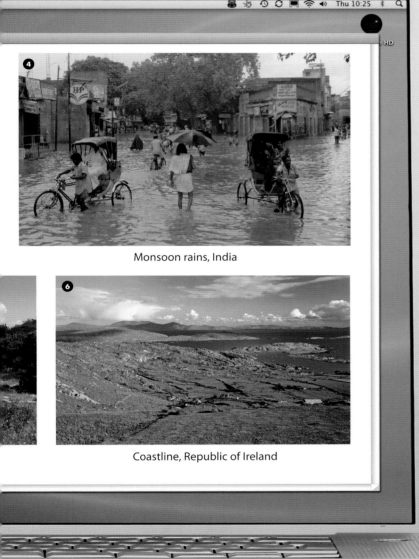

Monsoon rains, India

Coastline, Republic of Ireland

GREEN GLOW
Hardy trees glow with the vivid green of life amid the volcanic rock formations of Cappadocian Valley in Turkey. Life can flourish in the most hostile terrain, thanks to the amazing processes of evolution.

Life zones

STORY OF LIFE

No one really knows how life began. Some people suggest that the seeds of life might have been delivered to Earth in some of the many frozen, watery comets that crashed into the planet early in its history. This may be possible, but any organic material that arrived in this way must have been formed somewhere, by a process that assembled simple chemicals into the extremely complex molecules that are vital to even the most primitive life forms. Most scientists believe that this happened here on Earth, roughly 3.8 billion years ago, within 800 million years of the formation of the planet.

Moss

Paleozoic 540–250 million years ago

Coelacanth

Sea spider

Jellyfish

Precambrian 4.6 billion–540 million years ago

❶ FORMATION OF EARTH
When Earth formed out of a mass of gas and dust some 4.6 billion years ago, it was a biologically dead planet. But its cooling rocks contained all the elements that are vital to the chemistry of living organisms. Its gravity and position in the Solar System also enabled it to retain an atmosphere and oceans of liquid water—both essential conditions for the evolution of life.

❷ ORGANIC MOLECULES
All life depends on the carbon-based molecules that form complex organic materials such as proteins. Living organisms make their own proteins, using coded instructions contained in the spiral molecules of DNA (deoxyribonucleic acid) inherited from their parents. But the very first organic molecules must have been formed by a purely chemical reaction, possibly triggered by the electrical energy of lightning.

❸ LIVING CELLS
The DNA molecule can reproduce itself by splitting in two and adding raw chemicals to each half. To do this—and to make proteins—it needs a reliable supply of chemical nutrients. Key to the evolution of life was the development of the cell—a microscopic package containing water and vital nutrients, as well as DNA and other organic molecules. The first such cells were bacteria, the simplest of all life forms.

❹ ENERGY FROM LIGHT
Life needs energy. Some 3.8 billion years ago, the first bacteria relied on the energy locked up in chemicals. Similar organisms still survive in hot springs. More than a billion years later, bacteria evolved a way to absorb the energy of sunlight, and use it to turn carbon dioxide and water into sugar and oxygen. By this process, called photosynthesis, these cyanobacteria created all the oxygen in the atmosphere.

❺ SUPERCELLS
Bacteria are simple "prokaryotic" cells—tiny bags of chemicals and organic molecules. Approximately 2.5 billion years ago, a more complex type of cell evolved, with structures specialized for different tasks. These include a nucleus that contains the cell's DNA and controls other structures such as those that turn food into energy. Such "eukaryotic" cells are more diverse than bacteria and include a huge variety of single-celled organisms such as planktonic diatoms.

❻ CELL COLONIES
All the earliest living things were single-celled organisms, like most microbes today. Over time, however, some joined together to form colonies like *Volvox*—a modern freshwater organism that is made up of more than 500 eukaryotic cells linked in a sphere. By about 2.2 billion years ago, similar colonies included specialized cells that relied on the others for vital support. Such colonies were becoming the first multicelled organisms.

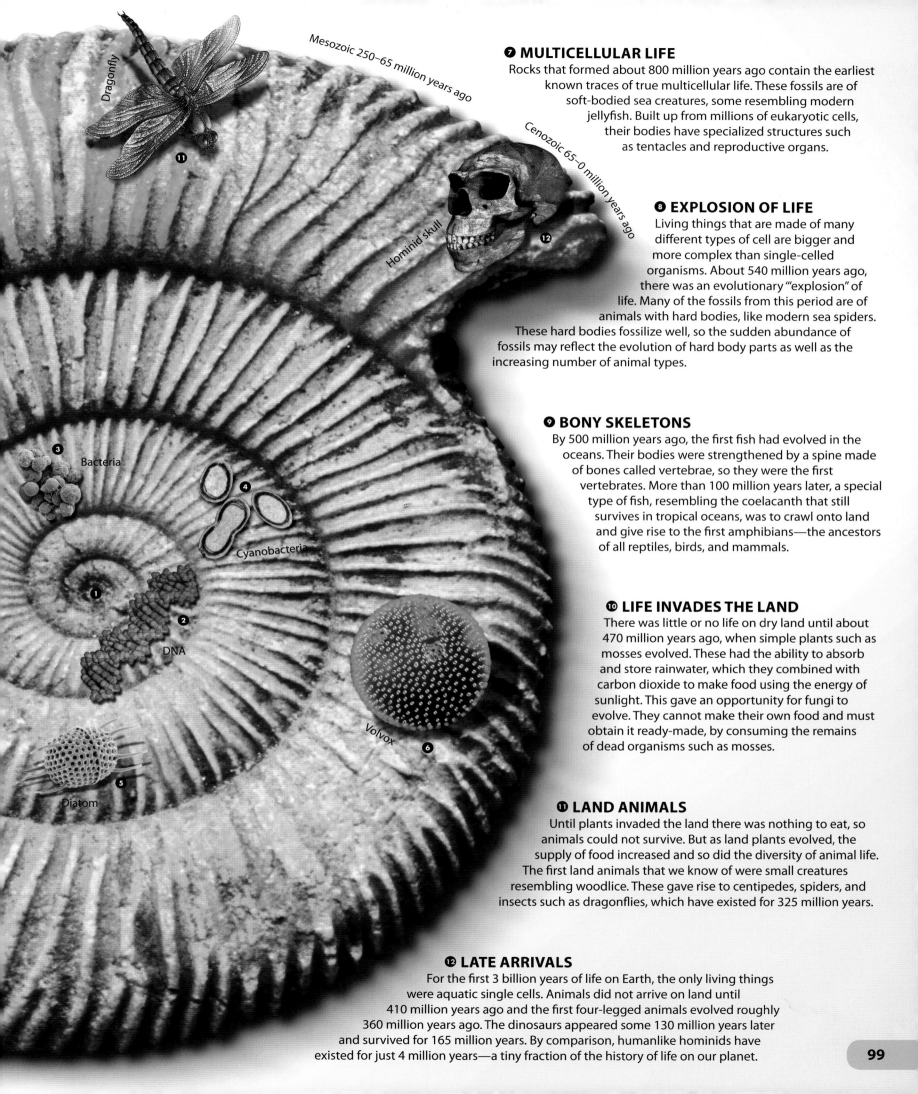

Dragonfly

Mesozoic 250–65 million years ago

Cenozoic 65–0 million years ago

Hominid skull

⑦ MULTICELLULAR LIFE

Rocks that formed about 800 million years ago contain the earliest known traces of true multicellular life. These fossils are of soft-bodied sea creatures, some resembling modern jellyfish. Built up from millions of eukaryotic cells, their bodies have specialized structures such as tentacles and reproductive organs.

⑧ EXPLOSION OF LIFE

Living things that are made of many different types of cell are bigger and more complex than single-celled organisms. About 540 million years ago, there was an evolutionary "explosion" of life. Many of the fossils from this period are of animals with hard bodies, like modern sea spiders. These hard bodies fossilize well, so the sudden abundance of fossils may reflect the evolution of hard body parts as well as the increasing number of animal types.

⑨ BONY SKELETONS

By 500 million years ago, the first fish had evolved in the oceans. Their bodies were strengthened by a spine made of bones called vertebrae, so they were the first vertebrates. More than 100 million years later, a special type of fish, resembling the coelacanth that still survives in tropical oceans, was to crawl onto land and give rise to the first amphibians—the ancestors of all reptiles, birds, and mammals.

Bacteria

Cyanobacteria

DNA

Diatom

Volvox

⑩ LIFE INVADES THE LAND

There was little or no life on dry land until about 470 million years ago, when simple plants such as mosses evolved. These had the ability to absorb and store rainwater, which they combined with carbon dioxide to make food using the energy of sunlight. This gave an opportunity for fungi to evolve. They cannot make their own food and must obtain it ready-made, by consuming the remains of dead organisms such as mosses.

⑪ LAND ANIMALS

Until plants invaded the land there was nothing to eat, so animals could not survive. But as land plants evolved, the supply of food increased and so did the diversity of animal life. The first land animals that we know of were small creatures resembling woodlice. These gave rise to centipedes, spiders, and insects such as dragonflies, which have existed for 325 million years.

⑫ LATE ARRIVALS

For the first 3 billion years of life on Earth, the only living things were aquatic single cells. Animals did not arrive on land until 410 million years ago and the first four-legged animals evolved roughly 360 million years ago. The dinosaurs appeared some 130 million years later and survived for 165 million years. By comparison, humanlike hominids have existed for just 4 million years—a tiny fraction of the history of life on our planet.

BIODIVERSITY

The last 800 million years have seen a spectacular diversification of life in all its forms. The single-celled organisms that dominated life for the previous 3 billion years have been joined by fungi, plants, and animals which, together with bacteria and the mainly single-celled protists, make up the five kingdoms of life. While millions of species have evolved, millions more have suffered extinction, in an endless process that is constantly transforming the nature of life on Earth.

Conifer

Cycad

▼FUNGI
Unlike a plant, a fungus cannot make its own food and must consume it in ready-made form, just like an animal. Microscopic yeasts are single-celled, but most fungi are multicelled, with networks of threadlike stems that may produce the spore-bearing structures we call mushrooms. Some fungi contain food-making algae, forming tough, compound organisms called lichens.

Yeast

◄ PLANTS
Nearly all plants use energy from the Sun to turn carbon dioxide and water into food using a process called photosynthesis. This creates the food that is vital to other forms of life on land. The first plants were low-growing mosses, later joined by ferns and cycads, and the conifers and flowering plants that include many trees.

Lichen

Sunflower

Fern

Moss

Vole

Poison-dart frog

Land crab

▲ANIMAL LIFE—ON LAND
As animals became adapted to life on land, they had to evolve ways of stopping their bodies from drying out. Some retained a connection with water for breeding, but others developed ways of breeding that did not involve water. Some animals, such as snails, land crabs, and frogs, are still tied to moist places. Others, such as insects, reptiles, mammals, and birds, have been able to colonize every viable habitat on dry land.

Garden snail

Diatom skeleton

Foraminiferan skeleton

Radiolarian skeleton

Seaweed

Cyanobacteria

E. coli bacteria

▲ BACTERIA

The simplest of all life forms, bacteria consist of a single "prokaryotic" cell, which has a much simpler structure than the eukaryotic cells of protists and multicelled organisms. Despite this, some forms—cyanobacteria—use photosynthesis to make food, releasing oxygen in the process. In the distant past, this produced the oxygen that made animal life possible.

▲ PROTISTS

Most protists are microscopic organisms, each consisting of a single "eukaryotic" cell. Some, such as diatoms and algae, make food in the same way as plants. Others, such as foraminiferans and radiolarians, are consumers that behave as animals. All these drift in oceans as plankton. Seaweeds are multicelled algae, which can grow very much bigger.

▶ ANIMAL LIFE—IN WATER

All animals are multicelled organisms that get their nutrients from food produced by other living things. They also need oxygen to turn some of these nutrients into energy. The first animals evolved in water, and most still live in aquatic habitats. They range from sponges, which are little more than colonies of cells, to highly active vertebrates such as fish.

Butterfly

Siphonophore

Golden jack

Cobra

Starfish

Mushroom

Hawfinch

Sponge

OCEAN LIFE

Most of the life on Earth lives in the surface zone of the oceans. Here, sunlight provides the energy for plankton and seaweeds to produce food by photosynthesis, and this supports the animals. The deep oceans are too dark for photosynthesis, so animals survive by eating debris drifting down from above, or by eating each other. In general, energy passes up the food chain from microscopic plankton to the most powerful hunters.

❶ Phytoplankton These microscopic single-celled protists turn raw chemicals into the organic tissue that other organisms rely on for food. They thrive only in nutrient-rich water, especially around coasts and in polar oceans.

❷ Zooplankton Swarms of mainly tiny animals drift with the phytoplankton, eating it and preying upon each other. They include adult animals such as copepods and the larvae of creatures such as crabs and mollusks that change their way of life when they mature.

❸ Herring The shoals of small or medium-sized fish, such as anchovy and herring, feed on the plankton, using their gill rakers to strain the small organisms from the water. These shoals can build up to immense sizes in plankton-rich seas.

These plankton swarms attract bigger, predatory fish, such as salmon and tuna. These also form shoals, but are more mobile, crossing oceans in search of prey. Tuna are fast swimmers and travel very long distances.

❹ Seabirds Fish shoals are attacked from the air by squadrons of seabirds, such as gannets. These birds plunge headlong into the water to seize the fish in their long bills. They spend most of their time hunting at sea, but breed in vast coastal colonies.

❻ Sharks Hunters such as tuna are hunted in turn by bigger predators such as marlin, swordfish, and oceanic sharks. The tiger shark is one of the most powerful and dangerous, with sharp teeth that can slice straight through a turtle shell.

❼ Filter-feeding giant The biggest animals in the sea are giant sharks and whales that feed by straining small animals from the water. The basking shark may grow to more than 40 ft (12 m) long.

Streamlined body is packed with muscle

Baby sperm whale is nursed by its mother

Gills are protected by grids that trap food

▲ SUNLIT ZONE

Extending down from the surface to 660 ft (200 m) in clear water, the sunlit zone is just a small fraction of the ocean, which has an average depth of 12,50 ft (3,800 m). Despite this, it contains most of the ocean's animals. They form a complex food web based on clouds of food-producing phytoplankton and the zooplankton swarms that drift with them.

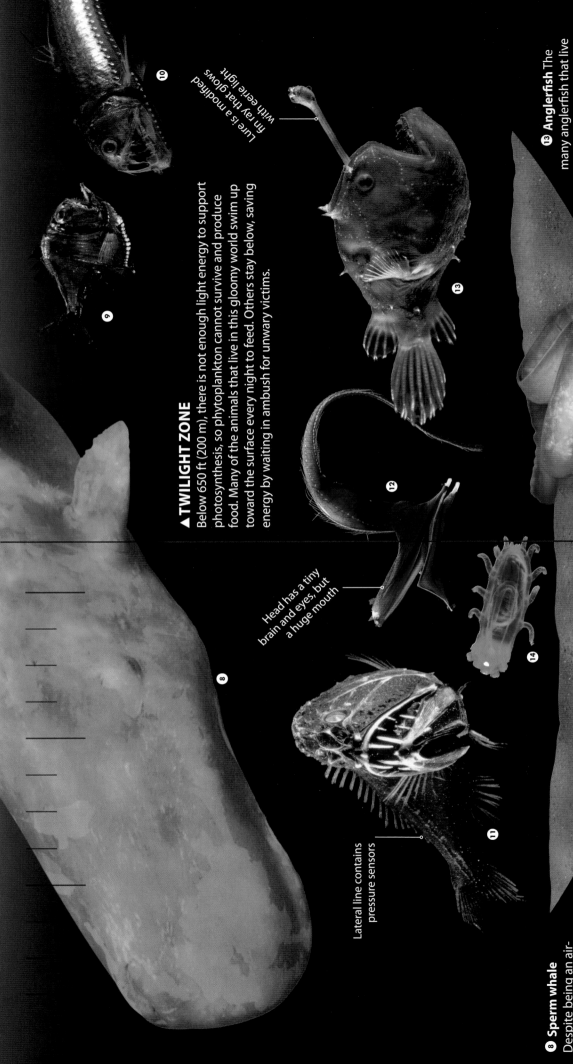

Lure is a modified fin ray that glows with eerie light

▲TWILIGHT ZONE

Below 650 ft (200 m), there is not enough light energy to support photosynthesis, so phytoplankton cannot survive and produce food. Many of the animals that live in this gloomy world swim up toward the surface every night to feed. Others stay below, saving energy by waiting in ambush for unwary victims.

⑬ Anglerfish The many anglerfish that live in the deep ocean tempt their prey with luminous lures. Any fish that decides to investigate is likely to stray within range of the angler's gaping mouth—with fatal consequences.

⑭ Sea cucumber Most sea cucumbers crawl over the ocean floor, sucking up the soft sediment, swallowing it, and digesting anything edible. But some deepwater species like this one can also swim a little.

⑮ Hagfish One of many deepwater scavengers, the slimy hagfish burrows into the carcasses of dead animals to eat them from the inside out. Its acute sense of smell enables it to locate food from far away.

Head has a tiny brain and eyes, but a huge mouth

▲DARK ZONE

Below 3,300 ft (1,000 m), the last glimmer of blue twilight fades out, and the water is pitch black except for the mysterious glow of the luminous animals that live here. Many fish are nightmarish hunters with long teeth and huge, gaping mouths. The deep ocean floor is populated by debris feeders that recycle the remains of dead animals drifting down from above.

⑪ Fangtooth Like the viperfish, the fangtooth has an impressive array of weapons for catching its victims. It has highly developed senses for detecting prey in the dark, including an acute awareness of pressure changes and vibrations in the water.

⑫ Gulper eel The bizarre gulper eels are nearly all mouth, with colossal gapes and flexible, balloonlike stomachs. This enables some species to engulf animals that are their own size or bigger, providing them with enough food to last for several weeks.

⑧ Sperm whale
Despite being an air-breathing mammal, the amazing sperm whale may dive to 3,300 ft (1,000 m) or more to hunt giant squid. It stores vital oxygen in its muscles, and may stay submerged for 45 minutes or more.

⑨ Hatchetfish These flattened fish eat small animals that live in the twilight zone by day but migrate to the surface at night. Their bellies glow with blue light that matches the glow from the surface, hiding their silhouette.

⑩ Viperfish Prey is scarce in the ocean depths, so like most hunters of the deep, the viperfish has extremely long, needlelike teeth to ensure that anything it catches has no chance of escaping.

Lateral line contains pressure sensors

CORAL REEFS AND ATOLLS

Tropical coral reefs are among the richest ecosystems on Earth. Their wealth is based on a partnership between corals, which are colonial animals related to sea anemones, and microscopic organisms living in their tissues that are able to make food by photosynthesis. Since these depend on light for their energy supply, the reefs are restricted to the clear, shallow, sunlit waters around tropical coasts and islands. They provide habitats for a dazzling diversity of marine life, ranging from tiny reef fish to giant clams.

Blue angelfish

Copperband butterfly fish

Lionfish

❶ BARRIER REEFS AND ATOLLS

Many coral reefs have formed around extinct volcanoes that are steadily subsiding under their own weight. The living coral keeps growing upward as the bedrock of the island sinks, to create an offshore barrier reef sheltering a shallow lagoon. When the original volcanic island finally sinks from sight, all that remains is a ring of coral, often capped with sandy islands, known as an atoll.

❷ STONY CORALS

Coral polyps are small cylindrical animals crowned with a ring of stinging tentacles, but they live in interconnected colonies that form branches, broad plates, massive blocks, and other shapes. The colonies are supported by skeletons of limestone secreted by the coral tissues. When individual corals die, the limestone remains. Living coral grows on top of the dead coral, so the limestone gradually builds up into rocky reefs.

Indo-Pacific sergeant

North America

Atlantic Ocean

Pacific Ocean

South America

Key
Tropical coral reef zone
Major reefs

Individual corals are too small to be visible

Some corals form branching colonies

Emperor angelfish

Sea fan

❸ REEF FISH

The total weight of fish, or biomass, on a coral reef is not large compared with some other marine habitats, but there is an amazing diversity of species. They have evolved because there are so many different ways to make a living on the reef. Some, such as parrotfish, eat the coral itself. Others nibble at algae, catch plankton, or prey on each other.

Gray reef sharks

❹ INVERTEBRATES

All kinds of colorful invertebrates live on coral reefs, including delicate prawns, flamboyant sea slugs, and deadly venomous cone shells. The biggest is the giant clam which, like corals, has masses of photosynthetic organisms called zooxanthellae living within its tissues. These provide the clam with sugar in exchange for nutrients that the clam obtains by filtering plankton from the water.

❺ CORAL ISLANDS

The tropical southwest Pacific is dotted with tens of thousands of coral islands. Most are too small to have names, and rise only a metre or two above the waves, but many are crowned with groves of coconut palm and other trees. These provide nesting sites for seabirds, while the beaches are used by breeding sea turtles.

Europe

Asia

Africa

Indian Ocean

Australia

Southern Ocean

❺

Potato cod

Giant clam

❹

❻ THREATS

Tropical stony corals thrive in sea temperatures of 68–84°F (20–29°C). If the water gets warmer than this, they may expel their microscopic, food-making partners and turn white, often with fatal results. Known as coral bleaching, this is posing an increasing threat to coral reefs as ocean temperatures rise. Another threat is the crown-of-thorns starfish, a coral-eater that can multiply rapidly and destroy large areas of coral.

Brightly colored sea slugs nibble at encrusting animals on the reef

Crown-of-thorns starfish

❻

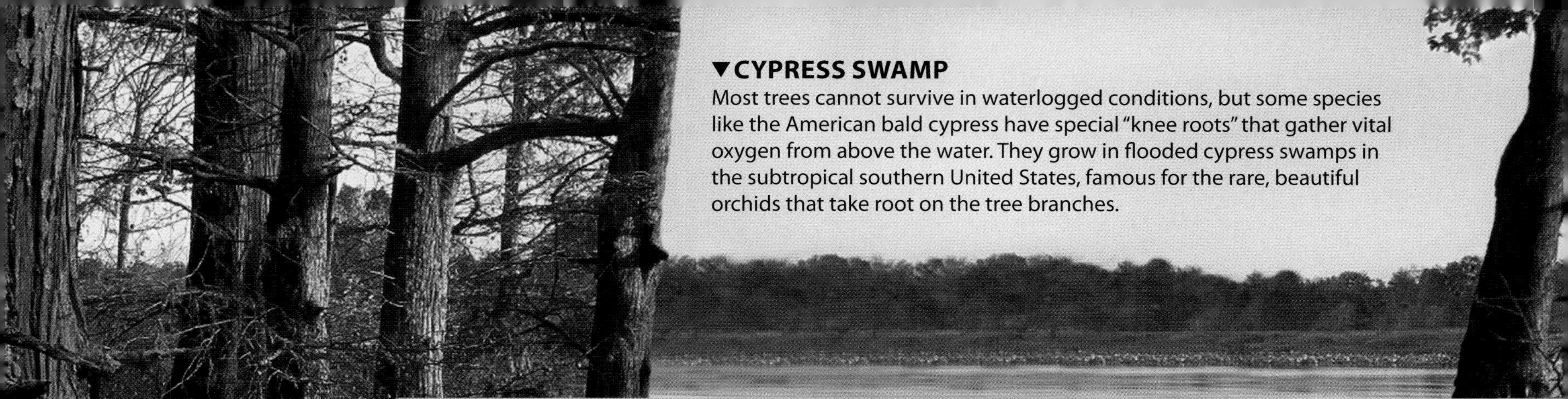

▼CYPRESS SWAMP

Most trees cannot survive in waterlogged conditions, but some species like the American bald cypress have special "knee roots" that gather vital oxygen from above the water. They grow in flooded cypress swamps in the subtropical southern United States, famous for the rare, beautiful orchids that take root on the tree branches.

WETLANDS

Most wetlands are freshwater habitats where most of the water is hidden by dense vegetation. Many are transition zones between open water and dry forest or grassland. They range from overgrown lake and river margins to waterlogged forests with tall trees. Many support a wide diversity of wildlife. Others, such as acid peat bogs, are colonized by only a few specialized plants and animals. Yet even these are rich habitats compared to deserts, because they are so well supplied with the substance vital to all life—water.

▲PAPYRUS SWAMP

The margins of many African lakes and rivers are choked with a type of giant sedge called papyrus, as seen here in the Okavango Delta in Botswana. The matted plants can also form floating islands. Virtually nothing else grows in these papyrus swamps, but they provide safe refuges for a great variety of animal life including waterbirds, crocodiles, and herds of hippos that spend their days in the water and emerge at night to feed on the surrounding grasslands.

▲MARSH AND FEN

Low-lying waterlogged land supports grasses, sedges, and reeds that root in the mud, forming a marsh. As the plants die they do not decay fully in the waterlogged soil, but build up as peat. Over time, water-tolerant trees such as willow and alder take root, dry out the peat, and turn the marsh into fen woodland.

Cattle egret

▶ MANGROVES

Sheltered tropical coasts and river estuaries are colonized by mangroves—evergreen trees that can grow in salty, waterlogged soil thanks to root modifications like those of swamp cypresses. The mangrove forests are flooded at high tide, providing safe havens for many fish. Low tide reveals muddy swamps, alive with fiddler crabs and air-breathing fish called mudskippers.

▶ ACID PEAT BOG

In cool, wet regions, spongy sphagnum moss grows on top of waterlogged plant remains to create acid peat bogs. Few other plants can grow in the acid, infertile conditions, but those that can include specialists such as carnivorous fly-traps, which feed on the mosquitoes that breed in the bog pools.

Mosquitoes

◀ TUNDRA SWAMP

In the far north, evergreen forest gives way to the open tundra that surrounds the poles. Here, the ground is permanently frozen at depth, forming a layer of permafrost. The surface thaws in summer, but the waterproof permafrost layer prevents the meltwater from draining away, so the defrosted tundra becomes a waterlogged swamp. It resembles an acid peat bog, but colder, and only a few tough plants can survive the combination of waterlogged soils, icy winds, and winter freezing.

◀ TROPICAL SEASONAL WETLAND

During the tropical rainy season, the great rivers that drain the forests and savannas burst their banks to flood the landscape. In southern Amazonia this creates the Pantanal, which at peak flood covers 75,000 sq miles (195,000 sq km), making it the largest wetland in the world. The whole area becomes a habitat for aquatic animals, such as these spectacled caymans, the anaconda—the world's biggest snake—and the giant river otter.

Anaconda

▶ SALT MARSH

Muddy estuaries in temperate regions are colonized by low-growing salt-tolerant plants, forming tidal salt marshes. The regions nearest to the coast are dominated by fleshy plants and grasses, but other areas are more shrubby. They provide homes for a variety of small animals, including the endangered salt marsh harvest mouse of California.

Salt marsh harvest mouse

Red-eyed tree frog,
Central America

FORESTS

Forests and woodlands are dense stands of trees growing so closely together that their crowns form a virtually continuous canopy, shading the ground below. Trees cannot grow so densely in dry climates, so forests are restricted to regions that experience regular rainfall, or where the climate is so cool that the ground never dries out. Other plants grow among the trees where they can get enough light. The trees also provide food-rich habitats for a wide variety of animals.

▼ TROPICAL RAIN FOREST

Near the equator, heavy rain and high temperatures throughout the year create ideal conditions for tree growth, and these are the most luxuriant forests in the world. The trees are broad-leaved evergreens that grow to immense heights, creating a multilayered habitat that teems with life—most of it living high above the forest floor.

Wooly monkey,
Amazonia

▲ DRY WOODLAND

The delicate leaves of rain-forest trees are destroyed by long droughts, so many trees that live in dryer climates, such as in Mediterranean and eucalypt forests, have evolved tougher types of leaves. The leaves of these Spanish cork oaks have thicker outer layers so they do not dry up. The bark of these trees has been harvested to be turned into cork.

Green rosella,
Tasmania

◄ TEMPERATE RAIN FOREST

Rain forests are not restricted to the tropics. Similar trees also grow in temperate rain forests, where the climate is cooler but still very wet, with mild, often frost-free winters. Forests of this type grow in Japan, New Zealand, and Tasmania, and include the giant redwood forests on the northern Pacific coast of North America.

North
America

Pacific
Ocean

South
America

Key
Taiga forest
Temperate rain forest
Tropical rain forest
Temperate deciduous/mixed forest
Dry woodland/eucalypt forest

◀ CONIFER FOREST

Coniferous trees such as cedar and cypress that grow in dry regions have leaves that are reduced to waxy needles to resist moisture loss. This leaf form also resists freezing, so needle-leafed conifers such as pine and spruce dominate the cold taiga forests that form a vast band around the north, through Alaska, Canada, Scandinavia, and Russia.

Two-tailed pasha, southern Europe

Europe

Asia

Africa

Atlantic Ocean

Indian Ocean

Australia

Southern Ocean

▲ BAMBOO FOREST

Many parts of the world have forests that are dominated by a particular type of tree. Unusually the forests of southwest China are dominated by bamboo, which is a type of giant grass. Along with rhododendron, it forms a dense undergrowth beneath the tall trees, and provides food for the bamboo-eating giant panda.

Fallow deer, UK

◀ DRY EUCALYPT FOREST

Most of the native trees of Australia are various types of eucalypt, with about 450 species altogether. They typically have fire-resistant bark and thick, leathery leaves that resist drying out in the hot sunshine. The leaves are full of oils that make them taste bad, but depite this they are the sole food of the koala, which is specially adapted to digest them.

▶ TEMPERATE DECIDUOUS FOREST

Some trees that live in temperate regions, such as oaks, beeches, and maples, have evolved thin, delicate leaves that make the most of the summer sun to photosynthesize. These leaves turn brown, die, and are discarded as winter closes in, and are replaced with a new set in spring.

The tropical grasslands of Africa are typically vast seas of grass dotted with drought-resistant acacia and baobab trees. Only a few of the world's grasslands, such as the Serengeti Plains of Tanzania, have retained their original wildlife. Vast herds of antelope and zebra migrate across the plains to find good grazing. They provide food for hunters such as lions and hyenas.

GRASSLANDS

In regions that are too dry for forests, but not quite dry enough to be described as deserts, the natural vegetation is grass. Other plants are dotted among the grasses, including scattered trees, but grass dominates the landscape. Temperate grasslands tend to be dry throughout the year, but tropical grasslands have long rainy seasons followed by long droughts. They support herds of large grazing mammals, many of which migrate over long distances to exploit seasonal flushes of lush growth.

North American prairie

Brazilian cerrado

Pampas

Key
☐ Tropical grassland
☐ Temperate grassland

Black-tailed prairie dog

▲ PAMPAS
Many dry grasslands develop in the lee (sheltered side) of high mountain ranges that intercept all the rain carried on prevailing winds. In South America, the Andes strip the moisture from winds blowing off the Pacific, and the lands in the "rain shadow" to the east of the mountains form the cool, dry Pampas of southern Argentina.

◄ NORTH AMERICAN PRAIRIE
The dry heartlands of North America were once vast grassy plains, grazed by huge, nomadic herds of bison and pronghorn antelope. They also provided a home for the ground squirrels known as prairie dogs, which lived in vast colonies bigger than many cities. Most of the original grassland has now been turned into farmland, but small pockets remain.

◀ ASIAN STEPPE

The temperate grasslands of central Eurasia have developed in the heart of the continent, and have hot, dry summers and cold, dry winters. Like many other grasslands they originally supported herds of big grazing animals, such as the saiga antelope and wild horses, but today the most numerous wild mammals are small species such as this ground squirrel.

◀ MOUNTAIN GRASSLANDS

Grasslands develop in mountains above the "tree line" or upper limit of tree growth. They resemble tundra, with tough, cold-adapted plants that can survive many months of snow cover and harsh, biting winds. They can be bleak places, but where there is a bedrock of nutrient-rich limestone, they are often bright with flowers such as this yellow alpine foxglove, being used as a perch by a false heath fritillary butterfly.

European souslik

Asian steppe

Indian savanna

African savanna

Australian bush

▲ INDIAN SAVANNA

Like many grasslands, the savannas of India are now mainly farmland, but patches survive in hilly regions and on desert fringes. One of the few areas left lies in the foothills of the Himalayas in northern India, where monsoon rains fuel the growth of tall grasses that help tigers stalk their prey undetected.

▼ BRAZILIAN CERRADO

The forests of Amazonia are flanked by two large tracts of tropical grassland—the Llanos in the north and the Cerrado in the east. The Cerrado is a rich habitat that grades into palm forest in wetter areas, and semi-desert in the drier south. It supports a wide variety of animals, such as ostrich-like rheas and the extraordinary giant anteater.

Giant anteater

▲ AUSTRALIAN BUSH

Dry grassland covers vast areas of Australia, grading into the deserts of the continent's arid interior. The main vegetation is spinifex, a tough form of tussock grass, dotted with eucalyptus trees and scrub. The grassland is regularly swept by fire, but the grasses and trees are adapted to survive this, and some plants even need regular fires to reproduce.

DESERTS

Deserts develop in very dry regions at the hearts of continents, in areas sheltered from rain by high mountains, or in the subtropical desert zone where sinking dry air prevents clouds forming. The scant vegetation is dominated by drought-resistant plants such as cacti, euphorbias, and tough woody shrubs. The animal life consists mainly of insects, spiders, scorpions, and reptiles, but there are some birds and a few mammals. The few large animals are nomadic, and most of the smaller ones hide in burrows by day and come out only at night.

Saguaro can grow to 40 ft (12 m)

◀ATACAMA DESERT
The driest desert in the world, the Atacama lies along the northwestern coast of Chile, where the only moisture is delivered by fog rolling in from the Pacific. This supports sparse vegetation in places, providing food for animals such as these guanacos—relatives of llamas—but most of the desert is a barren wasteland.

Sonoran Desert

Sahara

◀ SONORAN DESERT
One of a complex of deserts in the southwestern United States and Mexico, the Sonoran Desert is famous for its giant saguaro cacti and the drifts of short-lived flowers that bloom in the wake of winter rains. To the north lies the Mohave Desert, site of the infamous Death Valley—the hottest place in the US with a record high of 134°F (57°C).

Atacama Desert

Namib Desert

Kalahari Desert

Key
Desert

Patagonian Desert

Cactus wren perches on a saguaro flower

▶ PATAGONIAN DESERT
Oceanic winds blowing toward the east over the southern Andes mountains lose all their moisture on the western flanks, so the land to the east gets very little rain. This creates the cool Patagonian Desert—a largely barren, stony landscape inhabited by a few tough animals such as this hairy armadillo.

► KALAHARI DESERT

Lying at the heart of southern Africa, the Kalahari is a mixture of scorpion-infested desert with long sand dunes, and tree-dotted dry grasslands. The region contains the Okavango Delta, the remains of a huge prehistoric lake, that floods during the rainy season to create one of Africa's largest remaining wildlife havens.

Sting in the tail used for defense

Burrowing scorpion

▼ GOBI DESERT

The Gobi Desert of Mongolia and northern China is a region of high, waterless, stone-littered plains that suffers blistering summer heat and freezing winters. It owes its dry climate to its distance from the oceans. Over vast areas there are very few plants, yet bactrian camels, wild donkeys, and gazelles survive by wandering widely in search of food.

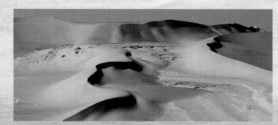

◄ ARABIAN DESERT

This is the classic sandy desert, with great expanses of sand dunes that, in the "Empty Quarter" to the south, cover an area the size of France. There is very little wildlife in the heart of the desert, but the sands lie above oil-rich sediments that have brought wealth to the few people who live here.

Gobi Desert

Arabian Desert

Australian Desert

▲ SAHARA

By far the world's largest desert, the Sahara has a total area of well over 3½ million sq miles (9 million sq km). It has immense "sand seas" with dunes up to 300 m (970 ft) high, and vast tracts of gravel and bare rock. Scattered oases of moist ground support palm trees and spiny shrubs, and provide vital water for desert animals and people.

White lady spiders communicate by drumming the sand with their legs

Humps used to store fat

Bactrian camel

► NAMIB DESERT

Lying along the Atlantic coast of Namibia, this is the African equivalent of the Atacama—a coastal desert created by the prevailing winds blowing from the shore to the ocean. Cold air that does blow in off the sea brings fog that supports the few plants and animals in the region, such as the white lady spider.

White lady spider

Thorny devil

Scaly skin stops lizard drying out

◄ AUSTRALIAN DESERT

Some 40 percent of Australia is desert, with vast expanses of red sand and bare rock, dotted with scrub. It is inhabited by venomous snakes, lizards such as the ant-eating thorny devil, nomadic birds, and native marsupial mammals—many of which are now very rare because of the competition from introduced rabbits.

RECLAIMED LAND
The massed flowers of tulips create a dazzling spring spectacle on the bulb fields near Lisse, in the Netherlands. This geometrical landscape is completely artificial, created on land reclaimed from the sea.

Human influence

FARMING

People first started farming the land in the late stone age. Since then, farming has had a bigger impact on the landscape than any other human activity, eliminating forests, wild grasslands, and wetlands to create fields to grow crops and raise animals. In traditional mixed farming, animals are run over the land to fertilize the soil, and a variety of crops are grown in rotation to prevent the buildup of disease. However, animals may be raised without growing any crops. The use of artificial fertilizers and pesticides now enables one valuable crop to be grown repeatedly on the same

❶ SLASH AND BURN

The most basic form of farming involves clearing the land of trees and other wild plants, burning the wood, spreading the nutrient-rich ash on the ground, and planting crops. When the fertility of the soil declines, the farmers move elsewhere. This "slash and burn" technique has been used for thousands of years, and is still employed in tropical forests. It can work well on a small scale, but if large areas are cleared there is less scope for moving on. The soil becomes exhausted and the land soon becomes waste ground.

❸ MIXED FARMING

Confining farm animals such as sheep or cattle to a fenced field ensures that all their dung falls within a well-defined area and fertilizes the land. The field can then be used to grow crops. This can be repeated indefinitely, especially if the crops are varied so that they take different nutrients from the soil. Some crops are grown for the animals, while others are harvested and eaten or sold.

❷ RANCHING

One of the most basic forms of farming involves running herds of domestic animals over large areas of land, and allowing them to graze the wild plants. The land is often not fenced in any way, and managing the animals may involve rounding them up from a wide area using horses, as here in Ecuador. Although crops are not planted, such ranching often involves clearing forests and eliminating wild grazing animals and predators. The grazing itself alters the nature of the vegetation, suppressing most plants and gradually creating grassland.

❹ MONOCULTURE

Modern fertilizers allow the same crop to be planted on a field year after year, without the need for farm animals. This enables farmers to specialize in the crops that yield most profit, so the whole farm may be given over to growing a single product such as wheat. Unfortunately, such monocultures are hostile to wildlife, partly because weeds and insects are controlled by chemicals, and this has brought many species close to extinction.

⑤ RICE GROWING

Some forms of agriculture have always been highly specialized. They include cultivating rice, which grows best in flooded paddy fields. Here in Bali, the hillsides have been terraced to create tiers of paddy fields. Unfortunately, microbes in the wet soil absorb carbon from the plants and turn it into methane, one of the gases causing climate change, and rice growing accounts for more than 10 percent of all methane emissions.

⑥ GREEN DESERTS

Modern technology can even allow crops to be grown in the desert, using water that is sprinkled by huge irrigation systems. These may travel slowly over the land, creating rectangles of green crops, or rotate to form discs. However, evaporation in the hot climate can make salts build up in the soil, so the land cannot be used like this forever. Eventually, it becomes too salty to grow any crops at all.

117

...NING

...nds of years, people have mined native ...h as gold, silver, and copper, and turned ...tools, weapons, and ornaments. At some ...y discovered that heating far more abundant ...s in a charcoal furnace separated the pure ...d this led to the widespread use of materials ...Other minerals such as flint, building stone, ...tones have also been mined since prehistory. ...n as coal, oil, and natural gas have been ...more recently. The three main techniques ...ying, deep shaft mining, and drilling into ...d to tap buried oil and gas reserves.

❶ STONE QUARRY

Building stone has always been a valuable resource. Originally chipped out and shaped using hand tools, it is now extracted using carefully placed explosive charges, or sliced out by machines. The stone being quarried here in Italy is Cararra marble, one of the finest of all stones. It has been used since Roman times for prestige building projects and sculptures such as the work of Michaelangelo.

❹ PANNING FOR GOLD

The fact that gold exists naturally in its native form makes it possible for people to extract it using the most basic methods, such as panning. This involves swirling water through gold-bearing sediments to carry away the lighter particles and leave the heavy gold. Gold is so rare, however, that days of work by these panners in Vietnam are likely to yield just a few grains of the precious metal.

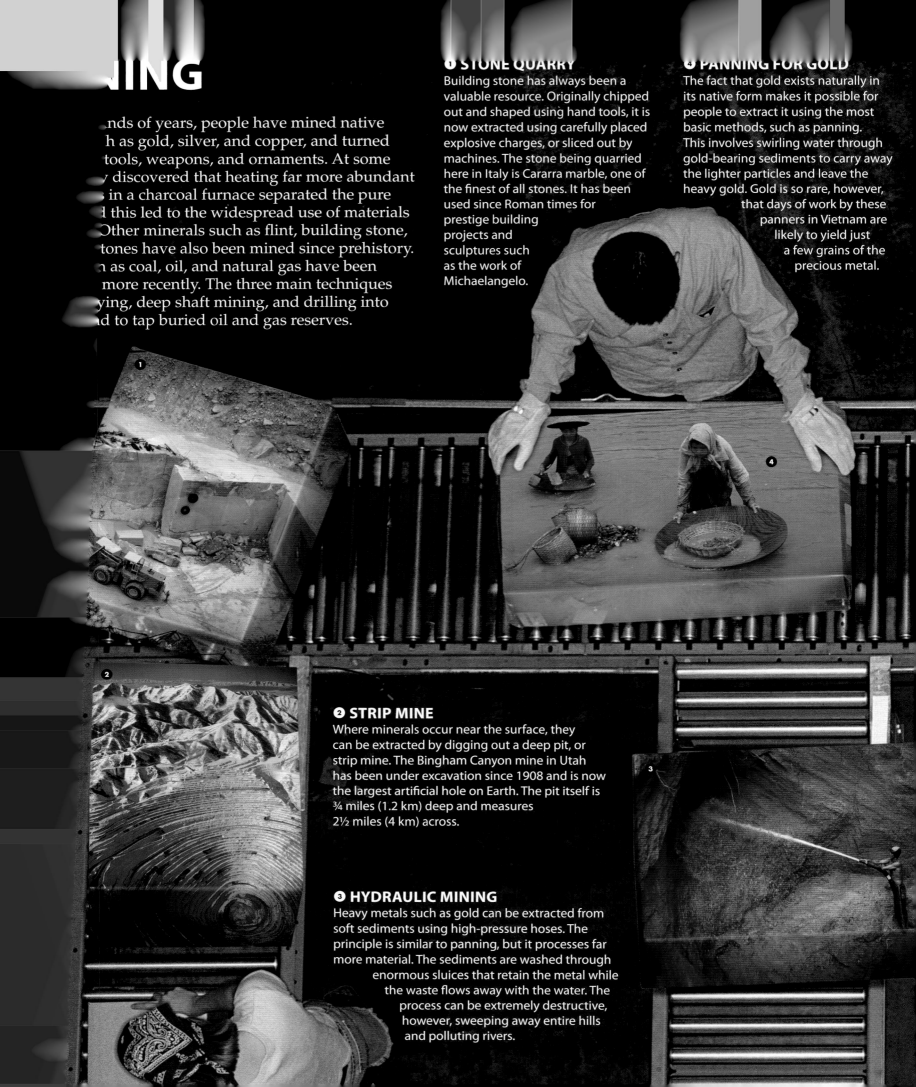

❷ STRIP MINE

Where minerals occur near the surface, they can be extracted by digging out a deep pit, or strip mine. The Bingham Canyon mine in Utah has been under excavation since 1908 and is now the largest artificial hole on Earth. The pit itself is ¾ miles (1.2 km) deep and measures 2½ miles (4 km) across.

❸ HYDRAULIC MINING

Heavy metals such as gold can be extracted from soft sediments using high-pressure hoses. The principle is similar to panning, but it processes far more material. The sediments are washed through enormous sluices that retain the metal while the waste flows away with the water. The process can be extremely destructive, however, sweeping away entire hills and polluting rivers.

❺ EMERALD MINE

Most mining is carried out on an industrial scale, using big, expensive machines. But in some parts of the world, valuable gold and gemstones are still mined at least partly by manual labor. At the Muzo emerald mine in Colombia, South America, one day a month is set aside for the swarms of workers to try their own luck, using simple picks and even their bare hands, and possibly dig out a fortune in gemstones.

❽ GRAVEL PIT

Not all mining operations involve obviously valuable minerals. Two of the most important products are sand and gravel, dug from vast pits and used to make the concrete that is so essential to the construction industry. Gravel is also gathered from the seabed using large dredgers. Some particularly pure forms of quartz sand are quarried for glass-making, and fine clays are mined for use in ceramics and papermaking.

❻ COAL MINE

The most dangerous and expensive type of mining involves sinking deep shafts and long galleries to extract minerals from far below the surface. A lot of coal is mined in this way, using big machines like this one in a mine in Germany. The mines must be drained of water, ventilated to remove gas, and cooled to reduce the high temperatures that exist deep below ground.

❼ OIL RIG

Crude oil is a relatively light liquid that seeps up through porous sediments until it reaches a layer of rock that it cannot pass through. It accumulates in underground reservoirs, often topped with natural gas. Both can be extracted by drilling through the rock, but locating big reservoirs is not easy. Many occur below shallow seabeds and are exploited using offshore rigs like this one.

INDUSTRY AND TRANSPORTATION

While farming and mining have had the most dramatic impacts on the landscape, industry and transportation have probably done more to change people's lives. The products of industry are now used routinely almost worldwide, and most countries have transportation networks that both distribute these products and allow people to move easily from place to place. Along with power supply networks, communications, water supplies, and drainage systems, they form the "infrastructure" of civilization that is now taken for granted in the developed world. Modern cities—and, in fact, modern life—could not exist without it.

◄ POWER SUPPLIES

Industry, homes, and some forms of transportation depend on a reliable electricity supply. Some is generated using wind or solar energy, or the power of flowing water. Other plants use nuclear reactors to heat water and drive steam turbines. Most, however, burn gas or coal, and get through vast amounts of fuel. A typical coal-fired plant burns enough coal every day to fill at least 100 of these big rail trucks.

◄ SHIPPING

Shipping is one of the oldest forms of transportation, yet still one of the most efficient for heavy, bulky goods. In the past, ships were loaded at city docks, but today many cargoes are put into containers at the factory and sent by rail and road to a dedicated cargo terminal. Here, the containers are stacked onto ships like this one—which can carry up to 7,500 containers—for delivery to similar cargo terminals all over the world.

▲ ROAD FREIGHT

A lot of the heavy freight that was once carried by rail is now transported by road, often using giant trucks like this tanker. This is a less efficient use of fuel than rail transportation, but it has the advantage of delivering goods directly to a destination, rather than to a rail terminal that can be a long distance away. The weight of such road trucks is immense, however, increasing highway maintenance costs.

▶ RAILROADS

Since the mid-19th century, railroads have been vital arteries of commerce. They are still important for carrying heavy items, such as these containers, each one of which would be a full load for a truck. The smooth, relatively flat railroad enables very heavy loads to be moved using relatively little energy. However, each track is very expensive to build.

▼ HIGHWAY NETWORKS

All developed countries now have complex networks of multilane highways like this, as well as local road systems. The driving force behind this development has been private car ownership. Traffic congestion and pollution are now becoming serious problems, however, and car use may soon lose some of its appeal.

► AIRPORTS

Air travel for both business and leisure is now a part of normal life for many people, especially in big countries such as the United States, where cities are far apart. Airports make a big impact on the landscape, however, and aircraft noise and pollution are serious problems that are only partly addressed by improved aircraft design. The massive growth in leisure air travel has also had profound effects on many tourist destinations, turning coastal communities into hotel resorts and virtually eliminating many traditional ways of life.

► CITY TRANSPORTATION

Many cities have rapid transportation systems that enable people to get around easily without using their cars. They include surface tramway systems like this one in southern France, and subways that run beneath the streets. Both use metal tracks and electric power, which keeps their energy requirements as low as possible. This is likely to become increasingly important in the future as energy costs rise.

CITIES

Some 7,000 years ago, the development of farming in ancient Mesopotamia—now Iraq—produced a surplus of wealth that encouraged the growth of the first cities. Since then, city living has spread around the world, but until recently most people still lived in small communities. Today, more than half the world's population lives in cities, some of which have grown to colossal size. Many historic cities are surrounded by new development, and many have been transformed by high-rise architecture.

❶ TINERHIR

The ancient town of Tinerhir in Morocco is very similar to the first cities, with houses made of mud brick and separated by narrow alleyways rather than wide roads suitable for vehicles. The town is located between two oases that provide vital water and surrounded by farmland and olive groves that, until recently, provided the main wealth of the citizens.

❷ ATHENS

The idea of the city as a center of civilization was born in city-states such as Athens about 2,500 years ago. The politicians of Athens are widely credited with inventing modern democracy. Many buildings of the era survive, including the Parthenon, seen here, which was built in about 440 BCE and still dominates the city.

❸ MACCHU PICCHU

This spectacular city was built by the Incas of Peru in about 1460. Although situated high in the Andes, it has reliable water sources and enough terraced farmland to support all the people who might have lived there. It was abandoned about a century after it was built—probably because of disease—and is now a ruin.

❹ CARCASSONNE

In the past, many rich cities were fortified to protect them from raiders. Carcassonne in southern France still retains its double ring of ramparts. From 1250, the town was extended beyond the fortifications, but this lower city was later destroyed by an invading army—demonstrating the value of the ancient city walls.

❺ VENICE

The richest cities were built on the wealth acquired through trade. During the Middle Ages, trade with the east brought rich rewards to Venice, a city built on 118 islands in a shallow coastal lagoon in northern Italy. Its many palaces and churches, rising directly from the water of its canals, make it one of the world's most beautiful cities.

❻ PARIS

Most old cities have been built up little by little, resulting in winding, narrow streets and a great variety of buildings. In the 19th century, much of Paris, the capital of France, was replaced with a planned city built around a geometrical network of wide avenues. Similar planning is now commonly used in new cities, often with the addition of open green spaces and road systems designed for use by high-speed traffic.

❼ TOKYO

Together with neighboring Yokohama, Kawasaki, and Chiba, Tokyo forms the biggest city in the world with more than 30 million inhabitants. It was virtually destroyed in 1923 by an earthquake. Since then, it has been rebuilt in the high-rise style typical of the world's richest cities. The steel-framed towers are more earthquake-proof than traditional masonry buildings.

❽ SHANTY TOWN

Cities are wealthy places that attract people looking for work. Many cannot afford to live in the city centers and in some countries rich cities are surrounded by squalid shanty towns housing poor workers and their families. They have no proper drainage or water supply, and suffer high rates of disease.

ENVIRONMENT AND CONSERVATION

Over the last 100 years, the world's population has risen from 1.5 billion to more than 6 billion. All these people have to live somewhere, and must eat. They also consume energy, and most now demand the luxuries of modern technology. As a result, vast areas of former wilderness have been built over or turned into farmland. Every day huge quantities of coal, oil, and gas are burned as fuel, and colossal amounts of waste and pollution are generated. Both the world's wildlife and the stability of the climate are under threat, and our future depends on solving the problem.

❶ INDUSTRIAL POLLUTION

The factories and power stations of the industrialized world release huge amounts of waste gas into the atmosphere every day. Much of this is carbon dioxide and nitrous oxide, which cause global warming. Other pollutants include sulfur dioxide, which combines with water vapor in the air to form acid rain, and soot particles that create choking smog.

❷ TRANSPORT EMISSIONS

Many forms of transportation—particularly on the roads and in the air—rely on burning hydrocarbon fuels derived from oil. This releases large amounts of waste gases into the air, particularly carbon dioxide. Modern cars are designed to minimize this, but there are more cars on the roads every year. Aircraft emissions at high altitude have a particularly serious impact.

❸ GARBAGE

Until the mid-20th century, most of the trash we produced could be broken down by natural decay. Most plastics, by contrast, are almost indestructible unless burned, which causes pollution. As a result, many countries are facing a mounting garbage problem. New York City alone produces 12,000 tons of domestic waste a day.

❹ CONTAMINATED RIVERS

Fresh, clean water is a vital resource, but all over the world streams and rivers are being polluted by industrial waste and sewage. This can poison wildlife and cause serious diseases, such as cholera. Fertilizers draining off farmland into rivers upset the balance of nature. Deforestation also allows soil to be swept into rivers by heavy rain, choking the water.

❺ POLLUTED OCEANS

The oceans are vast, but they are still affected by pollution. Oil spills at sea are deadly to wildlife like this penguin, and the oil that washes up on coasts is equally destructive. Drifting plastic garbage kills many seals, turtles, and seabirds, and engine noise from ships may make whales lose their way and become fatally stranded on beaches.

❻ DEFORESTATION

Over the past 50 years, a third of the world's rain forests have been felled and burned, and the rate of deforestation is increasing. This is destroying one of the world's richest habitats, and placing thousands of species of plants and animals in danger of extinction. It is also adding a huge amount of carbon dioxide to the atmosphere, contributing to climate change.

❼ CLIMATE CHANGE

Pollution of the atmosphere with carbon dioxide and other greenhouse gases is warming it up, raising world temperatures. Polar ice is melting, and by 2050—if not before—there may be no ice at the North Pole in the summer. Polar bears could become extinct, and if the polar ice sheets melt, sea levels could rise by up to 80 ft (25 m), drowning the world's coastal cities.

❽ CONSERVATION

Humanity relies on the web of life that produces our food and makes the air fit to breathe. We can help secure its future by protecting wildlife and wild places, and working to reduce climate change. Conservation can also provide tourist income for nations, such as Kenya, that still have spectacular wildlife.

❾ SAVING ENERGY

People in the industrialized world use a lot of energy every day, and most of it is generated in ways that add to climate change. We can reduce energy use by living in houses that need less heating or air-conditioning and that generate their own power. These "zero-carbon" homes in London, UK, are designed to produce the energy they need from sources such as solar panels.

❿ THINKING FOR THE FUTURE

Many environmental problems have been brought about by using scarce resources to produce things that are thrown away, or by wasting energy by moving goods around the world. Many people now try to reuse and recycle more, and by buying local produce in markets such as this one they save energy and help fight climate change.

ANIMALS

SAVANNA WILDLIFE
At a waterhole in the African savanna, giraffes, zebras, birds, and other thirsty animals gather to drink. These creatures are a tiny sample of the enormous variety of animals found worldwide.

Diversity

LIFE

From microscopic bacteria to massive blue whales, planet Earth is populated by a spectacular variety of life. But, despite their obvious differences, all living things share certain common features. They all obtain energy, grow, respond to their surroundings, and reproduce—things that nonliving objects, such as rocks, cannot do. Scientists divide life-forms into five distinct groups called kingdoms. Each has its own features, as you can see here.

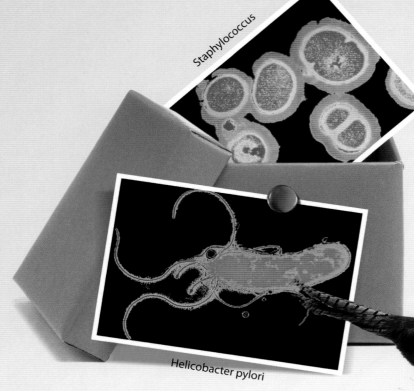

Staphylococcus

BACTERIA ▶
These are the tiniest, most abundant, and most widespread life-forms. Bacteria consist of single cells that, despite being simpler than those in other organisms, work in the same basic ways. Some take in food from their surroundings, while others make their own, using sunlight or other sources of energy.

Helicobacter pylori

Amoeba

◀ PROTISTS
Like bacteria, most protists also consist of single cells, but they are larger and just as complex as the cells that form animals and plants. Protists generally live in water or damp places. They are divided into animal-like protozoa, which take in food from their surroundings, and plantlike algae, which make food by photosynthesis.

Fly agaric

Paramecium

Puffballs

FUNGI ▶
Mushrooms, toadstools, molds, and yeasts are just some of the organisms that make up the fungi. Some resemble plants, but they live in a very different way. Fungi feed by releasing digestive chemicals called enzymes that break down dead or living matter, then absorb the simple nutrients that are released.

Dried yeast

Bread mold

Bracket fungus

ANIMALS ▼

Despite their diversity, all animals share certain key features. They are all multicellular (made from many cells), and get their food by eating other living things. All animals move at least part of their body, and many move around actively to find their food, using one or more senses to detect it.

Koala

South American tapir

Llama

Strawberry shrimp

Pheasant

Mudskipper

Mangrove rat snake

Porcupine

Horsefly

Nautilus

Iguana

Rat

Crab

Hissing cockroach

Armadillo

PLANTS ▶

From grasses to giant trees, all plants require water, sunlight, and soil in which to grow their roots. Most plants do not move actively or feed on other organisms. Instead, they use a process called photosynthesis, trapping sunlight energy to turn carbon dioxide and water into food.

Lily

Moss

Grass

Ivy

131

❶ PORIFERA

There are 5,000 species of sponge, all of which live either in the sea or fresh water. As larvae they drift until finding a suitable place to settle, then stay fixed to that spot as adults. Sponges are the simplest of all animals, with no regular shape. They feed by filtering out food particles from a current of water that they draw in through pores (holes) in their body.

❷ CNIDARIA

Corals, sea anemones, jellyfish, and their relatives make up the Cnidaria. Mostly marine animals, some swim or float freely while others, including anemones, are anchored to rocks. Many are carnivores that capture prey using their stinging tentacles. Some Cnidaria species are actually colonies of many individual organisms.

❸ WORMS

Animals that have long, soft bodies and no legs are commonly referred to as worms, yet they belong not to one but several distinct phyla. Phylum Annelida includes worms with bodies divided into segments, such as earthworms, leeches, and ragworms. Phylum Platyhelminthes includes the flatworms, with their flattened, ribbonlike bodies.

❹ ARTHROPODA

This is the biggest animal group, with well over a million known species. All arthropods have a tough outer exoskeleton or cuticle covering their distinct head and body segments, and legs with joints. The main arthropod groups are the insects, the crustaceans, such as crabs and crayfish, and the arachnids, which feature spiders and scorpions.

ANIMAL KINGDOM

The animal kingdom contains an extraordinary variety of different species, which can be arranged into 34 groups called phyla. Just one of these phyla, the Chordata, includes all vertebrates (animals with backbones, such as fish, ferrets, and frogs). The other more than 30 phyla contain 97 percent of known animal species, and are known collectively as invertebrates (animals without backbones), even though they are distantly related and share few common features. Here are some of the animal kingdom's main phyla.

❺ MOLLUSCA

This group of soft-bodied animals includes many that are protected by shells, such as slow-moving snails, whelks, and limpets, as well as bivalves (those with a shell in two hinged halves), such as mussels, that barely move at all. By contrast, the cephalopod branch of the phylum includes mollusks such as squid, cuttlefish, and octopuses that are intelligent and can shoot rapidly through water.

❻ ECHINODERMATA

Unlike other animals, the echinoderms, or "spiny-skinned animals," have a body divided into five parts arranged like the spokes of a wheel around a central point, and a supportive skeleton made of hard plates lying just beneath the skin. The phylum includes starfish, brittlestars, sea urchins, and sea cucumbers, all of which, as some of their names suggest, live in the sea.

❼ CHORDATA

The majority of chordates are vertebrates, which include the largest animals. They have a backbone that forms part of an internal, flexible skeleton that supports the body and is moved by attached muscles. They also have four limbs and a highly developed nervous system and sense organs. Vertebrates include birds, mammals, reptiles, amphibians, and the various types of fish. Chordates that are not vertebrates include sea squirts and lancelets.

7. KINGDOM ▶

At the top of the classification hierarchy is the animal kingdom, which contains more than 30 phyla. The other highly diverse phyla aside from the chordates are usually grouped together as "invertebrates" because they have no backbones, although this term has no meaning in classification. They include arthropods (insects, spiders, and crabs), mollusks, and worms.

6. PHYLUM ▶

Animals are grouped into phyla according to their main features. Mammals and related classes—including fish, birds, reptiles, and amphibians—belong to the phylum Chordata (the chordates). They all have a nerve cord running down their back and, at some stage in their life, a rod of tissue called a notochord. Most chordates are vertebrates—animals whose notochord grows into a

▼ 5. CLASS

There are 27 diverse orders that make up the class Mammalia (mammals), ranging from carnivores, bats, and seals, to primates (including humans) and kangaroos. Despite their diversity, all mammals are endothermic (warm-blooded), suckle their young with milk, and most have hair. No other class of animals shows these last two features.

Dragonfly

Butterfly

Toucan

Crab

Land snail

Octopus

Tarantula

Angelfish

Crocodile

Python

Frog

Bat

Parrot

Penguin

Kangaroo

Sea lion

Orang-utan

Tiger

Polar bear

CLASSIFICATION

There are 1.5 million known species (types) of animal on Earth, with millions more yet to be discovered. Scientists make sense of this vast array of creatures by looking for similarities and differences between species and organizing them into groups of increasing size—from a genus, which contains related species, through family, order, class, and phylum, to kingdom, which includes all animal species. In this example, you can see which groups the least weasel belongs to, and how it relates to other species.

1. SPECIES ▶

The least weasel has the scientific name *Mustela nivalis*, made up of the names of its genus (*Mustela*) and its species (*nivalis*). Each species has a two-part name like this that is understood by people worldwide. Members of the same species share similar features and can breed with each other in the wild.

Least weasel

▼ 2. GENUS

A genus (plural genera) is a group of species that are closely related but cannot breed together. The genus *Mustela* contains 16 species, including the least weasel, stoat, polecat, and mink. All are small, fierce predators, and each has its own slightly different lifestyle.

Stoat

▼ 3. FAMILY

Related genera are grouped together into families. *Mustela* is one of 24 genera, including otters and badgers, in the mustelid family (Mustelidae). All are active foragers that seek out prey, with some venturing into water or up trees in search of food.

Otter

European badger

▼ 4. ORDER

Eight families, including mustelids, cats, bears, dogs, and foxes, make up the order Carnivora. Those belonging to this order share certain features: most eat meat, are the predominant skilled hunters and predators on land, and have flesh-slicing teeth. Some, such as bears, have a broader diet. Members of this order are commonly called carnivores, although this term is also sometimes used to describe meat-eaters from other orders.

Red fox

INVERTEBRATES

Around 97 percent of animal species are invertebrates. Unlike vertebrates, they lack a backbone. The groups of invertebrate animals are diverse and have little in common. However, all share similar needs. They have to move, take in food and oxygen to supply energy, respond to their surroundings, and reproduce. In this snapshot of selected invertebrates, you can see the body organs and systems that meet these needs in three different types of invertebrate—flatworms, starfish, and lobsters.

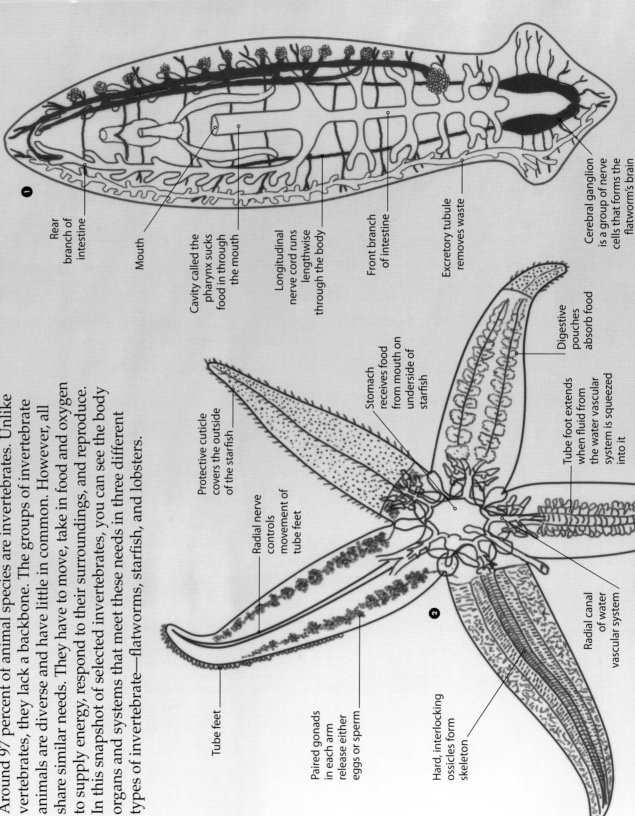

❶

Rear branch of intestine

Mouth

Cavity called the pharynx sucks food in through the mouth

Longitudinal nerve cord runs lengthwise through the body

Front branch of intestine

Excretory tubule removes waste

Cerebral ganglion is a group of nerve cells that forms the flatworm's brain

Protective cuticle covers the outside of the starfish

Radial nerve controls movement of tube feet

Tube feet

Paired gonads in each arm release either eggs or sperm

Hard, interlocking ossicles form skeleton

❷

Stomach receives food from mouth on underside of starfish

Digestive pouches absorb food

Tube foot extends when fluid from the water vascular system is squeezed into it

Radial canal of water vascular system

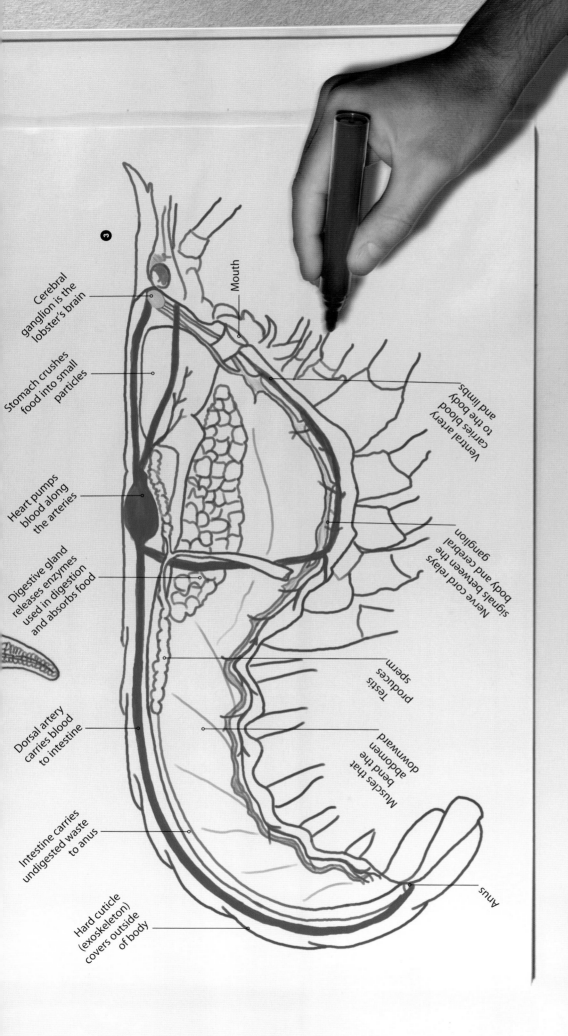

Cerebral ganglion is the lobster's brain

Stomach crushes food into small particles

Heart pumps blood along the arteries

Digestive gland releases enzymes used in digestion and absorbs food

Dorsal artery carries blood to intestine

Intestine carries undigested waste to anus

Hard cuticle (exoskeleton) covers outside of body

Mouth

Ventral artery carries blood to the body and limbs

Nerve cord relays signals between the body and cerebral ganglion

Testis produces sperm

Muscles that bend the abdomen downward

Anus

❶ FLATWORM

These simple invertebrates have neither respiratory (breathing) nor circulatory (blood) systems. Instead, oxygen is taken in directly through the flatworm's surface. Food enters—and undigested food exits—through the mouth, and is distributed to all body parts by the digestive system's many branches. A simple brain controls movement through nerve cords and picks up signals from the simple eyes.

❷ STARFISH

Each arm on this cutaway diagram of a starfish (a type of echinoderm) shows a different layer of the creature's insides. A skeleton of hard ossicles (small bones) lies just under skin. The digestive system consists of a mouth, stomach, and five sets of digestive pouches, one for each arm. Also projecting into each arm is a branch of the water vascular system, which pumps fluid into tiny tube feet, enabling the starfish to move.

❸ LOBSTER

A lobster is an arthropod, with a hard, jointed body, and limbs that are moved by muscles. These are controlled by the brain, which sends signals along a nerve cord. The brain also allows the lobster to see and feel. Food is digested by the digestive system—a tube with openings at each end (the mouth and anus). Blood pumped by the heart through blood vessels and body spaces distributes food and oxygen.

VERTEBRATES

Fish, amphibians, reptiles, birds, and mammals are called vertebrates because they have a vertebral column, or backbone. This is the part of an internal skeleton that supports the skull and to which the limbs are attached. Aside from the skeleton, several other body systems interact to produce a working vertebrate. Most are described here, using the rabbit as an example.

❶ SKIN, HAIR, AND CLAWS

All vertebrates have an outer skin. In fish and reptiles the skin is covered by scales, in birds it is covered by feathers, and in mammals, such as the rabbit, by hair or fur. Hair grows from the skin and helps insulate the animal so it can keep its internal temperature constant. Claws, and related structures such as hooves, are made from the same substance as hair, and help mammals grip the ground as they move.

❷ SKELETON

The bones of the skeleton form a flexible framework that supports the rabbit, protects its internal organs, and enables it to move. Where two or more bones meet they form a joint, and most of the skeleton's joints are freely movable.

❸ CIRCULATION

Blood carries oxygen, food, and other essentials to all parts of the body, and removes waste for disposal. The heart pumps oxygen-rich blood to the body along tubes called arteries. Oxygen-poor blood returns to the heart through veins.

❹ RESPIRATION

During respiration, air is drawn into the lungs. Here, oxygen from the air passes into the bloodstream and is carried to the animal's cells, where it is used to release energy from food. Waste carbon dioxide is carried back to the lungs and breathed out.

❺ NERVOUS SYSTEM

The nervous system controls the rabbit's movements and enables it to sense its surroundings. Located inside the skull, the brain is the control center of the nervous system, aided by the long spinal cord that connects to its base. Cablelike nerves attached to the brain and spinal cord relay signals to and from all parts of the body.

❻ DIGESTIVE SYSTEM

Food is essential for life since it supplies both energy and building materials. The digestive system consists of a long tube—including the mouth, stomach, and intestines—that digests (breaks down) food into simple, useful nutrients, absorbs those nutrients into the bloodstream, and then gets rid of undigested waste.

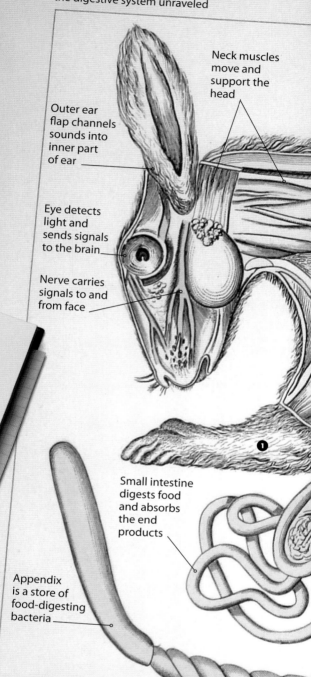

Inside view of a female rabbit with the digestive system unraveled

Neck muscles move and support the head

Outer ear flap channels sounds into inner part of ear

Eye detects light and sends signals to the brain

Nerve carries signals to and from face

Small intestine digests food and absorbs the end products

Appendix is a store of food-digesting bacteria

❼ URINARY SYSTEM

Two kidneys, the bladder, and the tubes that connect them make up the urinary system. The kidneys filter blood to remove wastes and excess water. These form urine that is stored in the baglike bladder before being released from the body.

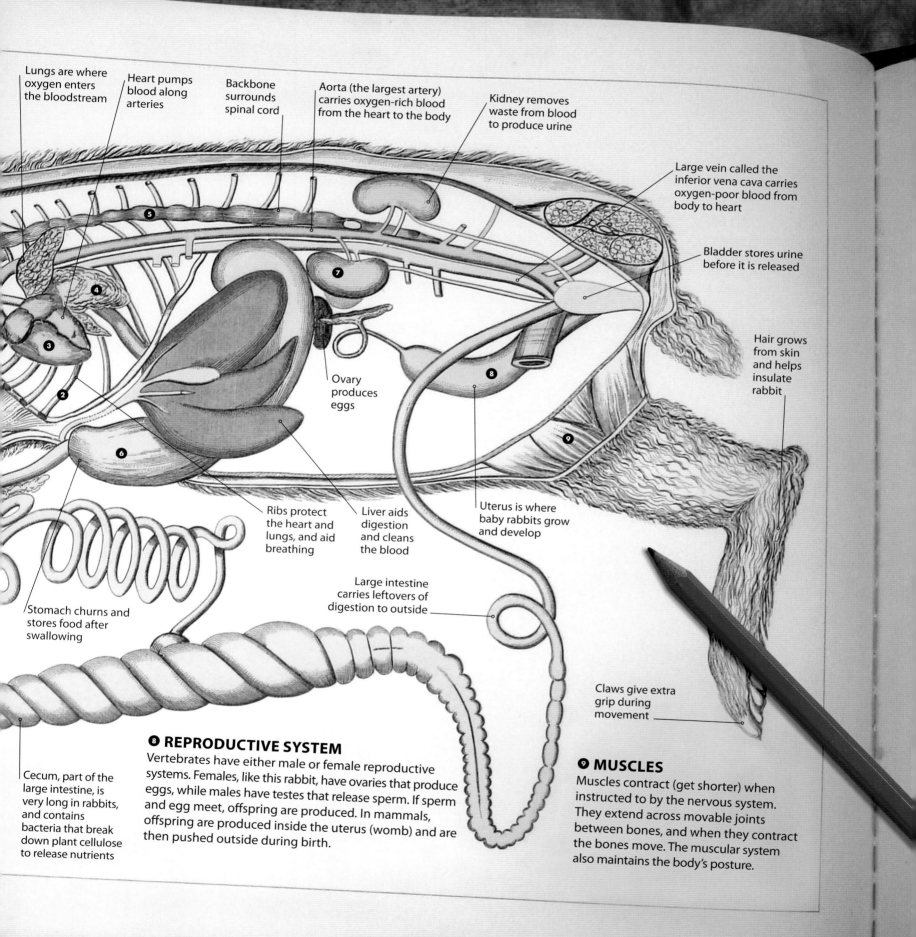

Lungs are where oxygen enters the bloodstream

Heart pumps blood along arteries

Backbone surrounds spinal cord

Aorta (the largest artery) carries oxygen-rich blood from the heart to the body

Kidney removes waste from blood to produce urine

Large vein called the inferior vena cava carries oxygen-poor blood from body to heart

Bladder stores urine before it is released

Hair grows from skin and helps insulate rabbit

Ovary produces eggs

Ribs protect the heart and lungs, and aid breathing

Liver aids digestion and cleans the blood

Uterus is where baby rabbits grow and develop

Stomach churns and stores food after swallowing

Large intestine carries leftovers of digestion to outside

Claws give extra grip during movement

Cecum, part of the large intestine, is very long in rabbits, and contains bacteria that break down plant cellulose to release nutrients

❽ REPRODUCTIVE SYSTEM

Vertebrates have either male or female reproductive systems. Females, like this rabbit, have ovaries that produce eggs, while males have testes that release sperm. If sperm and egg meet, offspring are produced. In mammals, offspring are produced inside the uterus (womb) and are then pushed outside during birth.

❾ MUSCLES

Muscles contract (get shorter) when instructed to by the nervous system. They extend across movable joints between bones, and when they contract the bones move. The muscular system also maintains the body's posture.

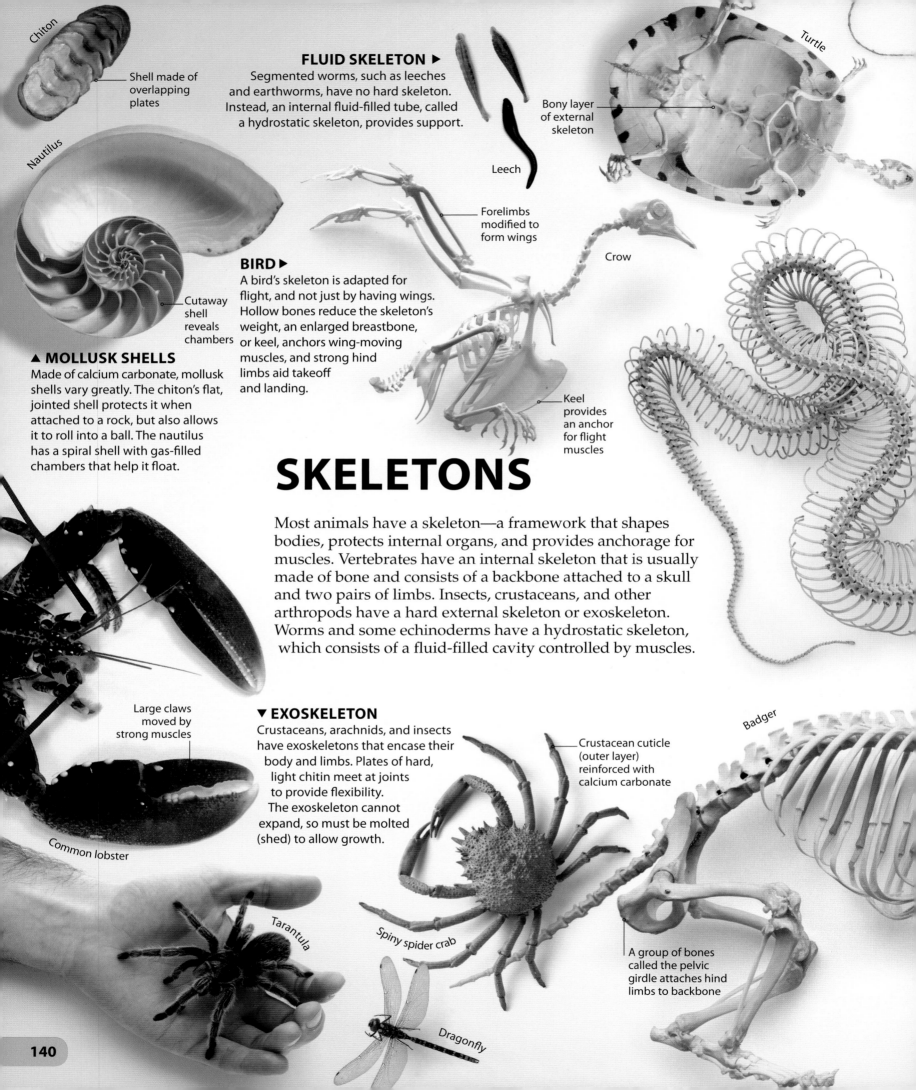

Chiton

Shell made of overlapping plates

Nautilus

Cutaway shell reveals chambers

▲ MOLLUSK SHELLS

Made of calcium carbonate, mollusk shells vary greatly. The chiton's flat, jointed shell protects it when attached to a rock, but also allows it to roll into a ball. The nautilus has a spiral shell with gas-filled chambers that help it float.

FLUID SKELETON ▶

Segmented worms, such as leeches and earthworms, have no hard skeleton. Instead, an internal fluid-filled tube, called a hydrostatic skeleton, provides support.

Leech

Forelimbs modified to form wings

BIRD ▶

A bird's skeleton is adapted for flight, and not just by having wings. Hollow bones reduce the skeleton's weight, an enlarged breastbone, or keel, anchors wing-moving muscles, and strong hind limbs aid takeoff and landing.

Crow

Keel provides an anchor for flight muscles

Turtle

Bony layer of external skeleton

SKELETONS

Most animals have a skeleton—a framework that shapes bodies, protects internal organs, and provides anchorage for muscles. Vertebrates have an internal skeleton that is usually made of bone and consists of a backbone attached to a skull and two pairs of limbs. Insects, crustaceans, and other arthropods have a hard external skeleton or exoskeleton. Worms and some echinoderms have a hydrostatic skeleton, which consists of a fluid-filled cavity controlled by muscles.

Large claws moved by strong muscles

Common lobster

▼ EXOSKELETON

Crustaceans, arachnids, and insects have exoskeletons that encase their body and limbs. Plates of hard, light chitin meet at joints to provide flexibility. The exoskeleton cannot expand, so must be molted (shed) to allow growth.

Tarantula

Spiny spider crab

Dragonfly

Crustacean cuticle (outer layer) reinforced with calcium carbonate

Badger

A group of bones called the pelvic girdle attaches hind limbs to backbone

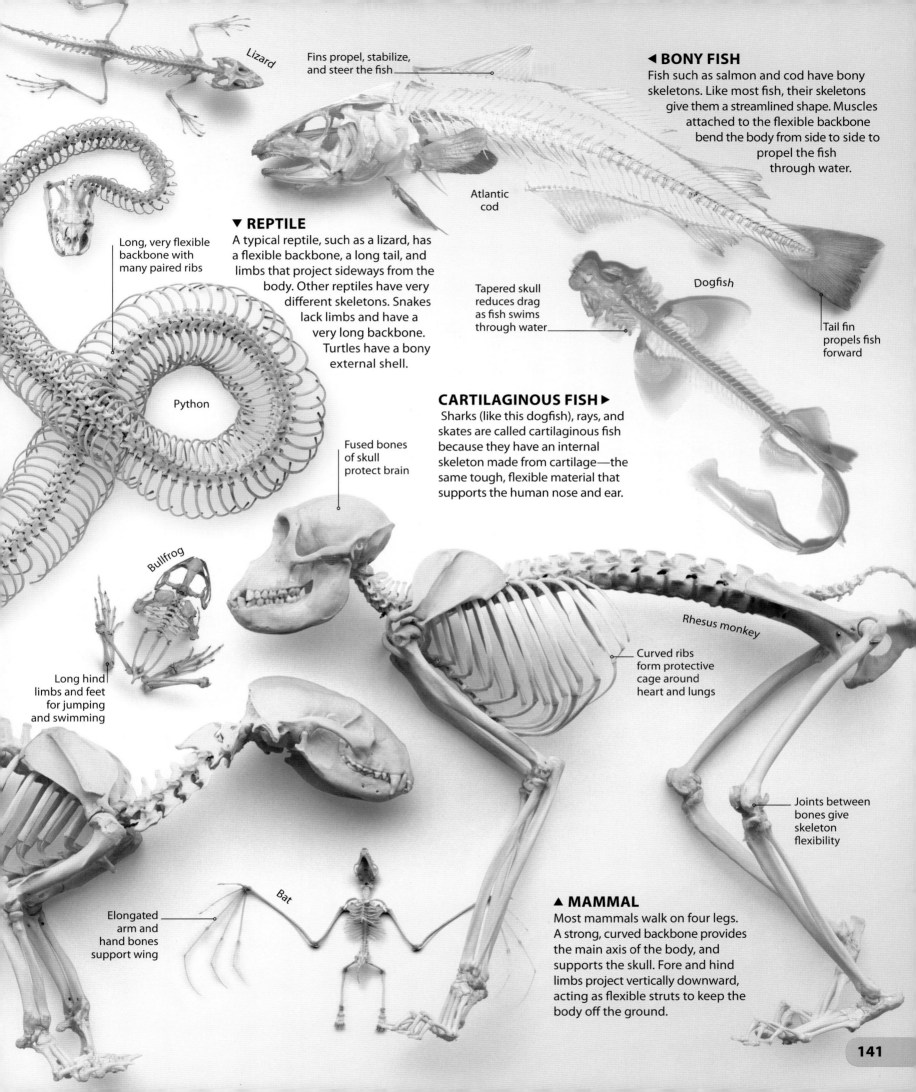

Lizard

Fins propel, stabilize, and steer the fish

◀ **BONY FISH**
Fish such as salmon and cod have bony skeletons. Like most fish, their skeletons give them a streamlined shape. Muscles attached to the flexible backbone bend the body from side to side to propel the fish through water.

Atlantic cod

Long, very flexible backbone with many paired ribs

▼ **REPTILE**
A typical reptile, such as a lizard, has a flexible backbone, a long tail, and limbs that project sideways from the body. Other reptiles have very different skeletons. Snakes lack limbs and have a very long backbone. Turtles have a bony external shell.

Tapered skull reduces drag as fish swims through water

Dogfish

Tail fin propels fish forward

Python

Fused bones of skull protect brain

CARTILAGINOUS FISH▶
Sharks (like this dogfish), rays, and skates are called cartilaginous fish because they have an internal skeleton made from cartilage—the same tough, flexible material that supports the human nose and ear.

Bullfrog

Rhesus monkey

Curved ribs form protective cage around heart and lungs

Long hind limbs and feet for jumping and swimming

Joints between bones give skeleton flexibility

Elongated arm and hand bones support wing

Bat

▲ **MAMMAL**
Most mammals walk on four legs. A strong, curved backbone provides the main axis of the body, and supports the skull. Fore and hind limbs project vertically downward, acting as flexible struts to keep the body off the ground.

141

SYMMETRY

The bodies of most animals show symmetry (balanced proportions). Some show radial symmetry, meaning they can be divided, like a cake, through a central point into two identical halves. Most animals are bilaterally symmetrical—they can be divided down their midline into two equal halves. Other animals have features that make them look strangely lopsided.

ASYMMETRY ▶

One group of animals, the sponges, lacks any sort of symmetry. These simple animals grow in a random fashion. Their asymmetric structure, cut in any direction, will not produce equal halves.

BILATERAL SYMMETRY ▼

From butterflies to buffalo, most animals show bilateral symmetry. This means that an imaginary line drawn along their length would divide them into identical left and right halves, each with front and back ends. A line anywhere else, however, would not produce equal halves.

Blue morpho butterfly

Head includes eyes, nose, whiskers, and mouth

Weddell seal

Right side of flounder is now its upper surface

▲ HEADS

Animals that are bilaterally symmetrical have a front end called the head. This contains the animal's sense organs, such as the eyes, ears, nose, and whiskers, which meet the environment before the rest of the body. They detect changes, which the brain, also contained in the head, analyzes and responds to.

Left eye has migrated over to the right (upper) side

142

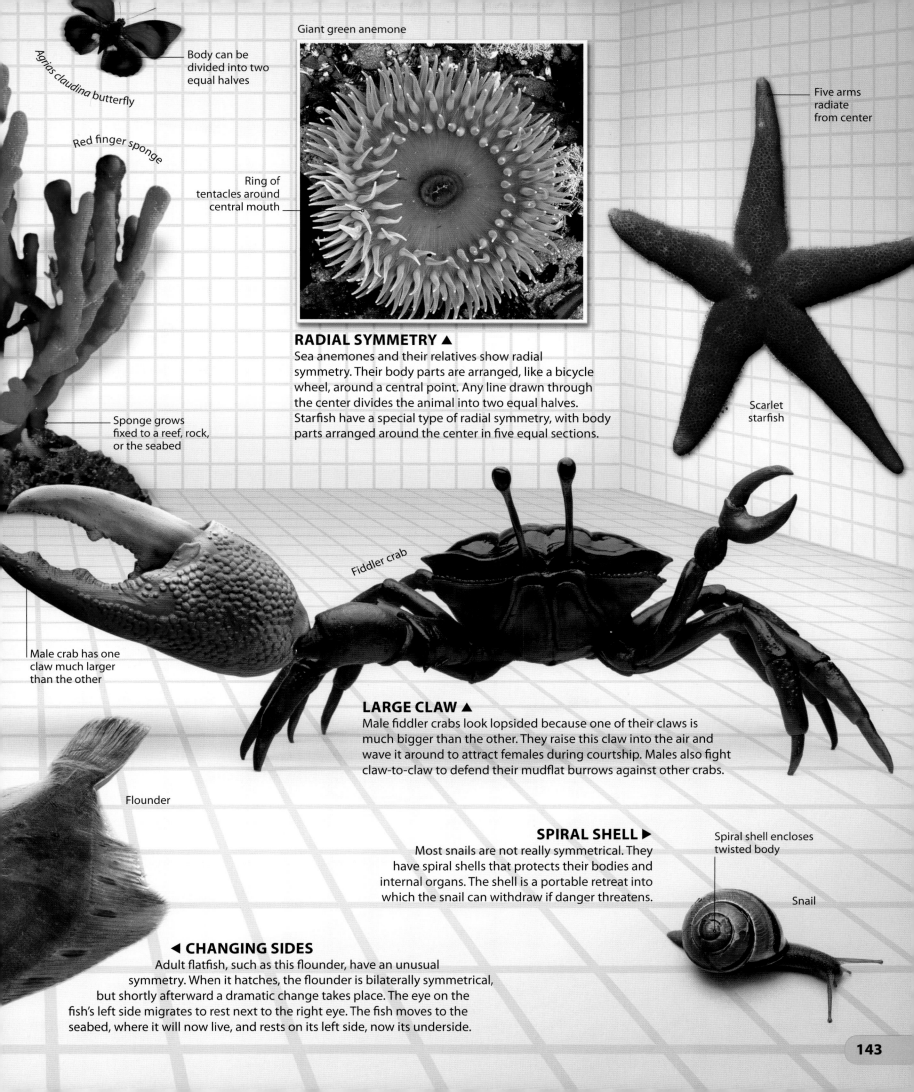

Agrias claudina butterfly

Body can be divided into two equal halves

Red finger sponge

Giant green anemone

Ring of tentacles around central mouth

Five arms radiate from center

RADIAL SYMMETRY ▲

Sea anemones and their relatives show radial symmetry. Their body parts are arranged, like a bicycle wheel, around a central point. Any line drawn through the center divides the animal into two equal halves. Starfish have a special type of radial symmetry, with body parts arranged around the center in five equal sections.

Scarlet starfish

Sponge grows fixed to a reef, rock, or the seabed

Fiddler crab

Male crab has one claw much larger than the other

LARGE CLAW ▲

Male fiddler crabs look lopsided because one of their claws is much bigger than the other. They raise this claw into the air and wave it around to attract females during courtship. Males also fight claw-to-claw to defend their mudflat burrows against other crabs.

Flounder

SPIRAL SHELL ▶

Most snails are not really symmetrical. They have spiral shells that protects their bodies and internal organs. The shell is a portable retreat into which the snail can withdraw if danger threatens.

Spiral shell encloses twisted body

Snail

◀ CHANGING SIDES

Adult flatfish, such as this flounder, have an unusual symmetry. When it hatches, the flounder is bilaterally symmetrical, but shortly afterward a dramatic change takes place. The eye on the fish's left side migrates to rest next to the right eye. The fish moves to the seabed, where it will now live, and rests on its left side, now its underside.

LIFE SPANS

Usually, the bigger an animal is, the longer its life span. But other factors are also involved. Animals that breed slowly, produce fewer offspring, and show parental care tend to live longer, as do animals with a large brain in relation to their body size, those that consume energy slowly, and those with fewer predators.

❷ Honeybee workers are sterile females that fulfill many roles within the bee colony. During their five hectic weeks of life they feed and clean bee larvae and pupae, construct new wax combs for eggs and honey, guard the entrance to the colony, and collect pollen and nectar from flowers.

❶ Kangaroos live for 10 years on average. They become mature within two years and are able to breed all year round. Young kangaroos may be preyed on by dingos and birds of prey.

❸ Giant salamanders have fairly long lives; they are big amphibians with low energy consumption.

❹ Sea lions, preyed upon by large sharks and killer whales, live for 15 years, on average.

❺ Giant tortoises live for a lengthy 120 years. Many factors contribute to their staying power: they are big creatures, they live on islands where there are few natural predators, and they are slow-moving, low energy consumers.

❻ Lobsters are among the largest crustaceans, protected from predators by their large claws and hard shell. Most live for around 15 years, but exceptional specimens can reach more than 100 years old.

❼ Domestic cats live long lives, with shelter, regular feeding, and protection against infection. Animals kept as pets generally live longer than those in the wild because they are fed and protected from predators.

144

8 Crocodiles are large, ectothermic (cold-blooded) creatures that feed occasionally during brief periods of intense activity but otherwise spend much time immobile—an ideal strategy for a long life.

9 Bottlenose dolphins are intelligent creatures that, in exceptional cases, can live to 40 or 50 years.

10 Albatrosses are large ocean birds that take years to become mature. They mate for life and produce just one egg during each breeding season.

11 Lake sturgeon females take more than 20 years to reach maturity, and only breed every five years.

12 Polar bears live for an average of 25 years in their harsh Arctic habitat.

13 Mice are small endothermic (warm-blooded) mammals with a high metabolic rate—a rapid energy consumption for their size. Animals like this tend to "burn out" faster and have shorter life spans.

75 YEARS

20 YEARS

50 YEARS

80 YEARS

25 YEARS

6 HOURS

2 YEARS

4 WEEKS

40 YEARS

14 Elephants are large, intelligent, social animals that look after their young. They live for around 40 years.

15 House flies have short lives, during which they feed and breed to produce another fly generation.

16 Ocean quahogs are bivalve mollusks (mollusks with two shells). Specimens collected off Iceland in 2007 were found to be more than 400 years old, making them the longest lived animals ever recorded.

17 Mayflies spend two to three years as nymphs feeding in streams and rivers. In summer they emerge as winged adults. They mate but do not feed, and die after just a few hours.

MAMMALS

They may appear very different, but all the animals shown here are mammals, a group that also includes humans. Mammals are endothermic (warm-blooded) vertebrates, and most are covered with insulating fur. Female mammals produce milk to feed their young. Mammals are found almost everywhere on Earth—from the poles to the equator—living on land, in water, and in the air. Most give birth to well-developed young.

❷ CARNIVORES

These mammals are hunters and scavengers that feed largely on meat. Carnivores include tigers and other members of the cat family, along with wolves, foxes, otters, and bears. Most are fast-moving, locate prey using their good senses of sight, smell, and hearing, and have sharp teeth to grip and cut flesh.

❸ MARSUPIALS

These pouched mammals are found in Australasia and the Americas, and include kangaroos, koalas, and opossums. Female marsupials give birth to tiny, immature young that complete their development inside their mother's pouch.

❹ ODD-TOED UNGULATES

Ungulates walk on the tips of their toes, each of which is capped with a hard hoof. Odd-toed ungulates have either one or three working toes, and include rhinos, horses, zebras, and tapirs. All are herbivores and many species are fast movers that live on open plains.

❺ LAGOMORPHS

Rabbits and hares are lagomorphs—fast-moving ground-dwellers that eat grasses, soft shoots, and tree bark. Their large ears are highly sensitive, and their bulging eyes provide all-around vision. At the first sound or sight of danger, they use their long hind legs to escape predators.

❶ CETACEANS

Whales, porpoises, and dolphins are cetaceans—mammals that spend their entire lives in water. They have a hairless body propelled by a powerful tail fin and steered by front flippers. Cetaceans include the blue whale, the largest animal that has ever lived.

Bottlenose dolphin ❶

Streamlined body adapted for life in the water

Tiger ❷

Kangaroo ❸

❹

Long hind legs and feet used like springs to hop at high speeds over long distances

❺

Baby rhinoceros

Hooves are made of keratin, the same material found in human hair and nails

Rabbit

Rat

❶❷

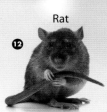

African elephant

❻ BATS

The only flying mammals, bats are generally nocturnal. The majority are small insect-eaters like the bumblebee-sized Kitti's hog-nosed bat—the world's smallest mammal. Bigger fruit bats eat fruit and nectar, and find food using their large eyes.

Fruit bat

Wing membrane stretches across long finger bones

❼ ELEPHANTS

The three species of elephant—two in Africa, one in Asia—are the largest land animals. Elephants are sociable animals that live in family groups and use their trunks to communicate through smell and touch.

Trunk is an extension of the nose that grasps vegetation and transfers it to the mouth

Deer

❽ EVEN-TOED UNGULATES

This group of hoofed mammals, including deer, cattle, camels, hippos, and pigs, usually have two hoof-tipped toes. These herbivores have large cheek teeth to grind tough vegetation and may also have large, four-chambered stomachs inside which bacteria aid the digestion of tough plants.

❾ PRIMATES

This group includes apes, monkeys, lemurs, bush babies—and humans. Most primates live in social groups in tropical and subtropical forests. The majority are agile climbers with long limbs and flexible, grasping fingers and toes. Primates also have forward-facing eyes and large brains compared to their body size.

❿ MONOTREMES

Found in Australasia, echidnas and the duck-billed platypus are monotremes— the only mammals to lay eggs. After hatching, their young feed on milk. The platypus is a good swimmer and probes for prey in the beds of streams and lakes. Spiky echidnas mostly feed on ants and termites.

⓫ INSECTIVORES

Insects and other small animals are the preferred prey of these mammals. Insectivores are typically small, solitary, nocturnal animals that have sharp teeth and depend on their senses of smell and touch to find food. They include shrews and hedgehogs. Moles are insectivores adapted for life underground.

⓬ RODENTS

With more than 2,000 species, rodents form the largest mammal group and are found everywhere except Antarctica. Rodents include mice, rats, squirrels, beavers, and porcupines. To gnaw tough foods they have two pairs of sharp incisor (front) teeth, which do not wear down because they never stop growing.

Baboon

Mole

Echidna

BIRDS

The ability to fly means that birds have been able to occupy an incredible range of habitats, including cliff faces, rain-forest canopies, and mountainsides. Birds have streamlined, lightweight bodies with wings that are covered and insulated by feathers. Their toothless beaks vary in shape and size according to their diet and feeding method. The near 10,000 species of birds are divided into 29 orders, most of which are represented here.

▲ **WOODPECKERS**
Tree-dwelling woodpeckers use their strong beaks as chisels to carve out tree holes and to probe for food. Their order includes toucans.

▲ **TROGONS**
Found in tropical forests worldwide, trogons have brilliantly colored feathers and feed mainly on insects.

▲ **PENGUINS**
These flightless seabirds use their wings as flippers to propel their streamlined bodies through the water in pursuit of fish and squid.

▲ **KIWIS**
Ostriches (the world's biggest birds), emus, and kiwis are flightless birds. Over time they have lost the ability to fly, so they run to escape predators.

▲ **TINAMOUS**
These ground-dwelling birds, found in the grasslands of South America, are well camouflaged, have small wings, and are fast fliers and runners.

▲ **HUMMINGBIRDS**
Long-beaked, multicolored hummingbirds hover in front of flowers to feed on nectar. Their close relatives, swifts, spend their lives in the air feeding on insects.

▲ **TURKEYS**
Living on the ground and rarely flying, turkeys belong to the game birds, an order that also includes pheasants and peacocks.

▲ **GREBES**
With a small head and thin neck to make diving easy, grebes are strong swimmers and live on sheltered lakes.

▲ **SWANS**
Together with ducks and geese, swans are waterfowl—excellent swimmers with large, webbed feet.

▲ **KINGFISHERS**
With a daggerlike beak, a kingfisher sits waiting on its riverside perch then dives into the water and grabs a fish.

▲ **DOVES**
Pigeons and doves are plump, strong fliers, with heads that bob up and down when they walk.

148

PELICANS
These birds, from the same order as gannets and tropic birds, scoop up fish in their pouched beaks.

HERONS
With long legs adapted to wading in shallow water, herons use their long beaks to capture fish and frogs.

THRUSHES
Thrushes belong to the vast order of perching songbirds that contains more than half of all bird species.

CRANES
The tallest flying birds in the world, long-legged cranes belong to an order that also includes coots and moorhens.

GULLS
Gulls and terns are seabirds, but other members of their order feed by the water's edge.

ROADRUNNERS
Members of the cuckoo family, roadrunners live mainly on the ground, running fast to flush out prey and avoid predators.

ALBATROSSES
Albatrosses migrate vast distances over the oceans, returning each year to the same breeding sites on land.

OWLS
Nighttime hunters, owls have excellent hearing and vision to detect and swoop on prey.

BIRDS OF PREY
Eagles and other birds of prey are formidable hunters with excellent eyesight, sharp talons to grab prey, and hooked, tearing beaks.

NIGHTJARS
These long-winged birds and their relatives roost in trees or on the ground during the day, then hunt for insects between dusk and dawn.

FLAMINGOS
Tall waders with long legs and necks, most flamingos live in flocks in tropical lakes, where they bend their necks to filter animals and plants from the water with their upturned beaks.

PARROTS
These forest birds are strong climbers and fliers that feed on fruit and nuts.

DIVERS
Also called loons, streamlined divers make excellent underwater swimmers but find it difficult to walk on land.

149

REPTILES

Alligators, cobras, tortoises, and geckos are just some of the animals found in this diverse group of vertebrates. Most reptiles live on land, and all have tough, scaly skin that stops them from drying out, even in hostile desert habitats. Many lay eggs with leathery shells, although some produce live young. Reptiles are ectothermic (cold-blooded). They bask in the Sun's heat to warm up and seek shade to cool down.

Jackson's chameleon

Male uses horns to fight other males over territory

American alligator

Mangrove snake

Adhesive foot pads enable gecko to cling to any surface

Tokay gecko

Strong jaws snap shut and teeth grip prey

Nile crocodile

Powerful, flat-sided tail lashes from side to side to propel crocodile through water

Komodo dragon

Green anolis

Corn snake

Powerful limbs ending in sharp claws

Pit organs detect heat given off by prey at night to create a "heat picture"

Toxic bacteria in saliva cause blood poisoning in prey

Royal python

Snake-necked turtle

Desert tortoise

❶ CROCODILIANS

These large, ferocious predators include crocodiles and alligators. They wait in rivers and lakes, then use their powerful jaws and sharp teeth to grab and drown unwary animals. Their eyes and nostrils are set on top of the head so they can see and breathe while in the water.

❷ LIZARDS

More than half of the 8,000 reptile species are lizards. Most are agile, fast-moving hunters. They include geckos, skinks, chameleons, slow worms, the Komodo dragon, and the venomous Gila monster.

❸ VENOMOUS SNAKES

All snakes are carnivorous, and around one-tenth, including adders, cobras, and rattlesnakes, immobilize prey by injecting venom, or poison, through special teeth called fangs.

❹ NONVENOMOUS SNAKES

Many snakes do not use venom. Constrictors, such as corn snakes and pythons, grab their quarry using sharp teeth, then wrap themselves around it and squeeze ever tighter until the animal suffocates. Then, like all snakes, they swallow their victim whole.

❺ TURTLES AND TORTOISES

The bodies of these reptiles are protected by a hard shell. Turtles live in the sea and fresh water, while tortoises live on land. All lay their eggs on land, with marine species migrating across oceans to do so. They lack teeth but their jaws have sharp edges to cut food.

❻ TUATARAS

These burrowing reptiles are found on islands off New Zealand, the sole survivors of an ancient group related to snakes and lizards. They are nocturnal and can live for more than 100 years.

❼ WORM LIZARDS

These wormlike reptiles live in hotter parts of the world. Most have no limbs, and all burrow underground, pushing through soil or sand using their blunt-shaped heads. Worm lizards have fairly simple eyes and feed on insects and worms that they find by touch.

Flying gecko

Skin along the sides of the body spreads out to allow lizard to glide

Puff adder

Brown and yellow markings camouflage the puff adder in its grassland habitat

Common iguana

Plumed basilisk lizard

Forked tongue "tastes" chemical particles in the air

Skink

Thorny devil

Sharp, protective spines collect water at night

Gila monster

As the snake strikes, hollow fangs swing forward to inject venom

Green tree python

Rattlesnake

Slowworm

Venom ejected from cobra's mouth can blind an attacker

Tuatara

Red spitting cobra

❻

Madagascar day gecko

Long tongue used to lick lidless eye clean

Worm lizard

❼

151

AMPHIBIANS

Most amphibians spend part of their lives on land and part in water, where they mate and breed. Females lay shell-less eggs, which hatch into swimming larvae called tadpoles that breathe using gills. As they grow into adults, amphibians develop lungs and they can also breathe through their skin. There are three groups of amphibians—the frogs and toads, the salamanders and newts, and the less familiar caecilians.

Flying frog

Webbing between outstretched toes allows frog to glide between trees

Goliath bullfrog

Brazilian gold frog

Smooth skin is moist and lacks scales

Asian horned toad

Poison dart frog

Leopard frog

Male carries string of eggs wrapped around its hind legs

Midwife toad

❷ NEWTS

Newts have long slender bodies and their tails are often flattened to assist movement in water, where many adult newts spend much of their lives. Some newts carry out courtship displays, such as tail swishing, to attract a mate during the breeding season.

European common frog

Leopard frog

Frog tadpoles

Tail moves from side to side to propel newt forward

Great-crested newt

❶ MUDPUPPIES

These North American salamanders spend their entire lives underwater. Unlike most other salamanders, mudpuppies retain their bright red external gills into adulthood. They live in streams and rivers, where they feed on fish, crayfish, and mollusks.

Mudpuppy

External gills

❸ FROGS

Frogs have wide mouths, bulging eyes, and short, compact, tail-less bodies with smooth skin. Their powerful back legs and webbed feet are ideally suited for jumping and swimming. Many frog species live in tropical forests.

American toad

Red-eyed tree frog

Sucker pad on the end of each digit aids grip

Couch's spadefoot toad

❻

Male keeps tadpoles inside his vocal sac until they become adult frogs

Darwin's frog

Oriental fire-bellied toad

Bright colors warn predators toad is poisonous

❺ SALAMANDERS

Found, like newts, in milder parts of the northern hemisphere, salamanders have long tails, slender bodies, and four legs of equal length. Although some live in water, most, including fire salamanders, live on land in damp locations where they hunt at night for prey.

❺

Fire salamander

Duck-billed tree frog

Odd-shaped head helps camouflage frog against tree bark

Green mantella frog

Glass frog

Heart and intestines can be seen through transparent skin

gless salamander

Salamander breathes through its skin

Caecilian

❹

Large vocal sac produces sounds to attract mates

Tungara frog

❻ TOADS

It can be difficult to tell them apart from frogs, but toads typically have dry, warty skins, little webbing between their toes, shorter legs for walking, and prefer living on land. Some, including Couch's spadefoot toad, live in deserts and burrow to avoid the heat.

Tiny legs form on tadpole

❹ CAECILIANS

These legless, wormlike amphibians are found in hot, humid places. Some live underwater. Others use their pointed heads to burrow into mud, where their keen sense of smell helps them detect earthworms and other prey, which they grab using their sharp teeth.

External gills

Blind olm lives in dark, watery depths of underground caves

Olm salamander

FISH

Found in oceans, lakes, and rivers, fish are vertebrates that are adapted for life in water. They have streamlined bodies covered with protective scales, and fins that propel and steer. The three types of fish are jawless fish, such as lampreys; cartilaginous fish, such as sharks and rays; and bony fish, the biggest and most diverse group, which includes most of those swimming here.

❶ Hammerhead shark

Bright markings break up fish's outline and confuse predators

Emperor angelfish

Seahorse

Body covered with bony plates

Barracuda

Thick, heavy scales cover the coelacanth's body

❺ Coelacanth

❷ Anglerfish

Lamprey

❸

❹ Lionfish

❶ SHARK
Found in oceans worldwide, these formidable predators have keen senses, powerful bodies covered with denticles (small toothlike skin growths), rigid fins, and rows of sharp teeth.

❷ ANGLERFISH
A growth projecting from the anglerfish's head lures curious prey close to the fish's mouth, which opens wide to consume the visitor whole.

❸ LAMPREY
This blood-sucking fish is one of the few survivors of the most ancient group of fish, the jawless fish. It has smooth, scaleless skin and a suckerlike mouth lined with rows of teeth, which it uses to clamp onto the side of a living fish.

❹ LIONFISH
This bony fish is one of the most poisonous in the sea. Its long, venomous spines disable predators. Brightly colored stripes warn of the danger.

❺ COELACANTH
The coelacanth's fleshy fins are pulled by muscles so it can swim or "walk" over the seabed. Thought to have died out 65 million years ago, it was rediscovered in 1938.

❻ RAY
With a mouth on their underside, flat rays feed off creatures on the seabed. They flap their winglike fins to move through the water.

Touch-sensitive barbels used to locate food

7 Sturgeon

9 Anchovies

8 Hatchetfish

Large, upward-pointing eyes detect prey moving overhead

Eyes are located on top of the ray's head

6 Spotted ray

10 Coho salmon

Moray eel **11**

Grouper

⓫ MORAY EEL
The moray eel lives in tropical waters and has a long, snakelike body that can reach up to 10 ft (3 m) in length. Moray eels ambush their prey. They hide in crevices in rocks and reefs, then launch a surprise attack, grabbing passing prey with their sharp teeth.

➓ SALMON
Like more than 90 percent of the 25,000 species of fish, salmon have bony skeletons and flexible fins. Salmon and their relatives, including trout, are fast-moving carnivores with sharp teeth that ambush prey or attack over a short distance.

❾ ANCHOVY
Silvery anchovies feed in shoals on tiny organisms filtered from the water. The dense shoals contain thousands of individuals and attract many predators.

❽ HATCHETFISH
This ax-shaped fish lives in the dark ocean midwaters. Light organs on the fish's underside confuse predators by disguising its outline.

❼ STURGEON
A long fish with scutes (bony plates) rather than scales, the sturgeon belongs to an ancient group with part-bony and part-cartilage skeletons.

ECHINODERMS

These distinctive animals are found only in the sea. Echinoderms, including starfish, sea urchins, and their relatives, have no distinct heads. Instead, the body is divided into five equal parts arranged around a central disk, with the mouth usually on its underside. The body is supported by an internal skeleton made of chalky plates covered by spiny, thin, skin. An internal hydraulic system pumps water into and out of sausagelike tube feet, each tipped with a sucker, that project from the body and are used for movement.

❶ SEA DAISY

These small echinoderms are flattened and disk-shaped, with no arms but a ring of spines around their margin. Their structure is similar to other echinoderms, with a body arranged in five parts. They probably feed on bacteria and microscopic mollusks.

❷ FEATHER STAR

Like their close relatives the sea lilies, plantlike feather stars are usually attached to the sea bottom by a stalk. Some, however, are free-swimming as adults. Feather stars feed by using their arms to transfer food particles from the surrounding water into their central, upward-facing mouth.

❸ SEA CUCUMBER

Sea cucumbers have more flexible bodies than other echinoderms. They also have a front end, with a mouth, and a back end, with an anus. The mouth is surrounded by tentacles that filter small particles of food from the water. Some species shoot sticky threads out of the anus to deter predators.

❹ BRITTLESTAR

With long, thin arms attached to a small, central disk, brittlestars move by wiggling their arms in a snakelike fashion. To evade predators, the arms can break off and be regrown. Brittlestars feed by scavenging, catching small animals, or filtering particles from the water.

❺ STARFISH

Familiar and star-shaped, starfish have five or more arms attached to a central disk. They are scavengers or predators that crawl over the sea bottom using their suckerlike tube feet. They feed by pushing their stomachs out through their mouths to surround food, digest it, and suck up the juices.

❻ SEA URCHIN

A sea urchin's globe-shaped body lacks arms but has a hard outer test or shell. Tube feet project through the test, which is armed with movable spines to deter enemies and aid movement. Sea urchins move slowly over rocks, grazing on algae or eating small animals.

❼ SAND DOLLAR

Close relatives of the sea urchins, sand dollars have irregular, flattened, and inflexible bodies covered by many small spines. Their body shape helps them to burrow easily into soft sand.

CRUSTACEANS

From tiny brine shrimps to large spider crabs, the 50,000 species of crustacean are very diverse and live mainly in the sea and fresh water. Crustaceans have a hard external skeleton, known as the exoskeleton or cuticle, jointed limbs, two pairs of sensory antennae, and compound eyes on stalks. Their heads and thoraxes are often covered by a shield or carapace.

BRANCHIOPODS ▼

These small crustaceans use leaflike limbs for movement, respiration, and to gather food particles. Branchiopods are found mostly in fresh water, although brine shrimps are a species of branchiopod that live in salty lakes and pools. Brine shrimps have a short life cycle and lay eggs that can remain dormant for years.

COPEPODS ▶

Superabundant in the plankton found near the ocean's surface, these tiny crustaceans are also found in fresh water. Copepods have a teardrop-shaped, transparent body, with a single compound eye, and large antennae that, along with the swimming legs, play a part in movement.

Peacock mantis shrimp

Freshwater copepod

Brine shrimp

Pill woodlouse rolling up

WOODLICE ▶

Among the few crustaceans that live on land, woodlice thrive in dark, damp places, such as rotting wood, where they feed on dead plant matter. Their upper surface is protected by tough, curved plates, and females carry their eggs in a special pouch on their undersides.

Woodlice

◀ MANTIS SHRIMP

This ferocious predator is neither a shrimp nor a praying mantis (a type of insect). Its second pair of legs—normally folded away, like those of a praying mantis—are adapted for either spearing or smashing prey. When the mantis shrimp ambushes prey, it shoots out these legs at high speed to kill or dismember its victim.

Crayfish

LOBSTER AND CRAYFISH ▶

Big crustaceans with a hard carapace and long abdomen, lobsters emerge from hiding at night and use their massive claws to crush and cut prey. Lobsters walk over the seabed, but can flip their tails to swim backward. Crayfish resemble small lobsters. They live in freshwater streams and rivers, where they make burrows in silt and mud.

CRABS ▶

Easily identified by their short, broad bodies protected by a hard carapace, most crabs live in the sea, although some prefer fresh water and even land. The first of their five pairs of legs have powerful pincers used to grasp and crush food, for defense, and even for signaling to other crabs. The remaining eight legs enable them to scuttle sideways quickly.

Shore crab

Common lobster

Spider crab

▼ KRILL

Tiny shrimplike krill are found in vast swarms in oceans worldwide. They are an important source of food for many larger marine animals.

Krill

Crayfish

Common shrimp

SHRIMPS ▶

These small bottom-dwellers have a near-transparent, highly flexible exoskeleton. Shrimps use their legs to swim or walk along the seabed. If threatened, they flick their tail downward to dart backward out of harm's way. Most shrimps eat almost anything, including pieces of dead animals plucked using their tiny pincers.

BARNACLES ▼

In early life, barnacles swim freely but they soon settle, forming large encrustations on rocks, ships, piers, whales, and even other crustaceans. The body of an adult barnacle is encased by chalky plates and either fixed directly onto a surface or, as in the case of these goose barnacles, attached by a stalk. Barnacles feed by opening the plates and extending feathery legs that filter tiny creatures from the water.

Goose barnacles

ARACHNIDS

Spiders, scorpions, and other arachnids are mainly land-dwelling predators. Most use venom to disable their prey, then douse it with digestive enzymes and suck up the resulting liquid. The arachnid body has two parts—a cephalothorax at the front and an abdomen at the rear. Attached to the cephalothorax are a pair of fanglike mouthparts called chelicerae, two appendages called pedipalps that are either leglike or clawlike, and four pairs of walking legs. In spiders, the abdomen contains silk-producing glands.

❶ HARVESTMEN

Commonly mistaken for spiders, harvestmen have an oval body with no "waist" between front and rear parts. Harvestmen use their second and longest pair of legs as feelers to find their way and detect prey. They feed on small insects, plants, dead animals, and dung. Some, if threatened, can detach their legs, which continue moving to confuse predators.

❷ SPIDERS

More than half of arachnid species are spiders. All produce silk threads, which some, such as orb web spiders, use to spin insect-trapping webs. Others, including tarantulas and jumping spiders, stalk their prey.

❻ SCORPIONS

Found in hotter regions, scorpions hunt at night, using special vibration sensors to detect prey. They hold prey in their clawlike pedipalps while picking off small morsels of food using their sharp chelicerae.

❼ WHIP SPIDERS

With broad, flat bodies, these tropical arachnids move sideways, feel for insect prey with their long, thin first legs, then grab it with their pincerlike pedipalps. Whip spiders are nocturnal, and spend the day hiding under stones, in leaf litter, or in caves.

❽ MITES AND TICKS

The smallest of the arachnids, some being barely visible, mites and ticks have rounded, one-piece bodies. Mites are found by the millions in soil and water, and also include parasites of both plants and animals. Ticks feed on the blood of mammals and birds. They penetrate the skin with their barbed mouthparts, expand enormously as they suck blood, and then drop off.

❹ PSEUDOSCORPIONS

Resembling smaller versions of scorpions, pseudoscorpions lack both a tail and sting. They have venom glands in their pedipalps, which they use to immobilize insects and other small prey. Pseudoscorpions hunt for prey in soil, leaf litter, and under logs and rocks.

❺ SUN SPIDERS

Also called wind scorpions, these fast-running arachnids are found in deserts. They locate prey with their long, sensitive pedipalps, which they also use to hold prey while they kill and chew it with their pincerlike chelicerae.

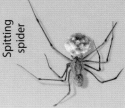
Spitting spider

Cave spider

Orb web spider

Funnel web spider

Crab spider

Chelicerae used to inject venom into prey

Abdomen, the rear part of the body

Harvestman

Mexican red-rumped tarantula

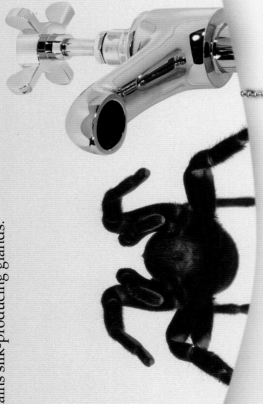
Huntsman spider

Cephalothorax, the front part of the body

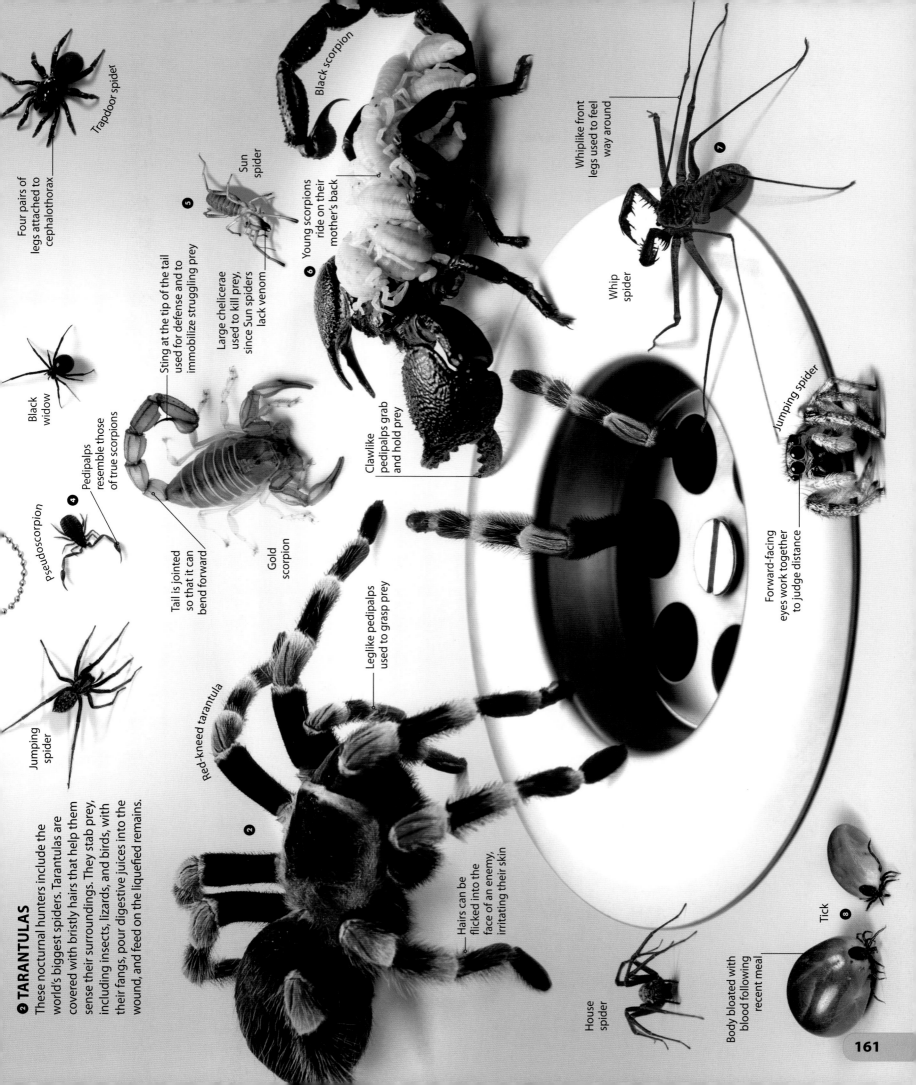

❷ TARANTULAS

These nocturnal hunters include the world's biggest spiders. Tarantulas are covered with bristly hairs that help them sense their surroundings. They stab prey, including insects, lizards, and birds, with their fangs, pour digestive juices into the wound, and feed on the liquefied remains.

Trapdoor spider

Four pairs of legs attached to cephalothorax

Black scorpion

Sun spider ❺

Young scorpions ride on their mother's back ❻

Sting at the tip of the tail used for defense and to immobilize struggling prey

Large chelicerae used to kill prey, since Sun spiders lack venom

Black widow

Pedipalps resemble those of true scorpions

❹ pseudoscorpion

Clawlike pedipalps grab and hold prey

Gold scorpion

Tail is jointed so that it can bend forward

Whiplike front legs used to feel way around

❼

Whip spider

Jumping spider

Jumping spider

Forward-facing eyes work together to judge distance

Red-kneed tarantula

Leglike pedipalps used to grasp prey

❷

Hairs can be flicked into the face of an enemy, irritating their skin

House spider

Body bloated with blood following recent meal

Tick ❽

161

INSECTS

From bees to butterflies, insects form the most successful animal group on Earth. There are more than one million named insect species, with probably another 10 to 30 million yet to be discovered. An insect body has three parts. The head has two compound eyes and a pair of antennae, the thorax carries three pairs of legs and, usually, two pairs of wings, and the abdomen contains reproductive organs. Insects are found everywhere, except for the oceans.

DRAGONFLIES

These fast-moving predators have alternately beating front and rear wings that allow them to fly through the air with incredible control. Equipped with large eyes, dragonflies use their excellent vision to detect unsuspecting prey, such as flies, then dart in to make the kill.

Southern hawker dragonfly has a slender body and long, thin wings

Southern hawker dragonfly

◀GRASSHOPPERS AND CRICKETS

Although grasshoppers and crickets have large wings, they usually employ their long hind legs to leap away from danger. All have chewing mouthparts. Grasshoppers and their relatives, such as locusts, are plant-eaters, while crickets are scavengers or omnivores.

Desert locust

Male locusts "sing" to attract females by rubbing hind legs against wings

COCKROACHES ▶

These mainly nocturnal insects are very sensitive to vibrations and scurry for cover if danger threatens. Most common in tropical and subtropical regions, cockroaches are generally scavengers. A few species are pests, infesting homes and feeding on food scraps.

American cockroach

Flattened body allows cockroach to squeeze into tiny crevices

Praying mantis

MANTIDS ▶

Also called praying mantises because of the way they hold their front legs, mantids are solitary predators, with a triangular head and large eyes. Their bodies blend in well with the leaves of forest trees. Mantids stay motionless, waiting for prey to wander within striking distance, then shoot their spiked front legs forward to grab their next meal.

Buff-tailed bumblebee

Emerald cockroach wasp

WASPS, BEES, AND ANTS ▶

These insects have a narrow waist between their thorax and abdomen, and, in females, a sting. Many, including wood ants and honeybees, live in large, highly organized colonies, and are important pollinators of flowers.

Cuckoo wasp

Leaf cutter ants

Two long antennae

Ichneumon wasp

Male driver ant

Wings only found on males

▼ BEETLES

With at least 370,000 species, beetles make up the largest group of insects. Their hard front wings form a wing case that folds over and protects the rear wings and abdomen. Beetles are found in fresh water and almost everywhere on land, and they use their biting mouthparts to feed on plants, fungi, other insects, dead animals, or even dung.

▼ BUGS

All bugs have a feeding tube that pierces their food and sucks out the juices. For example, most shield bugs and plant hoppers, such as the well-camouflaged thorn bug, suck sugar-rich sap from plants. Water bugs, such as the backswimmer, are predators of other invertebrates and small fish.

▼ FLIES

These agile fliers have just one pair of wings and feed by sucking up liquids. They include nectar-feeders, such as bee flies and crane flies, decomposers that feed on rotting matter, such as houseflies, and predators, such as robber flies, that feed on other insects.

BUTTERFLIES AND MOTHS ▶

Butterflies are generally brightly colored and active during the day, while most moths are nocturnal. Both use a long, coiled "tongue" to feed on nectar or other liquids.

Rove beetle

African ground beetle

Jewel beetle

Golden scarab beetle

Leaf weevil

Striped shield bug

Thorn bug

Long legs used for swimming

Common backswimmer (water boatman)

Darwin's beetle

Male Darwin's beetle has a large set of jaws

Moth's wings are covered with thousands of tiny scales

African Moon moth

Pericopine moth

Crane fly

True flies have just one pair of wings

Flattened body of violin beetle resembles a violin

Asterope sapphira butterfly

Robber fly

Bee fly

Verdant sphinx moth

MOLLUSKS

This amazingly diverse group includes more than 100,000 species, ranging from garden slugs to pearl-bearing oysters and terrifying giant squid. Despite their differences, most mollusks share some common features. They all have a soft body, often protected by a hard, chalky shell, and feed using a roughened strip called a radula. They have a muscular foot for movement and breathe using gills. Most belong to the gastropods—the group that includes snails and slugs.

CEPHALOPODS ▼

Octopuses, squid, nautiluses, cuttlefish, and other cephalopods are intelligent mollusks. They have a large head and a mouth surrounded by arms or tentacles, which are used for movement and catching fish and crabs. The mouth is equipped with a horny beak and a toothed radula for dragging in food. Cephalopods can move very quickly using a form of jet propulsion.

Common squid

Large eyes provide excellent vision

Shell contains chambers that provide buoyancy

Pearly nautilus

Common octopus

Blue giant clam

Suckers used to grip prey

◀ CHITONS

These inhabitants of rocky shores have a flat shell made up of eight overlapping plates. At low tide, chitons cling tightly to rocks and, if pulled off, curl up into a protective ball. At high tide they creep slowly over rocks using their muscular foot and feed on algae and other small organisms by scraping them off the rocky surface with their radula.

Chiton

Troschel's murex

Blue (common) mussels

Valves of shell open to draw in water current

Textile cone shell

Conus pertusus

Cone shell paralyzes prey with its poisonous, harpoonlike radula

BIVALVES ▶

Found in both fresh water and the sea, bivalves include clams and mussels. Bivalves have a hinged shell with two pieces or valves. They breathe by drawing a current of water into their shell from which large gills extract oxygen. The gills also trap food particles that are then transferred to the mouth, a process called filter feeding.

Bright colors warn predators that the sea slug is poisonous

Pair of nudibranch sea slugs

North's long whelk

Hooped whelk

Spiral shell protects soft-bodied whelk

Common limpet

TUSK SHELLS ▶

With shells that resemble miniature elephant's tusks, these sea-dwelling mollusks are found offshore where they burrow into the seabed. The small eyeless head that emerges from the shell's larger opening is surrounded by small tentacles. These sweep the seabed for tiny particles and draw them into the tusk shell's mouth.

GASTROPODS ▶

Most gastropods live in the sea. They have a head with eyes and tentacles, a muscular foot that produces creeping movements and all except the slugs have a large external—and often spiral—shell. Most, including cone shells, whelks, murexes, and sea slugs, are carnivores. Limpets are grazers with a simple cone-shaped shell.

WORMS

The term "worm" is a general one used to describe invertebrates that have long, soft bodies and, usually, no legs. Worms are found in a range of habitats including soil, tropical forests, lakes, rivers, and the sea. Flatworms are the simplest worms and have flattened, ribbonlike bodies. Annelids have bodies divided into segments. Other worm groups include peanut worms and velvet worms.

▼ LEECH

These annelid worms have a flattened body with a sucker at each end. Most live in fresh water, where they swim. Outside of water, they move by attaching their suckers to surfaces and arching their bodies. Some 75 percent of leeches are bloodsuckers. The rest are mostly predators of other invertebrates.

Most segments have tiny bristles called chaetae

▼ PEANUT WORM

Found in burrows in shallow seas, these worms have a slender front end, tipped with a tentacled mouth, and a swollen rear end. If threatened, they can retract their front end into their rear end, making them resemble a peanut shell. Peanut worms feed by filtering particles from sand using their tentacles.

Body coated with slippery mucus

VELVET WORM ▼

Inhabitants of tropical forests, velvet worms have a wormlike body and up to 43 pairs of short, stubby legs with clawed "feet." The head has sensory antennae, jaws, and glands that squirt slime over prey in order to disable it.

▼ LAND PLANARIAN

Flatworms like this one live in habitats with both high temperatures and humidity. They glide over soil or leaves on a thin film of slippery mucus. Land planarians feed on other worms, slugs, and insect larvae that they take in through the mouth in the middle of their underside.

MARINE FLATWORM ▶

Polyclads (marine flatworms) are oval-shaped and often brightly-colored, especially those that live on coral reefs. Bright colors serve as a warning to potential predators that the flatworm tastes bad. Most polyclads are predators that eat smaller invertebrates.

Rippling the edges of the body allows the worm to move

PEACOCK WORM ▶

The peacock worm is a bristleworm—a type of annelid—and lives attached to the sea bottom in a tube it constructs from mucus and sand grains. A feathery "crown" of filaments encircling its mouth traps tiny food particles that drift past. If danger threatens, the worm instantly folds its crown and retreats into its tube.

EARTHWORM ▲

With familiar rounded bodies, earthworms burrow through soil by changing shape. The front part of the body elongates, its tiny bristles gripping the burrow, while the rear part follows. Earthworms are annelids and eat soil, digesting the decaying plant material it contains.

BEARDED FIREWORM ▼

Like many bristleworms, the bearded fireworm moves using paddlelike lobes, reinforced with bristles, which project from its sides. The bearded fireworm's bristles carry a poison that can cause paralysis if touched. Fireworms live on reefs where they feed on corals, anemones, and small crustaceans.

Each segment carries a pair of lobes with bristles

Tentacles are
colonies of
tiny animals

Portuguese
man-of-war

3

Sea nettle

4

Box jellyfish

Tentacles
can inflict
lethal stings

Beroid comb jelly

1

SPONGES, JELLIES, AND CORALS

Some of the simplest members of the animal kingdom
belong to three phyla—Porifera, Cnidaria, and Ctenophora.
Poriferans are sponges, animals that feed by filtering food
from the water. Cnidarians include hydrozoans, jellyfish,
corals, and sea anemones. All have stinging tentacles that
immobilize and trap prey. Ctenophores, also known as
comb jellies, are related to the cnidarians.

❶ COMB JELLIES

Delicate and nearly transparent,
comb jellies swim among the ocean
plankton. Eight rows of hairlike cilia
extend from top to bottom, beating
in waves to move the comb jelly
around. Most catch prey with two
sticky tentacles, but this beroid comb
jelly uses its mouth to eat prey whole.

❷ SPONGES

The simplest of all animals, sponges
are unlike any other creatures. Most
attach themselves to the seabed,
where they grow without symmetry,
their bodies supported by a
"skeleton" made of tiny struts and
peppered with pores. Water is drawn
into the pores and food particles are
filtered out and digested.

❸ HYDROZOANS

This group of cnidarians shows
astonishing variety, from animals that
resemble tiny sea anemones to the
extraordinary Portuguese man-of-war.
This jellyfish is not one organism but
a colony of cooperating animals. One
forms the prominent gas balloon that
allows the colony to float and drift.
Others make up the tentacles.

❹ JELLYFISH

Scyphozoans or "true" jellyfish have
a bell-shaped body, filled with the
jellylike substance that gives the
animal its name, and prey-catching,
stinging tentacles. A jellyfish swims
by contracting its body to force out
water from its underside and propel
it in the opposite direction. Related
box jellyfish are notorious for their
toxic stings that can kill humans.

Opening through
which water current
leaves sponge

Water enters sponge
through tiny openings
in its surface

❺ SEA ANEMONES

They may look like colorful plants,
but sea anemones are predators
that eat small animals. On top of the
anemone's body is a central mouth
surrounded by stinging tentacles.
A base fixes the animal to a rock.
If threatened, many anemones
rapidly expel water from their
insides and shrink dramatically.

Yellow tube sponge

Sea sponge

2

5

Stinging
tentacles
capture prey,
then draw it into
central mouth

✪ CORAL
Resembling tiny sea anemones, corals live in vast groups in clear, shallow, tropical waters. They protect themselves by building hard cases of calcium carbonate into which they can withdraw. Over time, the massed cases form huge coral reefs that provide habitats for fish and many other marine animals.

Giant green sea anemone

Carpet anemone

169

ANCIENT ANIMALS

Around one billion years ago the first animals appeared on Earth. Since that time, a vast array of animal species have evolved, or developed gradually over successive generations. Extinction (when a species dies out) is a natural part of this process, even when whole groups disappear as a result of dramatic changes in their environment. These are just some examples from the history of animal life.

520 MILLION YEARS AGO

Anomalocaris

Opabinia

Opabinia had five eyes

▲ 520 MILLION YEARS AGO

Around this time there was a massive explosion in the numbers and types of invertebrates in Earth's warm oceans. Anomalocaris was a 2-ft- (60-cm-) long predator that swam using two winglike flaps. Opabinia grabbed prey with its long proboscis.

370 MILLION YEARS AGO

Dunkleosteus

Head of Dunkleosteus protected by bony plates

Cladoselache

Streamlined body shape allowed Cladoselache to move quickly through the water

▲ 370 MILLION YEARS AGO

The oceans abounded with many animals, including new types of fish. The placoderms—early fish with jaws—included Dunkleosteus, an armored giant that sliced through prey with its razor-sharp toothplates. The earliest sharks included Cladoselache, a predator that seized prey and swallowed it whole.

265 MILLION YEARS AGO

Dragonfly

▼ 265 MILLION YEARS AGO

Forests of conifers thrived in warm, dry conditions where mammal-like reptiles dominated life on land. One was Dimetrodon, a giant predator with a "sail" on its back that helped it to warm up and become active more rapidly. In the air, large dragonflies were the main hunters.

Dimetrodon's sail was used to control body temperature

10,000 YEARS AGO

Woolly mammoth

Giant sloth

▲ 10,000 YEARS AGO
The woolly mammoth and the giant sloth were among the large mammals that lived during the past two million years. All became extinct around 10,000 years ago, because of climate change at the end of the last ice age, and because of hunting by people.

RECENT HISTORY

Dodo

Thylacine

150 MILLION YEARS AGO

Allosaurus

Allosaurus tore its prey apart using its sharp teeth

Pterodactylus

▲ 150 MILLION YEARS AGO
At this time the climate was warm and dinosaurs dominated life on Earth. They included ferocious, fast-moving carnivores, such as *Allosaurus*, as well as giant, lumbering plant-eaters. Flying reptiles, such as *Pterodactylus*, preyed on smaller animals. By 65 million years ago, both groups were extinct.

RECENT HISTORY ▶
In recent times human activity has accelerated the rate of extinction. The dodo was a flightless bird discovered on Mauritius in 1598. By 1681, introduced cats, rats, and other egg-eaters had made it extinct. The presence of Europeans in Tasmania made the doglike thylacine extinct by the 1930s.

ON THE BRINK

Extinction is a natural part of life on Earth. Over millions of years, some species disappear while new species evolve. Since the 1600s, however, the rate of extinction has risen steadily, with species vanishing as a direct result of human activities. The World Conservation Union lists more than 16,000 animal species on the brink of extinction, including those shown here.

SIBERIAN TIGER ▼

Like other tigers, the Siberian tiger is critically endangered. Tigers are officially protected, but poachers kill them for their skins and for body parts, which are used in traditional Chinese medicine. The tiger's habitat is also shrinking because of intensive logging.

ECHO PARAKEET ▶

In the 1980s, only 10 echo parakeets remained on the Indian Ocean island of Mauritius, due to habitat loss and rats raiding their nests. Since then, however, conservation measures have resulted in a steady rise in the number of parakeets.

▲ PANAMANIAN GOLDEN FROG

Many frog species have gone into decline because of fungal infections. The Panamanian golden frog is no exception. The last specimens in the wild were seen in 2007 and have since been collected for breeding in captivity to save the species.

CALIFORNIA CONDOR ▶

Trapping, shooting, poisoning, and collisions with power lines brought this American vulture near to extinction. In 1987, all 22 surviving birds were taken into captivity, where they were bred successfully. Numbers are now steadily increasing.

AMERICAN BURYING BEETLE ▶

Once widespread across the US, this beetle buries the carcasses of rodents and birds to feed its young. Today, only a few remain, probably because of the use of pesticides (chemicals that kill insect pests) and changes in their habitat.

◀ SAIGA ANTELOPE

Numbers of saiga antelope have decreased by 90 percent since the 1980s. Their horns are used in traditional Chinese medicine. There are now just four isolated populations in the steppes (grasslands) of Russia and central Asia.

OAHU TREE SNAIL ▶

The Hawaiian island of Oahu was once home to 41 species of tree snails. Predation by the rosy wolf snail and loss of their natural habitat made most of them extinct. Today, just two species survive in the wild.

◀ WESTERN LOWLAND GORILLA

One of our closest relatives, this gorilla lives in the tropical forests of western Africa. Numbers have dropped as human populations have increased. Their forest home has been cut down to provide farmland, and people have hunted gorillas for meat. Deadly Ebola fever has killed gorillas and humans alike.

▲ FLOREANA CORAL

This rare species is found around the Galápagos Islands. Since 1982 the extent of the coral has decreased by 80 percent. The causes are believed to be heating of the Pacific Ocean, caused by global warming, and the El Niño effect, a change in ocean currents.

LEATHERBACK TURTLE ▶

The leatherback was once widespread in oceans around the world. Today, it faces a variety of threats. Its eggs, laid in burrows on sandy beaches, are targeted by egg thieves, while adult turtles can be trapped by fishing nets or mistakenly eat discarded plastic bags—which block their digestive system—instead of jellyfish, their natural food.

173

HEAD-TO-HEAD
Two male bison meet head-to-head to establish which is the stronger. Competition is just one of many life skills, such as feeding, communication, and defense, that animals perform daily in order to survive.

Life skills

RESPIRATION

Animals need oxygen to release the energy in their cells that powers all life activities. The energy-liberating process, called cell respiration, also releases waste carbon dioxide. How animals take in oxygen depends on their complexity and habitat. Many animals breathe in oxygen from air or water using structures such as lungs or gills, and have a blood system to carry the oxygen to their cells.

FLATWORM ▶

These simple animals have neither a respiratory system to take in oxygen nor a blood system to carry it to their cells. Instead, a flatworm takes in oxygen and loses carbon dioxide directly through its surface. This is possible because the flatworm, being extremely thin, possesses a very large outer surface through which oxygen can pass.

Air sacs connected to lungs

MOLLUSK ▶

How mollusks take in oxygen depends on their type and habitat. Land snails, slugs, and air-breathing pond snails have a lung. Marine mollusks, including sea slugs and clams, use gills to take in oxygen from the surrounding water, as do octopuses and squid.

▼ FISH

Red because of their rich blood supply, a fish's gills are located behind its mouth. The fish draws water into its mouth, across its gills, and back out again. Dissolved oxygen passes into the bloodstream and circulates around the body.

AMPHIBIAN LARVA ▶

This newt larva or tadpole—like other young amphibians—depends on feathery external gills to extract oxygen from water. When it becomes an adult newt it will lose its gills and develop lungs.

Pond snail

Newt tadpole

Goldfish

Feathery external gills

Flaplike operculum covers gills

As active fliers, birds need much more oxygen than mammals, and have a more efficient respiratory system. Nine air sacs work like bellows to maintain a one-way flow of air through the lungs, and to clear any used air quickly.

Holes called spiracles in an insect's thorax and abdomen allow air in and out of its body. Spiracles lead to branching tubes called tracheae that carry oxygen-rich air to all parts of the body, and remove carbon dioxide.

Spiracle in the side of a grasshopper's abdomen

MAMMAL ▼

Like other mammals, a hamster has two lungs. The lungs are made up of millions of tiny air sacs, each surrounded by blood capillaries that carry oxygen away. Air is sucked into or squeezed out of the lungs by muscles that make the chest cavity bigger or smaller.

AQUATIC MAMMAL ▲

Whales and other marine mammals have lungs and, unlike fish, cannot extract oxygen from seawater. They must come to the surface to breathe air, although they can wait much longer between breaths than land mammals. A whale has a nostril or nostrils—called a blowhole—on top of its head. When it surfaces, stale air (and any water lodged in the blowhole) is blown out as spray.

AMPHIBIAN ADULT ▶

Once it reaches adulthood, an amphibian, such as this frog, takes in oxygen through its lungs. In order to breathe, the mouth closes and air is drawn through the nostrils and into the lungs. Then the body wall contracts (squeezes) to push air out of the lungs. Frogs also take in oxygen through their moist skin.

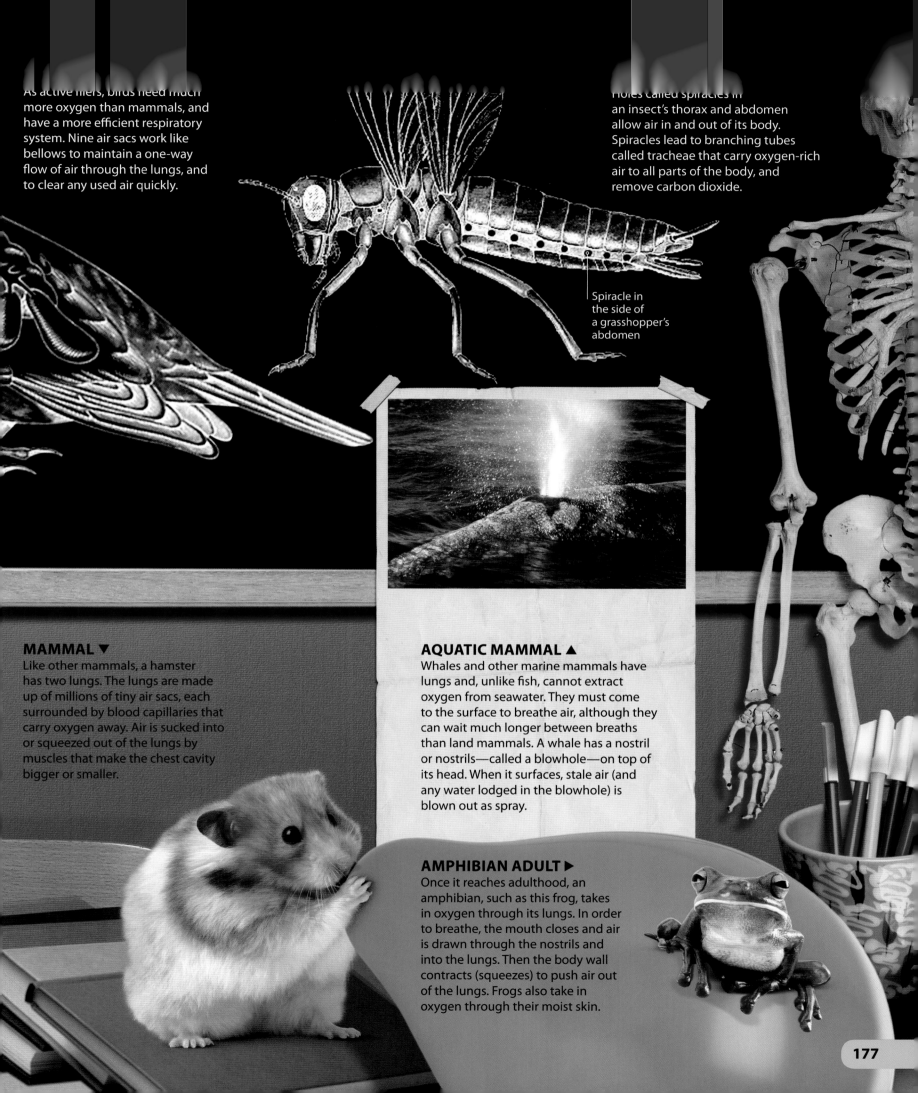

FEEDING

Animals eat to survive. They eat a wide range of foods and show many different feeding techniques. Animals are divided into different categories, such as herbivores and carnivores, according to their food preferences. Once an animal has eaten food, it is digested (broken down) to release its essential nutrients. These nutrients supply the energy needed for movement and the raw materials used for growth and repair.

Leopard

❶ CARNIVORES

These animals feed exclusively on meat or fish, food sources rich in nutrients. Carnivores are predators that either hunt or lie in wait for their prey. They include leopards, snakes, bullfrogs, and sea eagles. Many have large teeth and strong jaws, or sharp beaks and talons.

❷ SCAVENGERS

This clean-up squad of flesh-eaters feeds on dead animals. Vultures, for example, are scavenging specialists that use their sharp, hooked beaks to cut through skin and flesh, and their rough tongues to rasp meat from bones.

❸ INSECTIVORES

Animals that feed on insects are called insectivores. The giant anteater, for example, breaks open ant or termite nests using its powerful claws. It flicks its long, sticky tongue in and out of broken nests to scoop up the thousands of insects it needs to eat daily.

Farmyard pig

American black vulture

Vampire bat

Sharp teeth gnaw nut held in front paws

Gray squirrel

Fruit forms the main part of an orang-utan's diet

Guinea pig

Giant anteater

Narrow snout housing long tongue probes into ants' nests

Strong, sharp jaws cut margin of leaf

African bullfrog

Caterpillar

❽ DUNG FEEDERS

Certain insects feed on the feces (dung) of herbivores such as cattle. Dung beetles use smell to detect dung and suck nutritious fluid from it. They roll dung into a ball and bury it with their eggs to provide food for newly hatched larvae.

Dung beetle

Swallowtail butterfly

❹ BLOOD FEEDERS

These specialized fluid feeders have a substance in their saliva that stops blood from clotting. Female mosquitoes pierce their prey's skin, then suck up blood through special mouthparts. Vampire bats use razor-sharp teeth to bite cattle and other mammals, then lap up the blood.

❺ OMNIVORES

With a diet that includes both meat and plant foods, omnivores, such as pigs, squirrels, and orang-utans, tend to be opportunists that eat most things. Some, including raccoons and foxes, live in close proximity to humans, adding garbage and roadkill to their normal diet.

❻ FILTER FEEDERS

Most filter feeders, from small rock-bound barnacles to mighty baleen whales, live in water. They filter tiny organisms from the water around them using sievelike body parts. Flamingos, the only filter-feeding birds, eat tiny crustaceans.

❼ HERBIVORES

Pandas, muntjacs, caterpillars, and tortoises are herbivores—animals that eat plant parts using special teeth or other mouthparts. Leaves and stems are not very nutritious, so herbivores must consume large amounts to obtain enough nutrients.

❾ FLUID FEEDERS

Fluid feeders suck liquid food through tubelike mouthparts. Butterflies have a long, coiled-up proboscis that unrolls to drink energy-rich nectar from flowers. Aphids pierce plant stems using their mouthparts to suck up sugary sap.

Orang-utan

Bamboo forms 99 percent of this Chinese bear's diet

Giant Panda

❻ Flamingo

Muntjac

Large, flattened teeth grind up vegetation

Raccoon

Sea eagle

Snake suffocates its prey in its coils, then swallows it whole

Beak held upside down to strain food from water

Boa constrictor

Sharp talons grab fish from the water

Tortoise

Mosquito

MOVEMENT

One of the major things that makes animals stand out from other living things, such as plants and fungi, is their ability to move. While some stay rooted to one place and move body parts, most move about actively in the air, on land, or in water. Animals move in many different ways, from swimming to sidewinding, and looping to leaping.

❶ TIGER
Walking and running on four legs are movements performed not only by tigers and other cats, but also by many other mammals. Aside from supporting the body's weight, legs can be moved in coordinated ways by muscles under the control of the brain. The tiger's long tail helps it to balance when running or pouncing.

❷ FLAT-TAILED GECKO
These agile lizards make adept climbers, scaling vertical surfaces and even hanging upside down as they search for insect prey. They owe these skills to five wide toe pads on each foot that are covered with millions of tiny hairs. These create electrical forces that glue the gecko to any surface, even glass.

❸ LOOPER CATERPILLAR
Certain caterpillars travel with a looping movement. The caterpillar anchors itself with claspers at its rear end, and reaches forward with its front end. When it has fixed its front end in place using its legs, it pulls its back end forward to form a loop. It then repeats the sequence to continue moving forward.

❹ SIDEWINDING SNAKE
Most snakes move by wriggling from side to side to form S-shaped curves that push the body forward. In the desert, snakes have to move over hot sand. Some do this by sidewinding— throwing their bodies in sideways leaps so that they move diagonally and touch the hot ground as little as possible—leaving a trail of markings where they have landed.

❺ COMMON FROG
At home both on land and in water, frogs use different methods of movement for each environment. Frogs can walk, but they also leap, especially to escape enemies. Powerful hind legs push the body off the ground and shorter forelegs absorb the shock of landing. In water, the webbed hind feet kick out to propel the frog forward.

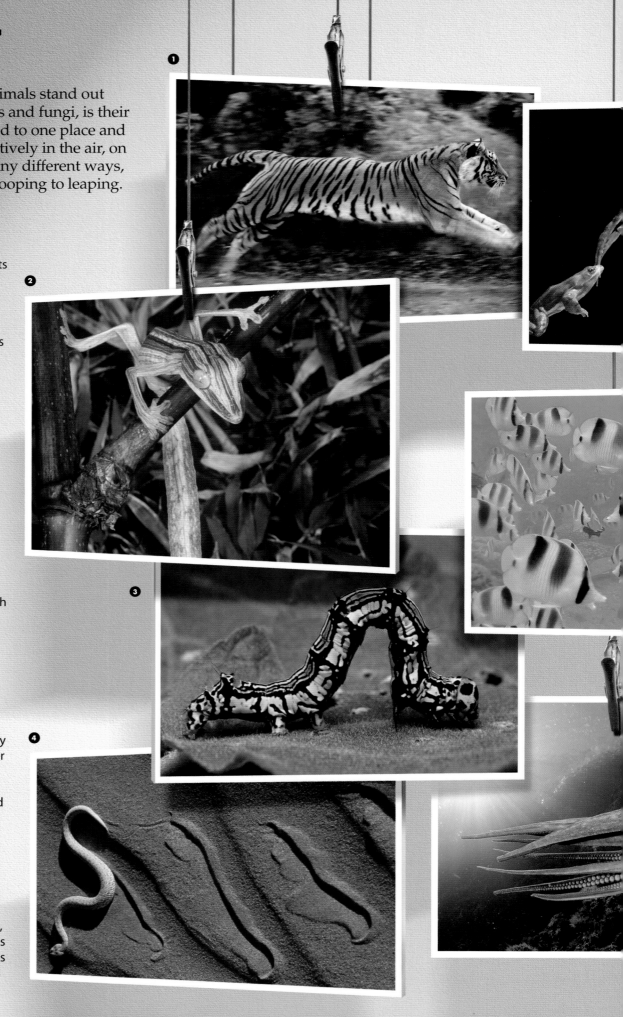

❻ FISH

On both sides of a fish's backbone there are muscles that contract (pull) to move the tail from side to side and push the fish forward. Fins also stabilize the fish's body, preventing it from tipping from side to side or up and down, and enable it to steer.

❼ OCTOPUS

The octopus uses its long tentacles and suckers to pull itself over the seafloor, but it can also swim rapidly, just as squid and cuttlefish do. It takes water into its body then expels it through a funnel-like siphon. This creates a jet of water that propels the octopus through the ocean, head first and with tentacles trailing.

❽ BLUE TIT

Most birds use their wings to fly. When the wings are pulled downward and backward, they push the bird forward. This forces air over the curved surfaces of the wings, creating the lift that keeps the bird airborne. Body feathers give this blue tit a streamlined shape, while the tail acts as a rudder.

❾ SNAIL

Slugs and snails have a single, large foot on which they creep across the ground or along plants. Muscles in the underside of the foot contract and relax to create wavelike ripples that push the snail slowly forward. The foot also produces slippery slime that makes creeping easier and protects the snail from any sharp objects in its path.

❿ GIBBON

Found in the tropical rain forests of southeast Asia, gibbons are apes with long arms and very flexible shoulder and wrist joints. These features enable them to perform an action called brachiation. Gibbons hurl themselves forward, swinging hand over hand from branch to branch to move with great speed and skill through the forest canopy.

⓫ HUMPBACK WHALE

This massive marine mammal swims using its tail. The tail fin has two horizontal paddles called flukes, which can be moved up and down by muscle action to propel the whale forward, downward, or upward to the surface to breathe air. Its broad front limbs or flippers steer the whale so it can turn.

SPEED

The members of the animal kingdom move at widely differing speeds. How fast an animal can move depends on many factors, including its size, shape, and weight, whether it lives in the air, on land, or in water, and the way it moves. In general, larger animals move fastest, especially those that live in open habitats such as grasslands or the ocean. Here are the slowest, the fastest, and some in between.

0.03 mph
(0.05 kph)

6 mph
(10 kph)

22 mph
(35 kph)

GARDEN SNAIL
Making leisurely progress on a film of slimy mucus, the garden snail is not built for speed. It creeps forward as a result of waves of contractions rippling down its single, muscular foot. If threatened the snail cannot flee, but retreats inside its protective shell.

BUMBLEBEE
Despite their apparent bulkiness, these flower-feeding insects can use their wings to reach a good flying speed. On cool days, they beat their wings to warm up their bodies before taking off.

25 mph
(40 kph)

3 mph
(5 kph)

GENTOO PENGUIN
With sleek, streamlined bodies, penguins move with ease in the ocean, powered by their flipperlike wings. The fastest, South Atlantic gentoo penguins, dart and turn to catch krill and fish, and to escape enemies.

COCKROACH
The fastest running insect, an American cockroach uses long legs to dart out of sight. It can conceal itself in the narrowest crevice.

BLACK RHINOCEROS
This heavily built, powerful African mammal browses on shrubs and low trees and has no natural enemies, aside from humans. Nonetheless, black rhinos have poor eyesight and will charge with speed and agility if spooked by strange smells or sounds.

33 mph
(53 kph)

TIGER SHARK
The ferocious tiger shark eats anything, including jellyfish, seals, turtles, dolphins, and even humans. It lives in warm coastal waters, where it uses rapid bursts of speed to catch its often fast-moving prey. It has a streamlined shape and powerful muscles that pull its tail from side to side.

SAILFISH
Powered by mighty muscles and a crescent-shaped tail, the sailfish is the fastest fish in the warmer oceans. Its sail-like dorsal fin is normally folded down, but raises to help the sailfish herd its prey, such as sardines, making them easier to catch.

70 mph
(110 kph)

55 mph
(88 kph)

PRONGHORN
One of the quickest land mammals, the North American pronghorn is related to deer and antelope. The pronghorn lives in scrub and open grassland and uses its long legs to move quickly over long distances.

175 mph
(280 kph)

60 mph
(100 kph)

45 mph
(72 kph)

PEREGRINE FALCON
This bird-hunting predator is the fastest animal on the planet. The peregrine falcon soars to a great height and then, with wings partially folded, dives at breathtaking speed on prey flying far below it. With a well-aimed slash of its talons, the peregrine knocks the prey to the ground, ready to be eaten.

OSTRICH
The world's biggest bird may not fly, but it can run faster than any other bird. In the African savanna, ostriches sustain high speeds over long distances as they seek food or escape predators, such as lions. Ostriches have long legs powered by massive muscles. These not only propel them at speed but can also deliver a deadly kick to enemies.

CHEETAH
Over short distances this daytime hunter is the fastest land animal. It pursues its prey with an explosive burst of speed, but if a kill is not made within 30 seconds, the cheetah stops to keep from overheating.

MAINTENANCE

The animal world is a tough, competitive place, and animals have to look after themselves and keep in peak condition in order to increase their chances of survival. Animals maintain themselves for many reasons: to enable them to move more efficiently, to help them attract a mate so they can breed, to remove pesky parasites, and to stay healthy. Maintenance methods include grooming, preening, eating special foods, and taking mud baths.

❶ SOCIAL GROOMING

Many primates, such as these Japanese macaques, live in tight-knit groups. Group members groom each other, using their nails and teeth to comb and clean each other's fur, and to remove any irritating parasites, such as lice.

❷ INSECT CLEAN-UP

Dust and food particles can cling to an insect's body parts and stop them from working well. Insects use their legs and mouthparts to clean themselves. This praying mantis is grooming the spines on its front legs.

❸ SELF-GROOMING

Cats and some other mammals groom themselves. A tiger, for example, uses its rough, moist tongue to clean its fur and remove pests. Kangaroos spread saliva on themselves, which then evaporates to give a cooling effect.

❹ CLAY LICK

A number of animals living in tropical forests, both birds and mammals, eat small amounts of clay each day. Flocks of colorful, squawking parrots descend on favoured spots, called clay licks. It appears that the clay makes harmless any poisons in the fruits, nuts, and seeds that the parrots eat.

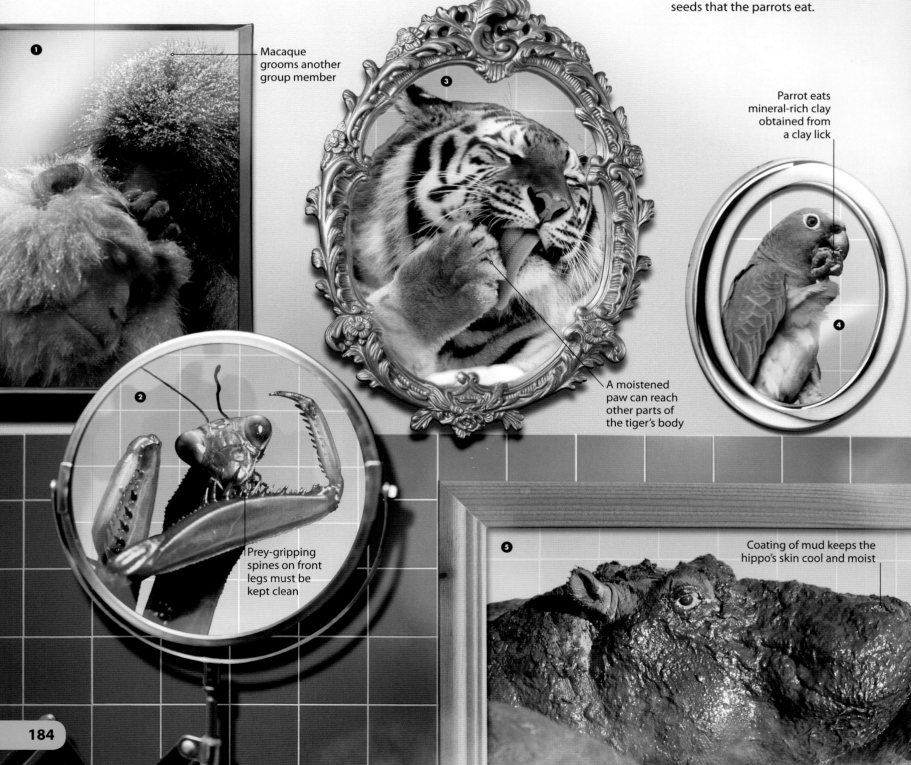

Macaque grooms another group member

Parrot eats mineral-rich clay obtained from a clay lick

A moistened paw can reach other parts of the tiger's body

Prey-gripping spines on front legs must be kept clean

Coating of mud keeps the hippo's skin cool and moist

❺ MUD BATH

Hippopotamuses depend on mud baths or water to keep themselves cool in the African heat. The water or mud also protects their sensitive skin from the bites of insects and other pests. If not regularly moistened, their skin dries out very easily, and can crack and become infected.

❻ SHOWERING

In the hot African savanna, elephants visit waterholes to drink and cool off. They use their trunks to suck up water, then squirt it into their mouths, or point it backward to shower cooling water over their thick skin. Wet skin traps a layer of dust that protects against parasites and sunlight.

❼ PREENING FEATHERS

To ensure flying is as efficent as possible, birds use their beaks to preen their feathers. The tip of the beak works like a comb to straighten and clean feathers. Preening also spreads an oily liquid over the feathers to waterproof them, and roots out any parasites living on the skin.

❽ BIRD ANTING

Eurasian jays are among the birds that use this type of maintenance. The bird lies on top of an ants' nest, provoking the irritated ants to spray chemicals, such as formic acid, onto its feathers. These chemicals kill irritating, blood-feeding parasites.

Flight feathers spread out for preening

Tail fanned out over ants' nest

SENSES

An animal's senses provide a constant stream of information about its surroundings, using receptors that send signals to the brain. This enables the animal to avoid danger, find food, locate a mate, navigate, and communicate. The main five senses are sight, hearing, smell, taste, and touch. Sharks are ocean predators. As well as the main five, sharks have two extra senses that enhance their hunting efficiency.

Lateral line runs along the length of the shark's body

❶ TOUCH
Most animals, including sharks, have touch receptors scattered throughout the skin. Receptors for other senses are usually found in special organs, such as the eyes. The shark's touch receptors detect water currents, temperature changes, and direct contact with other animals, especially when a shark goes in for the kill.

❷ VIBRATIONS
A fluid-filled tube called the lateral line runs along the length of the shark from head to tail. Pores in the skin connect the surrounding water to lateral-line receptors that detect vibrations and pressure changes. This provides the shark with a sense of "distant touch" that allows it to sense the intensity and direction of the movements of an approaching fish.

❸ HEARING AND BALANCE
Two small openings in the top of the shark's head mark the entrance to the inner parts of a shark's ears. Sounds travel farther and faster in water than in air, and sharks are able to pinpoint prey over several miles by detecting the low frequency sounds they produce. As in many other animals, balance organs in the shark's ears help it stay orientated and upright.

Position of lateral line as it extends toward tail

❹ SIGHT
A shark's large, well-developed eyes are more sensitive than human eyes. With increasing depths, light levels in the ocean decrease and the eye's pupils widen to admit more light. In addition, a layer called the tapetum lucidum lining the shark's eyes reflects light internally, maximizing the shark's vision so it can hunt in the darkness.

❺ TASTE
Sharks do not use their sense of taste to detect their prey, but to determine whether they want to eat it or not. Pits in the mouth and throat contain receptors called taste buds. As the shark bites, the taste buds detect chemicals in its prey's tissues. If the shark finds the animal "tasty," perhaps because it contains plenty of fat, it will continue eating.

Openings to
ears located on
top of head just
behind the eyes

3

Eye rolls backward
during feeding
for protection

4

Pores mark openings
to organs that detect
electrical signals

6

7

Water passing
through
nostrils
carries odors
to smell
receptors

5

Taste buds
located in lining
of mouth and gullet

1

Skin contains
touch, temperature,
and pain receptors

❻ SMELL

As a shark swims, water flows into
its nostrils and over highly sensitive
smell receptors. Once the shark
picks up on an odor trail, it swims
toward the source, moving its head
from side to side to pinpoint the
exact location.

❼ ELECTRICAL SIGNALS

When animals move, their muscles
give off very weak electrical signals.
Dotted around the shark's snout
are hundreds of pores leading to
sensory organs that can detect those
electrical signals. Once a shark has
seen, heard, or smelled its prey and
is closing in, its electrical detectors
take over, using the prey's weak
electrical signals to strike accurately.

VISION

For many animals, vision is their most important sense. They use it to create an image of their surroundings so that they can navigate, find food and mates, avoid predators, and communicate with each other. Animals can see because they have light receptors, usually housed inside special sense organs called eyes. These receptors turn light into nerve signals, which are then turned back into images by the brain. Quality of vision varies greatly between different species. Flatworms can distinguish only between light and dark, while some mammal eyes generate 3-D color images.

▲ SPIDER EYES

All spiders have eight simple eyes, but many depend more on their sense of touch to detect and trap their prey. However, active hunters, such as jumping spiders and this wolf spider, use large, forward-facing eyes to locate and catch prey.

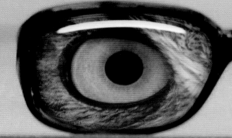

▲ CEPHALOPOD EYES

Octopuses and other cephalopod mollusks have highly developed eyes. They allow their owners to find and catch prey, and to navigate away from predators. Unlike other cephalopods, cuttlefish have unusual W-shaped pupils.

▲ FORWARD-FACING EYES

Forward-facing eyes enable hunters, like this eagle, to judge distances accurately so they can pounce on moving prey. Tree-dwelling primates, such as monkeys, also have forward-facing eyes, which allow them to jump safely from branch to branch.

▲ EYESPOTS

The most simple eyes are eyespots. In water-dwelling flatworms, cup-shaped eyespots act as simple light detectors, enabling the flatworm to shy away from bright light and move to darker, safer areas under rocks or plants.

▲ NIGHT VISION

Like many nocturnal animals, red-eyed tree frogs have large eyes in relation to their overall body size that are efficient at capturing light in dim conditions. In the tropical forests of South America, they use their keen night vision to ambush moths, flies, and crickets.

Thick eyelashes
protect eye from
dirt and insects

▲ EYES ON STALKS
Like many crabs, shore-dwelling ghost crabs have compound eyes on stalks, giving them an all-around view of their surroundings. If they spot danger, they disappear instantly into their burrows. The stalked eyes can also be folded down for protection.

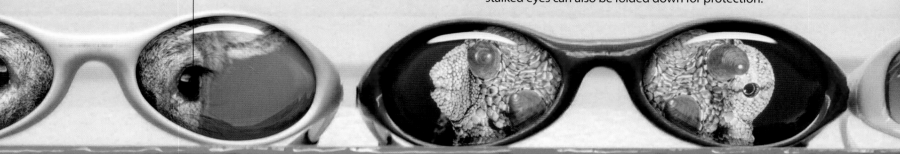

▲ ALL-AROUND VISION
Animals—such as rabbits, antelopes, and deer—that graze or browse on vegetation, have large eyes on the sides of their heads that allow them to see to the front, sideways, and behind. This all-around vision allows them to keep a constant lookout for predators.

▲ INDEPENDENT EYES
A chameleon swivels its two eyes independently of one another as it looks out for insects. Once prey is sighted, both eyes swivel forward so the lizard can judge the distance accurately as it shoots out a long, sticky tongue to grab its victim.

▲ COMPOUND EYES
Crustaceans, such as crabs, and insects, including this dragonfly, have compound eyes made up of lots of separate light-detection units, each with its own lens for focusing light. The animal's brain receives signals from all these units to produce a "mosaic" image.

▲ MIRROR EYES
A scallop, like a mussel, is a mollusk that has two hinged shells enclosing its body. When the shells open, they expose two rows of small eyes. Inside each eye, a mirrorlike surface reflects light onto receptors to form images.

▲ ABOVE AND BELOW
The four-eyed fish floats on the surface of fresh water. It has two eyes, each divided into two parts. The upper half of each eye is adapted for vision in air, so it can see insect prey on the water's surface. The lower half sees underwater.

▲ WIDELY SEPARATED EYES
The hammerhead shark has eyes located at the tips of extensions on each side of its head. Being widely separated, they give the hammerhead a much bigger visual range than other sharks as it swims along in search of prey.

Eardrum just
below knee of
front leg

BAT ▶
Finding food at night is not a problem for insect-eating bats. They produce high-pitched sounds that bounce off potential prey, such as moths. Their highly sensitive ears detect these echoes and the bat then uses them to pinpoint the position of its prey.

◀ CRICKET
A keen sense of hearing enables crickets to hear the chirping sounds produced by potential mates or rivals. Sounds are picked up by a thin membrane located on the cricket's knee.

◀ AFRICAN ELEPHANT
Elephants communicate using sounds that humans can hear. But they also produce very low-pitched sounds that travel over long distances to keep the herd in touch. African elephants pick up these sounds with their ears, and from the ground through their feet and trunks.

SERVAL ▼
An African savanna cat, the serval has long legs that allow it to see over tall grasses and large ear flaps that move to pick up even the faintest sounds made by small prey, especially rodents. Once the prey's position is pinpointed, the serval leaps and pounces.

Large ears
open wide to
capture sounds

Large, movable
ears detect prey

HEARING

Whether it is used to find food, recognize mates, pick up sounds made by rivals, or detect the approach of a hungry predator, hearing is a vitally important sense for many animals. Sound waves travel through air or water from a vibrating source, such as an elephant's vocal cords or a cricket's wings. Many animals pick up sound waves using a membrane called the eardrum that is linked to sound receptors within the ear.

◀ DOLPHIN

Although dolphins have excellent eyesight, these marine mammals also use echolocation to find food. They produce bursts of high-pitched clicks that are beamed in front of the dolphin, focused by a lump of fatty tissue called the melon. Sounds bounce off objects and their echoes are channeled via the lower jaw to the ears. The dolphin can then analyze the echoes to pinpoint prey.

Bulge contains fat-filled melon

BARN OWL ▼

This nocturnal hunter uses its acute sense of hearing to detect rustling sounds made by potential prey. A ruff of feathers channels sounds into the ear openings, which are asymmetrical to pinpoint prey accurately.

Right ear opening is higher than the left one

◀ BULLFROG

Hearing is a very important sense in amphibians. It enables them to identify and pinpoint calls made by mates and potential rivals, and to detect predators. Bullfrogs have no external ears but pick up sounds through large eardrums on the sides of the head.

Eardrum is just behind the eye

◀ KANGAROO RAT

As it hops across American deserts at night, a kangaroo rat listens for danger. its ears can amplify (make louder) sounds by 100 times, so it can detect a rustling rattlesnake, its main predator.

SMELL AND TASTE

The ability to smell and taste varies enormously throughout the animal kingdom. An animal with a sense of smell has detectors that pick up odor molecules from objects, enabling it to find food or mates, identify other members of its species, detect predators, or find its way home. A sense of taste involves direct contact with food in order to test if it is a tasty meal that is safe to eat.

❶ AFRICAN WILD DOG

African wild dogs, like other members of the dog family, are predators with a powerful sense of smell. Dogs use smell to track prey over long distances, to identify other members of the pack, and to pick up scents left by outsiders marking their territory.

❷ FRUIT BAT

While insect-eating bats depend on their acute sense of hearing to detect prey, larger fruit-eating bats use their excellent senses of smell and vision to find food. Also called flying foxes, they live in tropical areas where there is a constant supply of fruit. Some species of fruit bat feed on flowers, nectar, and pollen, also found in tropical areas.

❸ KIWI

Native to New Zealand, this nocturnal, flightless bird has poor sight, but, unlike most birds, it has a great sense of smell. The kiwi has two nostrils at the tip of its long beak. As it looks for food, the kiwi pushes its beak into the soil to sniff out worms, beetle larvae, centipedes, and other juicy food items.

❹ TAPIR

A tapir lifts its upper lip to expose the opening of its Jacobson's organ, located in the roof of the mouth, which enhances the ability to smell and taste. This action, called a flehmen response, draws in airborne scents. It is also performed by lions and some other mammals, and is used mainly to pick up smells given off by potential mates.

❺ MOTH

Insects use the two antennae attached to their heads to detect smells and tastes, as well as to touch. Some male moths have feathery antennae that are supersensitive to pheromones (chemical signals) released by females, often hundreds of yards away. As they fly at night, males pick up the scent trail and follow it to find a potential mate.

❻ MONKEY

Japanese macaques, like other monkeys, use their excellent sense of vision to spot fruit. Their senses of smell and taste then take over. As the macaque bites into a fruit, smell detectors in its nose pick up odors from the flesh, and taste buds on its tongue detect tastes, such as sweetness. A bitter taste warns that the fruit may be poisonous and should be discarded.

❼ OCTOPUS

These intelligent mollusks hunt mainly at night for fish, crabs, and other prey. An octopus's eight flexible, muscular arms reach out to move and to grasp food. Each arm is equipped with numerous suckers that grip the seabed and hold onto prey. The suckers also taste prey to see if it is worth eating.

❽ SNAKE

Like a tapir, a snake has a Jacobson's organ housed in the roof of its mouth, which detects both tastes and smells. By flicking out its tongue, the snake collects odor molecules. These are identified when the tongue is pressed against the Jacobson's organ. Snakes use this combined sense to locate food and potential mates.

❾ TURKEY VULTURE

While other vultures use sight to find the dead animals on which they feed, turkey vultures employ a different strategy. Found in North and South America, the turkey vulture uses its sense of smell. As it soars and glides, the vulture can pick up odors given off by rotting corpses on the ground, even if they are hidden in dense forest.

❿ CATFISH

Named for the whiskerlike barbels around their mouths, catfish have poor vision and live in the murky depths of lakes and rivers. Their long barbels are equipped with lots of taste sensors. As the catfish's snout probes the lake or riverbed, the barbels feel for food and taste it to determine whether it is edible.

COMMUNICATION

Animals communicate with each other in a huge number of different ways. They make sounds, release odors, use touch, gestures, and body language, and even produce flashing lights. Communication is an important tool for attracting a mate, holding a social group together, marking a territory, or alerting other group members to a food source, rival, or an approaching predator.

❶ CHIMPANZEE
Like many other animals, chimps use gestures and body language to communicate with other members of their social group. But these intelligent primates also use facial expressions to show anger, fear, happiness, playfulness, and hunger, and to indicate their status in the group.

Grimace made when higher-ranking chimp approaches

Stripy tail used for visual signaling

❷ FIREFLY

These night-flying beetles use light to communicate with each other. An organ in the firefly's abdomen produces flashes of light that it uses to attract mates. Some female fireflies imitate the light flashes of other species to lure male fireflies, which they then eat.

❸ RING-TAILED LEMUR

Relatives of monkeys, lemurs depend heavily on their sense of smell for communication. Male ring-tailed lemurs use a scent gland in their wrist to mark their territory. They also have stink fights against rivals—rubbing their tails against their scent glands and waving them in the air as "smelly flags."

❹ HONEYBEE

When foraging worker honeybees return to the hive, they perform "dances" to tell other workers the direction and distance of good sources of nectar and pollen. The other bees use their antennae to detect the smell of nectar and to track the movements of the newly returned worker through touch.

❺ GANNET

Many male and female birds use body language during courtship and, if they stay together for a long time, to reinforce the bond between them. Gannets perform special greeting ceremonies, stretching their necks and beaks skyward and gently tapping or rubbing their beaks together.

❻ ANT

When ants from the same colony meet they smell each other using their antennae. In this way, they can detect whether or not they belong to the same group, and if one has discovered a good food source that others can exploit. Such communication allows ants to function as complex societies.

❼ TREE FROG

Communicating by sound can be risky, because it may attract predators. Yet many male frogs, including tree frogs, make a loud, croaky call to attract females or deter rivals. Sounds are produced by the vocal cords and amplified when air is forced into the bulging vocal sac.

IP 82.184

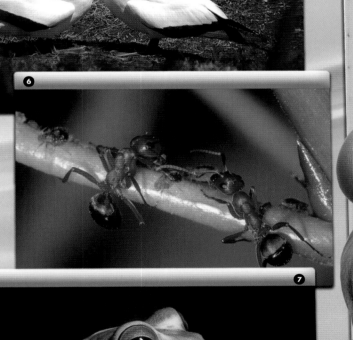

❽ WOLF

Although they live in packs, wolves often get separated when they go hunting. To maintain contact and identify themselves, they howl. Howling sounds travel over long distances and bring the pack back together.

DEFENSES

For many animals there is a near-constant threat of attack by predators in search of food. Those with keen senses and quick reactions can make a dash for safety and hide themselves. Others employ a wide range of strategies—including armor, chemical warfare, or even pretending to be dead—to defend themselves against hungry attackers.

❶ LOOKING BIGGER

With fur raised and back arched, a cat makes itself appear bigger to frighten off an enemy. Many animals use the same method. The Australian frilled lizard expands its neck collar, opens its mouth, and waves its tail to look bigger and more scary.

❷ ARMOR

Many insects, crustaceans, and some mammals, such as armadillos, have a hard outer covering that provides a degree of protection from hungry predators. Certain types of woodlice, called pill bugs, have jointed armor and can roll into a ball to protect their softer underparts.

❸ SPINES

Sharp spines provide a very effective deterrent, as any porcupine illustrates. Inhabitants of rocky shores and reefs, black sea urchins are armed with movable spines that put off all but the most determined of predators. The spines also inject poison if they penetrate the skin.

❹ CHEMICAL ATTACK

Many animals, especially insects, contain poisonous or irritating chemicals that make them inedible. Some launch a more direct attack. The bombardier beetle bends its abdomen forward and squirts out a cocktail of chemicals that distracts, burns, and may even blind its enemy.

❺ SAFETY IN NUMBERS

Living as a group—be it a shoal of fish, a herd of wildebeest, or this flock of snow geese—has great defense benefits. It is more difficult for a predator to pick off individuals from a moving group, and members can warn others of approaching danger.

❻ SMOKESCREEN

A threatened octopus squirts a billowing cloud of brown ink into the water around it. While the confused predator attacks the cloud, the octopus is able to make a jet-propelled escape. Squid use the same means of defense.

❼ SCARE TACTICS

Many butterflies and moths have patterned spots on their upper wing surfaces that resemble large eyes. When this owl butterfly opens its wings, a predator sees the "eyes" and backs off, thinking its potential prey is big and fierce.

❽ PLAYING DEAD

Many predators are only attracted to moving prey, so they lose interest if their target plays dead. By lying still with its mouth open, this grass snake appears to have died, but it will soon come back to life once its attacker has moved on.

❾ LOSING BODY PARTS

As a dramatic defense ploy, a threatened blue-tailed skink sheds the tip of its tail. The lost tip continues to wiggle for a while, distracting the predator while the lizard makes its escape. Amazingly, the tail grows back over the following weeks and months.

Lizard expands collar of skin in order to appear bigger

⑩ HIDING

What could be simpler than running away and hiding when an enemy appears? A burrow provides a safe haven for these ground squirrels. They feed near the entrance so they can make a rapid escape when trouble threatens.

Eyes appear suddenly when butterfly opens its wings

Gaping mouth makes the snake appear dead

Blood vessels close up at the fracture point to reduce bleeding

Cloud of ink left by octopus as it escapes

❶ NATURAL MATCH

Many animals naturally merge into their habitat. The tan color of a lion is a perfect match for the tall savanna grasses that conceal it as it stalks prey. The wings of the willow beauty moth match the color and texture of a tree trunk, making it all but invisible to birds that prey on it.

❷ SEASONAL CHANGE

Arctic regions have short summers and long, snowy winters. Some animals change color seasonally to maintain their camouflage all year round. In the fall, the ptarmigan's brown plumage turns white, making it less visible in the snow. In spring it turns brown again.

❸ RAPID COLOR CHANGE

An octopus can change the color and pattern of its body within seconds to match its surroundings by either shrinking or expanding packets of pigment (coloring) in its skin. The chameleon is another rapid changer, although it also alters its colors in order to communicate.

❹ DECORATION

Some animals adorn themselves with objects from their surroundings to conceal their identity. The decorator crab attaches pieces of seaweed, pebbles, shells, and even corals and sponges, to blend in with the seabed. This camouflage covering is held in place by tiny hooks on the crab's shell.

Decorator crab

Sponge attached to crab

Camouflaged octopus matches stony seabed

Octopus

Chameleon

Plumage matches pebbles and rocks

Fur and eye colorings match grasses

Ptarmigan in summer

Ptarmigan in winter

Lion

Willow beauty moth

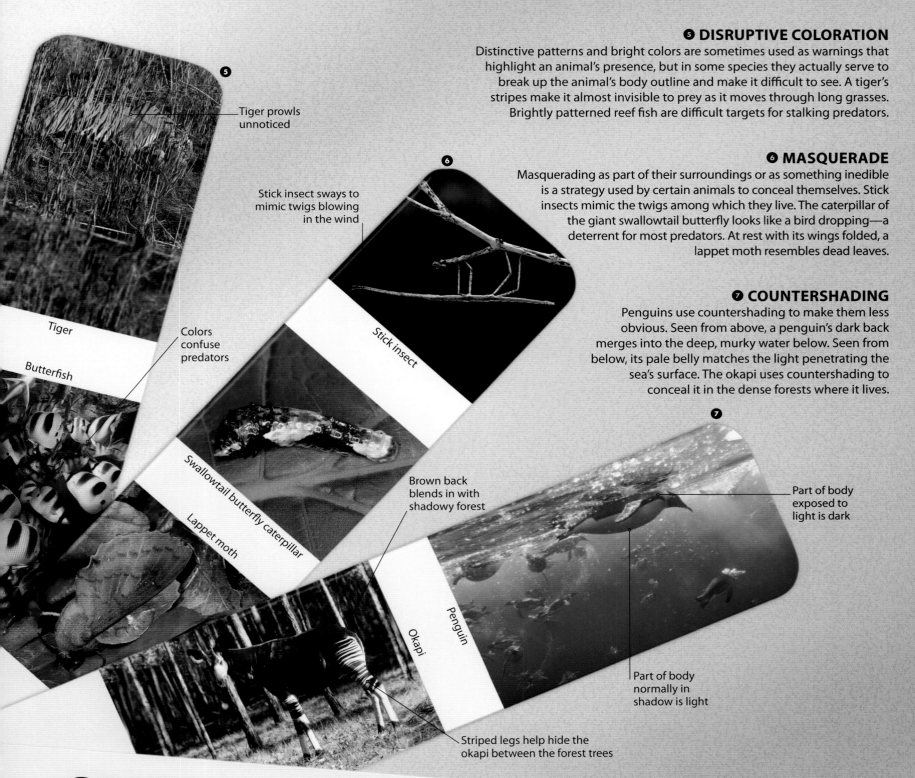

❺ DISRUPTIVE COLORATION

Distinctive patterns and bright colors are sometimes used as warnings that highlight an animal's presence, but in some species they actually serve to break up the animal's body outline and make it difficult to see. A tiger's stripes make it almost invisible to prey as it moves through long grasses. Brightly patterned reef fish are difficult targets for stalking predators.

❻ MASQUERADE

Masquerading as part of their surroundings or as something inedible is a strategy used by certain animals to conceal themselves. Stick insects mimic the twigs among which they live. The caterpillar of the giant swallowtail butterfly looks like a bird dropping—a deterrent for most predators. At rest with its wings folded, a lappet moth resembles dead leaves.

❼ COUNTERSHADING

Penguins use countershading to make them less obvious. Seen from above, a penguin's dark back merges into the deep, murky water below. Seen from below, its pale belly matches the light penetrating the sea's surface. The okapi uses countershading to conceal it in the dense forests where it lives.

Tiger prowls unnoticed

Stick insect sways to mimic twigs blowing in the wind

Tiger

Butterfish

Colors confuse predators

Stick insect

Swallowtail butterfly caterpillar

Lappet moth

Brown back blends in with shadowy forest

Part of body exposed to light is dark

Penguin

Okapi

Part of body normally in shadow is light

Striped legs help hide the okapi between the forest trees

CAMOUFLAGE

A predator has a much greater chance of catching prey if it cannot easily be seen, while its victim is less likely to be caught and eaten if it blends into its surroundings. Some animals have natural camouflage that makes them less visible. Body color, stripes and patterns, or even looking like something inedible can provide a life-saving cloak of invisibility.

199

WARNINGS

Rather than hiding themselves, or having elaborate defenses, some animals give clear warnings to predators or competitors either to stay away or risk getting hurt. Warnings can take the form of sounds, gestures, or bright colors, which announce that an animal is dangerous, poisonous, or both. A few animals even mimic the colors or shapes of other poisonous animals in order to trick enemies into believing that they are dangerous.

❷ POISON DART FROG

These small, brightly colored frogs from Central and South America release poison from glands in their skin that can kill predators, such as snakes and spiders. Their bright colors and patterns advertise the fact that they are not good to eat.

❸ LION

Big cats roar to warn others to stay out of their territory. In addition to the loud sound, an open mouth displays the lion's sharp teeth and makes its head looks bigger and scarier. Other animals that display their teeth include monkeys.

❶ RATTLESNAKE

These highly venomous snakes have a warning rattle at the end of their tail. If threatened by a predator or a large animal that might step on it, the rattlesnake vibrates its rattle, producing a loud buzz.

Wide open mouth shows off the lion's sharp teeth

Rattle is made from modified scales

Bright colors mark the frog as being poisonous

Bright red stripes are a sign of danger

❹ BLISTER BEETLE

Its red and black coloration identifies the blister beetle as an animal to be avoided. If attacked, it releases a poisonous chemical that causes blistering and deters would-be predators from disturbing the beetle again.

❺ WASP AND HOVERFLY

The yellow and black colors of a common wasp provide a warning to predators that it has a powerful sting. The unrelated hoverfly mimics the wasp's stripey appearance, thereby deterring predators even though it is harmless.

❻ SKUNK

Even a predator as big as a bear can get into trouble if it ignores a skunk's warning colors. After hissing and foot-stamping, the skunk sprays its attacker with a stinking fluid that can irritate or even cause blindness.

❼ VENOMOUS FISH

The colored stripes of the zebra lionfish send out a clear message to potential predators that its long spines are highly poisonous. If threatened, the fish puts its head down so the spines point forward, ready for action.

❽ SCARY CATERPILLARS

Being vulnerable to bird predators, some caterpillars attempt to scare them away. The puss moth caterpillar raises its facelike head, waves its tails, and may squirt acid. The hawkmoth caterpillar mimics a poisonous snake.

❾ BUTTERFLY MARKINGS

Birds that try to eat the foul-tasting monarch butterfly do not repeat the experience and remember the patterns of their wings for the future. The viceroy butterfly has a similar appearance, and also tastes horrible.

Hoverfly's markings mimic those of the wasp

Wasp has clear yellow and black stripes

Hawkmoth caterpillar

Startling eyespots mimic a snake's eyes

Long spines filled with venom

Black and white warning colors

Head raised to reveal a colorful but false face

"Tails" are lifted and waved when caterpillar is threatened

Puss moth caterpillar

Viceroy butterfly

Monarch butterfly

COMPETITION

Animals are constantly competing for access to vitally important but limited resources, such as food, mates, and territory. Competition happens between individuals of the same species, but may also occur between different species. Some animals attempt to assert their dominance and deter rivals through a threat display or a ritualized fight—a strategy that prevents harm to either side. But sometimes competition involves real fights in which one or both animals may suffer injury.

❶ NECK WRESTLING

Male giraffes engage in ritualized fights known as necking. Two males stand with their necks entwined and then push from side to side. Necking establishes which are the strongest males. These are the only ones that will mate with females.

❷ STANDOFF

If an animal can avoid injury in a fight by deterring a rival, so much the better. In standoffs between some mammals, the open mouth is a common threat display. By "yawning," this hippopotamus bares its enormous mouth and teeth.

Male giraffes push with their long necks

Wide open mouth warns off enemies and rivals

Bighorn sheep's thick skull absorbs the head-on impact

Strong jaws used to lift rival during a fight

❸ BETWEEN SPECIES

In the African savanna, when an animal dies or is killed, vultures crowd around the remains, fighting among themselves for scraps. When scavenging hyenas arrive, the vultures scatter, returning to the carcass to feed warily in the presence of these powerful carnivores.

❹ STAG BEETLES

With their massive jaws it might appear that male stag beetles catch large prey. In fact, they feed on tree sap and use their jaws to fight other males for mates and favored mating sites. The winning male lifts an opponent and turns him onto his back. The loser then retreats uninjured.

❺ HEAD ON

At the start of their breeding season in the fall, male bighorn sheep have head-butting contests. Two males run at each other, ramming their heads together. This can go on for hours until one male gives up. The overall "winner" within the herd mates with the most females.

❻ DECLARING TERRITORY

Songbirds do not sing to give us pleasure but to tell other members of their species to keep out of their territory. European robins, for example, defend the territory that supplies them and their offspring with food. Persistent intruders are attacked and driven out.

❼ WARNING CALL

In the fall, male red deer round up females to prevent them from mating with other males. They roar at their rivals, the loudness of their bellowing indicating their fighting ability. Roaring alone may ensure a stag's success, but if not, he locks antlers with rivals and fights.

❽ ON THE BEACH

During their breeding season, male elephant seals strive to command the largest territory and the most females. Initially, a male makes booming noises to intimidate rivals. If that fails, the enormous creatures fight on the beach, inflicting wounds until one retreats.

Antlers used for fighting

Competing male seals bite and push against each other

Beak opens wide as the European robin sings to defend its territory

Pink dewlap exposed as a threat

❾ LIZARD THREAT

Many lizards change color or perform some other display when their territory is threatened. A male green anole flicks down its pink dewlap (throat fan) to warn off intruders. It emphasizes the message by bobbing its head up and down.

INSTINCT

Everything an animal does—and the way in which it does it—makes up its behavior. Some behaviors are learned during an animal's lifetime, but many are inbuilt or instinctive. They are performed automatically in situations such as courtship, breeding, or nest building.

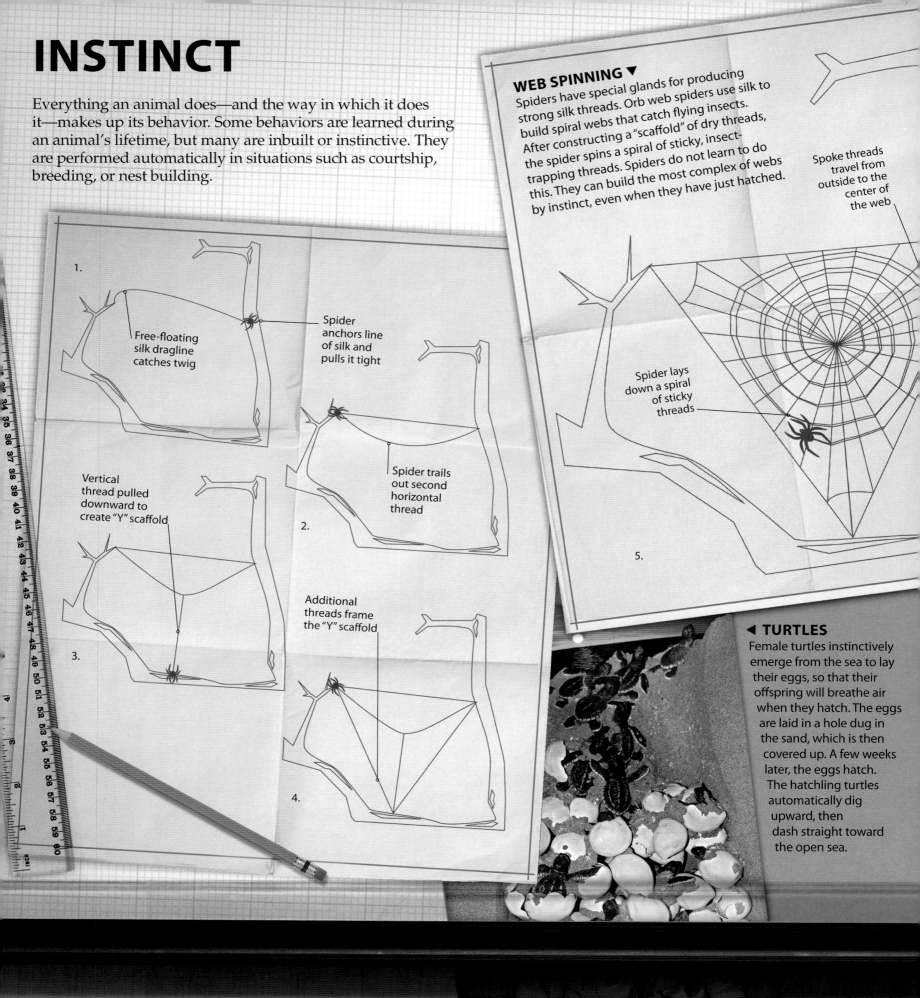

1.

Free-floating silk dragline catches twig

Spider anchors line of silk and pulls it tight

Spider trails out second horizontal thread

Vertical thread pulled downward to create "Y" scaffold

2.

Additional threads frame the "Y" scaffold

3.

4.

WEB SPINNING ▼

Spiders have special glands for producing strong silk threads. Orb web spiders use silk to build spiral webs that catch flying insects. After constructing a "scaffold" of dry threads, the spider spins a spiral of sticky, insect-trapping threads. Spiders do not learn to do this. They can build the most complex of webs by instinct, even when they have just hatched.

Spoke threads travel from outside to the center of the web

Spider lays down a spiral of sticky threads

5.

◀ TURTLES

Female turtles instinctively emerge from the sea to lay their eggs, so that their offspring will breathe air when they hatch. The eggs are laid in a hole dug in the sand, which is then covered up. A few weeks later, the eggs hatch. The hatchling turtles automatically dig upward, then dash straight toward the open sea.

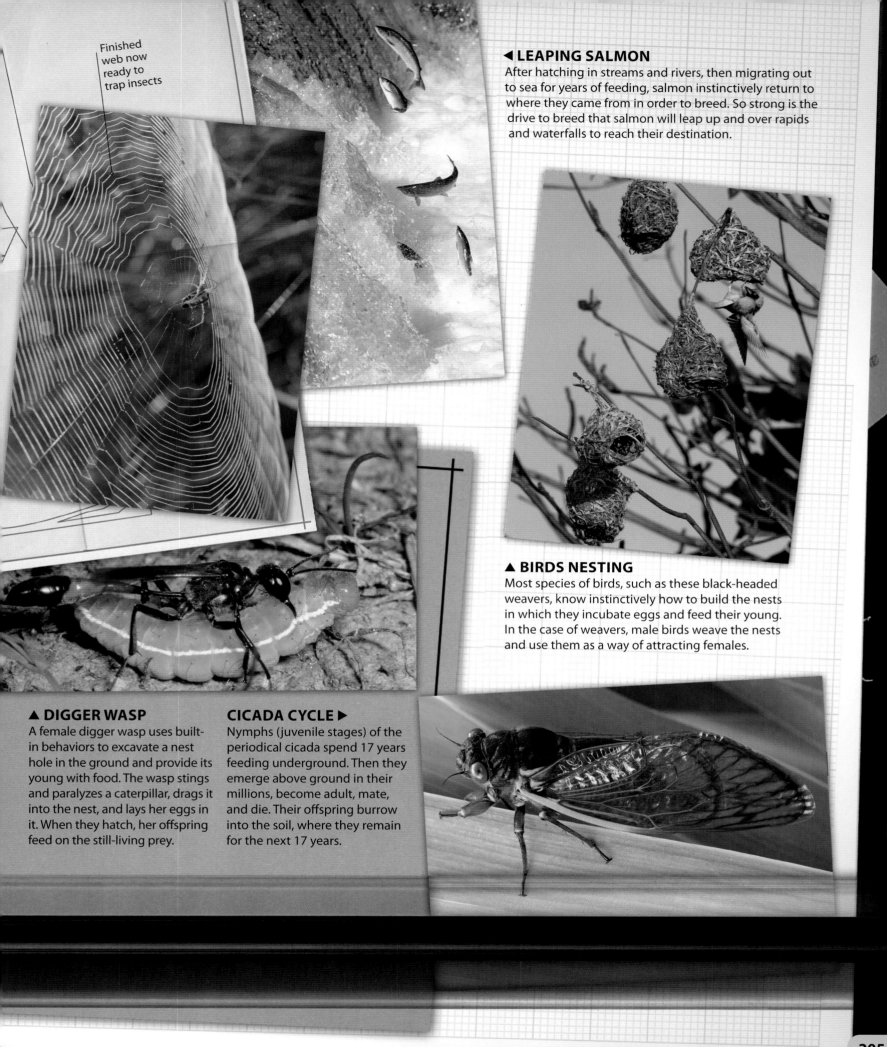

Finished web now ready to trap insects

◄ LEAPING SALMON

After hatching in streams and rivers, then migrating out to sea for years of feeding, salmon instinctively return to where they came from in order to breed. So strong is the drive to breed that salmon will leap up and over rapids and waterfalls to reach their destination.

▲ BIRDS NESTING

Most species of birds, such as these black-headed weavers, know instinctively how to build the nests in which they incubate eggs and feed their young. In the case of weavers, male birds weave the nests and use them as a way of attracting females.

▲ DIGGER WASP

A female digger wasp uses built-in behaviors to excavate a nest hole in the ground and provide its young with food. The wasp stings and paralyzes a caterpillar, drags it into the nest, and lays her eggs in it. When they hatch, her offspring feed on the still-living prey.

CICADA CYCLE ►

Nymphs (juvenile stages) of the periodical cicada spend 17 years feeding underground. Then they emerge above ground in their millions, become adult, mate, and die. Their offspring burrow into the soil, where they remain for the next 17 years.

LEARNING

Animals learn to change their behavior as a result of experiences, thereby increasing their chances of survival. Learning is more common in birds and mammals that have a period in their life when they are looked after by their parents, although learning can continue throughout life. Learning is often achieved through copying or by trial and error, when animals alter their behavior according to their successes and failures.

Stick provides a handy tool to extract ants from a nest

Young cheetah practises its hunting skills on a baby antelope

Young duckling soon learns to follow its mother

Oystercatcher teaches its young how to collect food

❶ CHEETAH
The skills needed to hunt and kill prey must be learned by young predators such as cheetahs so that as adults they can get enough food to survive. A cheetah learns by watching its mother, who provides her offspring with live prey, so they can learn by trial and error the right ways to catch and kill it.

❷ DUCKLING
Soon after they hatch, ground-nesting birds such as ducks and geese show a type of learning called imprinting. They learn to identify their mother, following and staying close to her for protection and to find food. Imprinting lasts for the first weeks of life and improves the young birds' chances of survival.

❸ CHIMPANZEE
Like humans, chimpanzees show insight learning—the ability to solve new problems by "putting two and two together." A chimpanzee unable to get tasty ants from a nest will figure out that if it probes the nest with a stick it can pull out a mouthful of ants. This skill will then be copied by other chimps.

❹ OYSTERCATCHER
Eurasian oystercatchers are shorebirds that probe soft sand or mud with their long, strong beaks, then use them to prize open cockles and other shelled mollusks, or to pull out marine worms. Young oystercatchers learn how to feed by watching and copying their parents.

Females constantly touch young elephants, providing guidance and protection

❽ ELEPHANT

These intelligent animals live in family units of related females. Over many years a young elephant learns both social and survival skills, such as where to find food and water, or which paths to follow. It is taught not just by its mother, but also by its aunts and cousins.

❾ JAPANESE MACAQUE

When researchers left sweet potatoes on a beach for a group of these intelligent monkeys, a female took one into the sea and washed it to remove sand—a behavior never seen before. Other group members copied this learned behavior, as did their offspring, so that food washing passed from generation to generation.

Sweet potato is washed before being eaten

❺ BOWERBIRD

Some birds mimic the sounds of other birds to defend territories and attract mates. Among the most talented mimics are the bowerbirds of Australia and New Guinea. They learn other bird songs, but also copy sounds such as cell phone ring tones, chainsaws, and car alarms.

❻ FOX CUB

Play is an enormously important part of learning in many young mammals, such as fox cubs. By "going through the motions," they learn through trial and error how to fine-tune life skills such as fighting and catching food, so that they will be able to survive and compete as adults.

Butterfly feeds on nectar from brightly colored flower

❼ BUTTERFLY

When butterflies emerge from their pupae (transition stage between caterpillar and butterfly), they have an instinctive attraction to brightly colored flowers that they will feed on. Butterflies learn by trial and error which flowers provide more or sweeter nectar.

MALE AND FEMALE

All animals reproduce to create new generations of offspring that will replace them when they die. In many species, reproduction involves males and females meeting so that mating can take place. Males and females may look very similar or, as in the examples shown here, they may differ in size and color. In these species, such differences are important in attracting mates.

Female green birdwing butterfly

Inflatable throat pouch

❶ GREAT FRIGATE BIRDS
These large seabirds spend most of their lives over the ocean, snatching prey from the water's surface or stealing from other birds. During the breeding season they gather on oceanic islands where each male inflates his distinctive red throat pouch to attract a female.

❷ PROBOSCIS MONKEYS
In many primates, including Borneo's proboscis monkeys, males are bigger than females. A male proboscis monkey also has a large, pendulous nose that attracts females. The huge nose amplifies the honking noises he makes to warn other males to stay away from his females and their young.

❸ MAROON CLOWNFISH
Some fish, especially those that live on coral reefs, change sex. The maroon clownfish lives in groups of one female and several males. If the female dies, one of the males changes to a female and takes over her role in breeding. Flame angelfish live in groups of one male and several females. If the male leaves, a female becomes male to replace him.

❹ PRAYING MANTIS
Mating can be a dangerous time for male praying mantises. The females of these predatory insects are larger than their potential mates and have been known to eat the males when mating is still in progress. When the male moves onto the female's back she may grab him with her front legs and bite his head off.

❺ BIRDWING BUTTERFLIES
Named for their large size and birdlike flying, many birdwing butterflies show differences between males and females. Spotting a vividly colored male green birdwing in an Australasian tropical forest would be easier than seeing a female, which is larger but has a duller, brown coloration.

❻ GIBBONS
Crested black gibbons are found in the tropical forests of southeast Asia. They start life with pale fur, then turn black. The males remain black, but the females become light again.

Male praying mantis mates with a female

Maroon clownfish

Flame angelfish

⑦ ECLECTUS PARROTS

Many parrots show color differences between the sexes, but few differ as dramatically as eclectus parrots. Early naturalists believed they belonged to separate species. Unusually for parrots, the female's red plumage makes her stand out when feeding among foliage.

⑧ DEER

In summer, male deer grow bony antlers. During the mating season in the fall, stags use their antlers to attract females and to fight rival males. In winter, the antler bones die and the antlers are shed.

Large, branched antlers

⑨ GOLDEN ORB SPIDERS

The male golden orb web spider, as with many other spider species, is much smaller than the female and at risk of being eaten by her. The benefit of being so tiny is that the male can mate with the female, or steal her food, without being noticed.

Female deer is smaller than the male

Female eclectus parrot is crimson and blue

Female golden orb spider approached from behind by smaller male

COURTSHIP

Many male animals use courtship to attract females. The most spectacular courtship displays happen among birds. Male birds sing, dance, or use other strategies to impress potential mates. Some are brightly colored when compared to the females, and they advertise themselves using their plumage. For birds such as eagles, courtship begins a lifelong bond between partners.

KINGFISHER ▲
Courtship feeding is important for many birds, including kingfishers. The male offers food to a female to reinforce the bond between them. This may continue when she incubates the eggs so she does not go hungry.

▼ BLUE-FOOTED BOOBY
These Pacific Ocean seabirds have big, blue webbed feet. When courting, the male booby stamps his feet, lifts his tail, and then performs a strut, showing off his feet to impress a female and persuade her to mate.

LYREBIRD ▲
To attract females, the male Australian superb lyrebird fans his long, elegant tail feathers over his head. He then sings a complex song, mimicking other birds' calls as well as forest sounds, such as chainsaws.

BALD EAGLE ▼
Male and female bald eagles perform a dramatic courtship display that includes tumbling over each other in midair. They link talons and cartwheel downward through the air, separating just before they reach the ground.

In the spring, sage grouse congregate at communal areas called leks. Male sage grouse strut around, fanning their tail feathers, and puffing out large air sacs to show off yellow neck patches and attract as many females as possible.

BIRD OF PARADISE ▲
Male Raggiana's birds of paradise are flamboyant with long, brightly colored feathers. In the forests of New Guinea, males try to outdo their rivals by displaying their finery, including black tail wires.

NIGHTJAR ▲
During the breeding season in Africa, the male standard-winged nightjar develops elongated central wing feathers. He circles a potential mate and raises these feathers vertically to impress her during dusk display flights.

CRANE ▼
Generally mating for life, cranes engage in an elaborate courtship display at the beginning of the breeding season. These Japanese cranes perform an intricate dance by bowing and leaping into the air.

BLUE PEAFOWL ▼
A native of south Asia, the male peafowl, or peacock, is brightly colored with elongated, patterned tail feathers. Female peahens, on the other hand, have drab plumage. During courtship, the peacock raises his tail feathers into a magnificent fan.

EGGS

From cockroaches to cuckoos, many different types of animals lay eggs. Inside the egg, a young animal grows and develops, nurtured by its own food supply, until it is ready to hatch. Some animals lay a few eggs and look after them. Others lay lots of eggs and leave them to develop on their own.

Eggs suspended in a silk cocoon

Cave spider

Cockroach

Dogfish eggs

Leopard tortoise

Egg purse

Pattern of cuckoo's egg resembles its host's eggs

Yolk sac feeds developing dogfish

Cuckoo egg

Fish eggs

Soft-shelled rat snake's egg

Host nest

Rat snake

Rat snake emerging from its egg

❶ TORTOISE

Found in South Africa, female leopard tortoises lay a clutch of five to thirty soft-shelled eggs under the soil. Young tortoises use a special tooth to break through the shell, before they burrow upward and emerge on the soil's surface.

❷ SPIDER

Silk is used by spiders to make a protective cocoon around their eggs. This female cave spider is suspending her bag of eggs over an overhanging ledge. After hatching, some of the spiderlings may eat each other before they can escape and go in search of food.

❸ COCKROACH

During its two-year life span, a female cockroach can lay up to 1,000 eggs. Batches of around 15 eggs are contained in tough protective capsules called egg purses. The female cockroach carries the egg purse for a period before sticking it to a concealed surface, where the eggs later hatch.

❹ CUCKOO

A female cuckoo lays her egg in the nest of another bird, where it is incubated by the unaware host bird. The newly hatched cuckoo pushes any other eggs out of the nest to make sure it gets all the food for itself.

❺ SNAKE

Most snakes lay soft-shelled eggs, which they then abandon. The developing snake feeds on the yolk, cushioned within a bag of fluid, and receives oxygen absorbed through its eggshell. When ready, the snake hatches by slashing open the shell using a special egg tooth.

❻ DOGFISH

This small shark's eggs are protected within leathery cases called mermaid's purses. Tendrils anchor the case to seaweed to prevent it from being swept away. After months of development, during which it is fed by a yolk sac, the young dogfish pushes its way out.

Damp feathers soon dry out

Pheasant chick

Hard eggshell chipped open by young bird

Pheasant egg

Peregrine falcon egg

Guillemot egg

Mockingbird egg

Platypus egg

Ladybug eggs

Indian stick insect eggs

Butterfly leaf eggs

Frogspawn

Ostrich egg

Newt eggs

❼ GROUND-NESTING BIRD

Birds that nest on the ground, such as pheasants, lay large clutches of hard-shelled eggs. They have a long incubation period. When hatched, the young are soon able to feed themselves.

❽ CLIFF-NESTING BIRD

Female guillemots lay their eggs, rather precariously, on narrow cliff ledges. However, if disturbed, the pointed egg simply rolls around in a circle instead of falling off the ledge. Unique markings on the egg help returning parents identify it among so many others.

❾ PLATYPUS

The female duck-billed platypus is one of only a few mammals that lay eggs. Having excavated a breeding burrow next to her home stream, she lays two soft-shelled eggs. She incubates the eggs for 10 days, and feeds her young with milk after they hatch.

❿ BUTTERFLY

When female butterflies lay their eggs, they attach them to the leaves of plants that their offspring will feed on when they hatch. However, when the caterpillars emerge from their eggs, they consume their nutritious empty eggshells first, before eating the leaves.

⓫ NEWT

Like those of frogs, newt eggs do not have shells and are laid in water. A female newt lays her eggs one at a time, using her feet to wrap each one in the leaves of water weeds in order to protect them, until the newt tadpoles are ready to hatch.

213

LIFE HISTORIES

After it hatches from an egg or is born, an animal grows and develops until it becomes a mature adult that can breed. Some young animals, including mammals, birds, and fish, bear a resemblance to their parents, and their life histories simply involve growth to adult size. In contrast, the life history of animals such as insects and amphibians involves a metamorphosis (transformation) through several distinct stages.

▼ COW

Mammals develop inside their mother's body, are born, and then feed on her milk. Cattle and horses are born well developed, getting to their feet soon after birth. They grow and develop over the following years until they, too, can breed. Other mammals, such as foxes and mice, are born blind and helpless. They need constant parental care, and change shape as they grow.

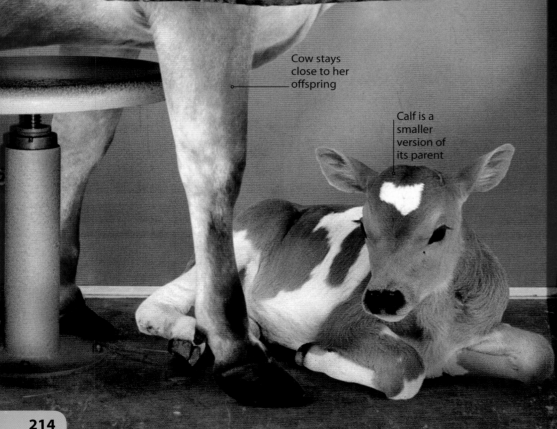

Cow stays close to her offspring

Calf is a smaller version of its parent

GOLDEN EAGLE ▼

When a golden eagle chick hatches, like many young birds, it is small and helpless. For 10 weeks it remains in or near the nest, dependent on its predator parents to feed it pieces of meat. When its wing feathers develop, the young eagle starts to fly and hunt. Once mature, males and females pair for life.

1. The newly hatched chick is covered with white, downy feathers.

2. After a few weeks the eagle chick has grown rapidly on a diet of fresh meat.

3. The young eagle is almost ready to fly. The parent ignores its offspring begging for food.

4. The eagle has reached maturity and can fly and hunt for food.

1. Tadpoles breathe through gills.

2. Front and back legs appear.

3. Body begins to look froglike and tail shrinks.

4. Adult frog has compact body shape.

▲ FROG

Amphibians, such as frogs, undergo metamorphosis between tadpole and adult stage. Tadpoles hatch from eggs laid in ponds. They feed on plants and breathe using gills. After a while the tadpole's back legs, and later its front legs, emerge. Its head and eyes become more distinct, it starts breathing air through lungs, and feeds on small animals. Finally, its tail shrinks and, fully frog-shaped, it leaves the water.

PHOTOS DELIVERED HERE

1. Butterfly egg is laid on a leaf.

2. Caterpillar uses biting mouthparts to eat plants.

3. Caterpillar turns into a pupa and remains immobile for days or weeks.

4. Adult butterfly emerges.

▲ BUTTERFLY

Most insects, including butterflies, show complete metamorphosis. This means that they pass through four distinct life stages. A female butterfly lays eggs that hatch into larvae called caterpillars. Each caterpillar feeds continuously on plants, then stops moving and forms a tough outer coat to become a pupa. Inside the pupa, body tissues are reorganized to make a butterfly, which emerges when the pupa splits open.

1. Nymph lives and hunts underwater.

2. Adult emerges.

3. Wings fill with blood and expand.

4. Adult flies in search of insect prey.

▲ DRAGONFLY

Some insects go through incomplete metamorphosis, with only three stages—egg, nymph, and adult. Dragonfly eggs hatch into wingless versions of adults called nymphs. As the nymph grows it molts (sheds and regrows its outer covering, or cuticle). Then the cuticle splits open and a winged adult emerges.

1. Egg laid in bed of stream.

2. Hatchling emerges from egg.

3. Young salmon migrates to sea.

4. Mature salmon in breeding colors.

▲ SALMON

Salmon spawn (lay eggs) in freshwater streams and rivers. After the eggs hatch, the young fish feed and grow in their native waters for months or years before migrating to the sea. Here they remain for several years as they mature. They then stop feeding, change color, and swim back up their home river to spawn before, exhausted, they die.

PARENTAL CARE

For many animals, reproduction is a matter of laying eggs and leaving them to hatch. But some animals, notably birds and mammals, show parental care by looking after their young. Parental care makes it more likely that an animal will survive the dangerous early days of life.

▲ DOMESTIC CAT

Many young mammals, including cats, are born helpless—often blind and unable to move much. They are totally dependent on their mother for warmth, protection, and food in the form of milk, which they suckle from her nipples.

▲ ELEPHANT

Some mammals, including elephants and hoofed mammals, give birth to young that can walk and run soon after birth. A young elephant is nurtured by its mother and her female relatives within the herd, who devote many years to its care.

◄ KANGAROO

Young marsupial mammals, such as kangaroos, are born tiny and underdeveloped. They migrate to their mother's pouch and remain there for months, protected and feeding on milk, as they grow and develop.

▲ SCORPION

After giving birth to live young, a female scorpion carries them on her back until they can fend for themselves. Some other arachnids, including certain types of spiders, guard their eggs, even wrapping them in a ball of silk and hauling them around.

SWAN ▶

Ground-nesting birds hatch from eggs in a well-developed state and are soon moving around. They still receive parental care, however. They usually follow their parent, and sometimes, as in the case of swans, are carried on a parent's back.

▲ BLUE TIT

The young of tree-nesting birds, such as blue tits, hatch blind, naked, and helpless. Both parents spend all day finding insects to feed their offsprings' wide-open beaks so the brood grows and develops rapidly.

GOLDEN STINK BUG ▶

While bees and other social insects look after the young in their colony, most insects just lay eggs and leave them to hatch. However, the golden stink bug guards her eggs and stands over the young hatchlings to protect them from predators.

▲ ALLIGATOR

Aside from the few lizards and snakes that guard their eggs, alligators and their relatives are the only reptiles to show parental care. Having laid her eggs, a female guards the nest until they hatch. She then protects her young until they are old enough to be independent.

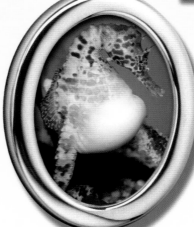

◀ SEAHORSE

Around a quarter of fish species show parental care, often by the male. Female seahorses, for example, lay their eggs in a brood pouch on the front of the male's body, where they are incubated until they hatch.

▼ COLLARED POISON FROG

Some frogs lay a small number of eggs and guard them until, and sometimes after, hatching. The male collared poison frog stays with the eggs until they hatch, then carries the tadpoles to a nearby stream to complete their development.

PENGUIN COLONY
In the cold Antarctic, emperor penguins spend part of their lives on land and part in the ocean. These hardy birds do not exist in isolation, however, but live together in colonies.

Lifestyles

HABITATS

Most animals have a particular set of surroundings, called their habitat, in which they thrive and survive. Each habitat, be it a desert or a tropical forest, is shaped by a number of features including rainfall, altitude (height above sea level), temperature, and what kind of plants grow there. Here is a selection of just some of the many habitats found on Earth, with examples of the animals that live in them.

▲ CONIFEROUS FOREST

Blanketing northern North America, Europe, and Asia, these dense forests of pines and other conifers tolerate long, cold winters. In the short summer they are alive with animals, including insects, seed-eating birds, hares, moose, wolves, and lynx. To survive in winter, many animals migrate or hibernate.

CORAL REEF ▶

Found in shallow, tropical seas, coral reefs are constructed by tiny animals. They provide food and shelter for a rich variety of small fish and other creatures, including predators such as octopuses and sharks.

◀ AFRICAN SAVANNA

This vast grassland, dotted with trees, is rich in animal life. It is hot, with alternating rainy and dry seasons. Large herds of grazing animals, such as zebras, are stalked by predators including lions and hyenas.

MOUNTAIN ▶

Mountainous regions have several habitats. The higher the altitude, the colder and windier the conditions, and the fewer animals that can survive there. These grazing guanaco in the Andes live between lower forested areas and craggy mountain peaks.

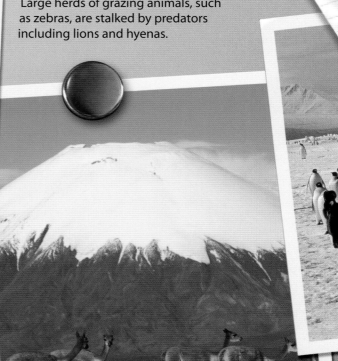

▲ DESERT

In this dry, harsh habitat, temperatures soar during the day and plummet at night. Yet animals do survive there. Many, such as these meerkats, dig burrows for protection from heat, cold, and predators.

TROPICAL FOREST ▶

These dense forests grow in warm, wet areas near the equator and are home to more than half of all animal species. Each level of the forest provides shelter or food for birds, monkeys, and other animals.

◀ ANTARCTICA

Covered by a layer of ice, lacking in vegetation, and cold all year round, especially during the dark winter, the continent of Antarctica has few permanent animal residents. However, the seas around the continent are rich in animal life including seals, whales, and penguins, some of which breed on Antarctica itself.

DECIDUOUS FOREST ▶

These forests grow where there are warm summers and cool winters, during which the trees lose their leaves. They support many insects that provide food for birds. Other forest animals include squirrels, foxes, bears, and owls, and deer that graze in forest clearings.

HOMES

Although many animals are constantly on the move, others construct homes to provide shelter from the weather and protection from predators for themselves and their young. Some homes, such as a mole's tunnels, last longer than temporary structures, such as birds' nests. On a larger scale, many animals hold and defend a territory in order to protect access to food and water.

❶

Chimpanzee lies back in its leafy nest

❶ OVERNIGHT STAY

After a day's foraging for food in the forest, chimpanzees make simple nests up in the trees where they sleep during the night. They build their nests by folding branches to make a platform that they line with leafy twigs. The next morning the chimps move on, rarely returning to old nests.

❸ TUNNEL AND TRAPDOOR

Trapdoor spiders dig a vertical burrow, closed at the surface by a hinged silk lid camouflaged by twigs and soil. The spider waits in its tunnel home until it feels vibrations produced by passing prey, then darts through the trapdoor to grab its next meal.

❷

A beaver's lodge is built from branches, sticks, and mud

❷ WATER LODGE

Beavers are nature's engineers. These water-loving rodents use their sharp incisor teeth to cut down trees and branches in order to dam streams and create a pond. In the pond they build a lodge—a family home with an underwater entrance. Here beavers feed, breed, and bring up their young, secure from predators.

❸

❹

Trapdoor flies open as spider emerges from tunnel home

❺

A mole eats an earthworm that has fallen into its tunnel

❻

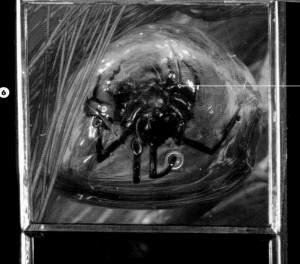

Water spider breathes the air inside its bubble

❹ MOBILE HOME

Some animals carry their homes around with them as extra protection from predators. The hermit crab, which has a soft, vulnerable abdomen, borrows a home by occupying an empty mollusk shell. If danger threatens, it simply withdraws into the shell. When it grows too large for its borrowed shell it moves into a new, larger one.

❺ UNDERGROUND HOME

With cylindrical bodies, short fur, spadelike front feet, and excellent senses of smell and touch, moles are perfectly adapted for building a network of tunnels around a nest or nests. They regularly patrol their tunnels to make repairs and to collect any juicy insects or worms.

❻ AIR BUBBLE HOME

The water spider is the only spider to have a permanent watery home. It spins a web underwater, fills the web with air, and waits in the resulting air bubble, darting out to grab passing prey. The spider goes to the surface occasionally to collect tiny air bubbles on its hairy body to replenish supplies inside the bubble.

❼ BIRD'S NEST

These temporary homes, built by birds during the breeding season, come in many shapes and sizes. Nests provide a place where eggs can be incubated and kept warm, as well as shelter for young birds. Great crested grebes build their nests on water, denying access to land-dwelling predators.

❽ TERRITORY

Some animals claim and defend a large home area called a territory. They do this in order to protect their food, water, and mates from rivals. This male cheetah is marking the boundaries of its territory by spraying a jet of strong-smelling urine on a tree.

❾ TREE HOLE

Whether a tree hole is natural or has been excavated, it may provide a home for many species, including woodpeckers and squirrels. A female mountain bluebird builds a nest and lays her eggs in a tree hole, while the male guards her.

❿ PLANT HOME FOR ANTS

Azteca ants are among several species of ants that have a special relationship with plants—in their case, Cecropia trees. The biting ants defend their trees by driving off plant-eating insects and cutting away strangling vines. The tree provides food for the ants, and they nest in hollows within its soft tissues.

Grebe's nest floats on the water

Male mountain bluebird emerges from a tree-hole nest

Azteca ants tend their eggs inside opened tree nest

IN THE DARK

Many animal species are not active in daylight, preferring to feed under the cover of darkness. Some are nocturnal, becoming active at night in order to avoid high daytime temperatures, predators, or competition with other species. Others live in habitats, such as the deep ocean, burrows, or caves, where darkness is permanent. All have their own ways of navigating and finding food without the benefit of light.

Fringed wing feathers help to produce silent flight

BARN OWL ▼
This nocturnal hunter is remarkable because it can hunt in pitch darkness. It uses its acute sense of hearing to locate prey, then swoops down soundlessly and grabs its victim with razor sharp talons. Like other owls, the barn owl has big eyes, ideally suited for vision in dim light.

EUROPEAN MOLE ▼
Life underground means that sight and hearing are not important to these champion burrowers. Instead, their heads have a very sensitive, mobile snout with whiskers linked to touch receptors. Using smell and touch, the mole locates its food: earthworms, slugs, and insect larvae that fall into its tunnels.

BLACK-TAILED JACKRABBIT ▶
Like many desert animals, the black-tailed jackrabbit shelters in the shade during the intense daytime heat, emerging in the cool of the night to feed. The jackrabbit uses its long ears to listen for predators, such as coyotes.

TREE WETA ▶
These large relatives of crickets are found only in New Zealand. By day, tree wetas shelter in tree holes, originally excavated by beetles. At night they emerge to feed on plants and small insects. Wetas navigate and sense prey in the dark using their long antennae.

FIREFLY ▶
Also called lightning bugs, fireflies are nocturnal flying beetles that have light-producing organs in their abdomens. These organs contain a substance called luciferin that uses chemical energy to release light. As very little energy is wasted producing heat, it is a highly efficient process. Fireflies use light signals to attract potential mates.

VIPERFISH ▲
The viperfish lives deep in the ocean where no light penetrates. Like many other deep-sea fish, the viperfish has light-producing organs, or photophores. One at the tip of the dorsal fin flashes to lure prey toward the gaping jaws and long teeth. Photophores along the body are used to communicate with other viperfish.

◀ LONG-EARED BAT
Many bats prey on insects. Bats have poor vision, instead using echolocation to navigate and hunt. In flight, the bat releases pulses of high-pitched sounds that bounce off objects. Returning echoes picked up by the bat's ears create a "sound picture," enabling it to pinpoint its prey.

RED FOX ▶
This opportunistic, nocturnal hunter has excellent senses of hearing, smell, and vision. Foxes use their ears to listen for rodents rustling in grass. Their eyes, like those of many nocturnal mammals, have a reflective layer that improves night vision and produces the green glow seen here.

LESSER BUSH BABY ▶
Galagos or bush babies are active at night, jumping between branches in African forests. Their huge eyes allow them to see in near darkness. Large, movable ears enable them to track flying insects so accurately that they can snatch them from the air with their grasping fingers.

TEXAS BLIND SALAMANDER ▶
Animals that spend their entire lives in caves, such as the Texas blind salamander, have no need of sight. This pool-dwelling salamander's eyes are reduced to two tiny black dots. An active predator, it uses touch to locate shrimps and other invertebrates.

ECOSYSTEMS

Within an ecosystem, animals, plants, and other organisms interact with each other and their surroundings. Tropical rain forests are the world's richest ecosystems. Found around the equator, they are hot, wet, and packed with plants that provide food for herbivores, which in turn are eaten by carnivores. A South American rain-forest ecosystem, with a few of its animals, is described here.

❶ **Fruit bat** flies from tree to tree, eating ripe, sweet fruit.

❷ **Julia butterfly** feeds on nectar from flowers.

❸ **Harpy eagle** soars over the canopy, swooping on monkeys, snakes, and other prey.

❹ **Toucan** uses its long, brightly colored beak to reach fruit.

❺ **Howler monkey** eats leaves and lives in a group. Their cries can be heard over long distances.

❻ **Tamandua** is an anteater, which uses its long, sticky tongue to snare ants and termites.

❼ **Scarlet macaw** uses its curved beak to break open fruit or nuts.

❽ **Blue morpho butterfly** feeds on the juices of overripe fruits.

❾ **Kinkajou** is a mammal that grips branches with its prehensile (grasping) tail.

❿ **Hermit hummingbird** feeds on nectar from understory flowers.

⓫ **Tree frog** thrives in these humid surroundings, where it eats insects.

⓬ **Green iguana** eats leaves and fruits.

⓭ **Eyelash viper** is a poisonous snake that preys on frogs, lizards, and small birds.

⓮ **Brazilian tapir** uses its mobile snout to feed on grasses, leaves, shoots, and small branches.

⓯ **Wandering spider** is agressive, highly venomous, and hunts insects, small lizards, and mice.

⓰ **Elephant beetle** roams the forest floor in search of decaying fruit.

⓱ **Giant centipede** eats a wide range of prey including insects, lizards, and small birds.

⓲ **Agouti** is a rodent that eats fallen fruit and leaves as well as roots.

⓳ **Jaguar** is a large predator that stalks and ambushes prey, including tapirs and deer.

Howler monkey's gripping tail helps it cling to branches in its treetop home

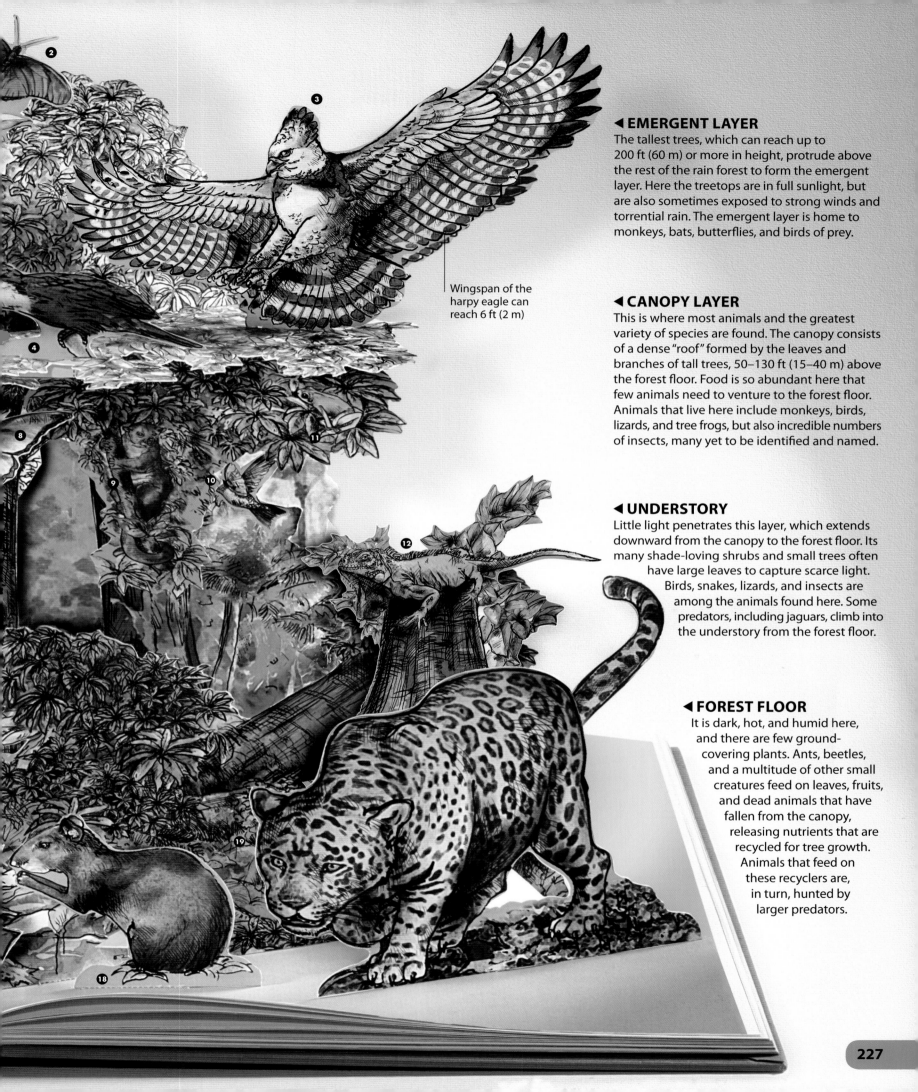

◀ EMERGENT LAYER

The tallest trees, which can reach up to 200 ft (60 m) or more in height, protrude above the rest of the rain forest to form the emergent layer. Here the treetops are in full sunlight, but are also sometimes exposed to strong winds and torrential rain. The emergent layer is home to monkeys, bats, butterflies, and birds of prey.

Wingspan of the harpy eagle can reach 6 ft (2 m)

◀ CANOPY LAYER

This is where most animals and the greatest variety of species are found. The canopy consists of a dense "roof" formed by the leaves and branches of tall trees, 50–130 ft (15–40 m) above the forest floor. Food is so abundant here that few animals need to venture to the forest floor. Animals that live here include monkeys, birds, lizards, and tree frogs, but also incredible numbers of insects, many yet to be identified and named.

◀ UNDERSTORY

Little light penetrates this layer, which extends downward from the canopy to the forest floor. Its many shade-loving shrubs and small trees often have large leaves to capture scarce light. Birds, snakes, lizards, and insects are among the animals found here. Some predators, including jaguars, climb into the understory from the forest floor.

◀ FOREST FLOOR

It is dark, hot, and humid here, and there are few ground-covering plants. Ants, beetles, and a multitude of other small creatures feed on leaves, fruits, and dead animals that have fallen from the canopy, releasing nutrients that are recycled for tree growth. Animals that feed on these recyclers are, in turn, hunted by larger predators.

Killer whale

5

Leopard seal

5

Mouth opens wide to filter vast amounts of krill from the sea

3

Southern right whale

Crabeater seal

3

Flippers allow penguin to swim rapidly and gracefully in pursuit of marine prey

3

Penguin

3 Fish

FOOD WEBS

The icy, nutrient-rich oceans around Antarctica abound with life. Plantlike microorganisms use the Sun's energy to produce food that is consumed by shrimplike krill, which are, in turn, eaten by huge whales. This is one of many food chains that together form a food web connecting all the species in the ecosystem. Any ecosystem, whether a coral reef, woodland, or desert, has its own food web.

Krill

2

Phytoplankton

1

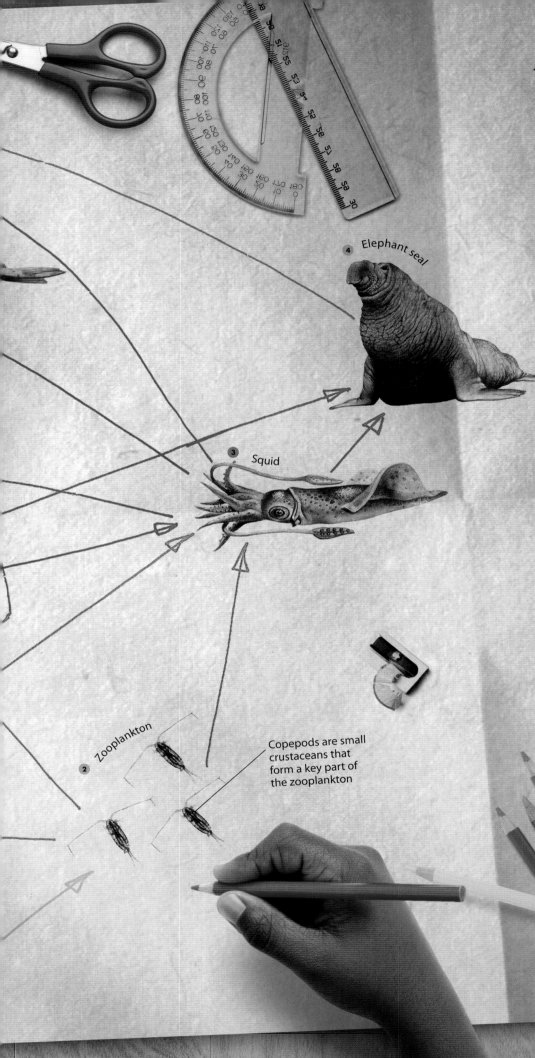

Elephant seal ④

Squid ③

Zooplankton ②

Copepods are small crustaceans that form a key part of the zooplankton

◄ HOW A FOOD WEB WORKS

A food web shows at a glance what eats what in an ecosystem. In each of the food chains that make up the web, arrows show the direction in which energy flows when one organism consumes another. At each step in a chain, energy is lost. Therefore, less energy is passed on to build and run an animal in the next level.

① PRODUCERS

All food webs start with producers—living things that use sunlight energy to make food by a process called photosynthesis. In the case of this Antarctic food web, the producers are microscopic phytoplankton—plantlike organisms that float in the well-lit surface waters. Producers provide the energy that supports all the other species in the food web.

② PRIMARY CONSUMERS

Unlike producers, primary consumers cannot make their own food. Instead, they survive by eating the producers, in this case the phytoplankton. Antarctic primary consumers include zooplankton (masses of tiny animals) and krill.

③ SECONDARY CONSUMERS

Crabeater seals, despite their name, feed almost exclusively on krill that they filter from the water using their unusually shaped teeth. Along with penguins, ice-tolerant fish, and squid they are secondary consumers—animals that feed on primary consumers. However, the categories in a food web are only for guidance: consumers often belong to more than one food chain, and occupy different levels in each.

④ TERTIARY CONSUMERS

In each food chain, an animal that is eaten passes on only around 10 percent of the energy it received from the animals it ate. The rest is used for movement and maintaining its body or it is lost as heat. Each level, therefore, supports fewer individuals than the one before. At tertiary consumer level these are the elephant seals.

⑤ TOP PREDATORS

Leopard seals and killer whales (orcas) are the top predators and consumers in this Antarctic food chain. They are the equivalent of lions in the African savanna, hunting a wide range of prey. They have no natural predators—although orcas will eat leopard seals—so this marks the upper limit of the food web.

TIME OUT

Animals thrive when adequate food, water, and warmth are available. But an animal's environment can change dramatically with the seasons, or even between day and night, especially in cooler, temperate parts of the world. To survive less favorable conditions, such as extreme cold or lack of food or water, some animals use resting strategies, including hibernation, torpor, or estivation. By being less active they conserve valuable energy.

❶ SUSPENDED ANIMATION

Tardigrades or water bears are microscopic creatures that normally live in water. If their surroundings dry out, they curl up and shut down their body systems. They can stay in this state of suspended animation for more than 25 years, but come back to life once water returns.

Tardigrade

Hummingbird

Wings beat so fast that the bird must spend all day searching for energy-rich nectar

American black bear

Desert toad

❷ ESTIVATION

The summer equivalent of hibernation, estivation is practiced by some animals in hot countries. Land snails, for example, seal themselves up to avoid the summer heat and cling together in a state of inactivity. Desert toads survive underground, emerging above ground to lay their eggs only when the rains come.

❸ WINTER SLEEP

In the fall, many bears enter a state of rest called torpor—during which their heart- and breathing rates drop considerably—to avoid cold weather and food shortages. They prepare for torpor by eating greedily to build up fat reserves. Torpid bears sleep in dens, such as hollow trees or caves, but are easily awakened.

❹ REPTILE REST

Reptiles, such as the North American red-sided garter snake, that live in places with cold winters take a winter rest called brumation. Garter snakes gather together in a sheltered location and become sluggish as the temperature falls. In spring, they emerge together to enjoy the warmth.

Mountain-living marmot's size means it must hibernate in a burrow during winter

Marmot

6 Cabbage white butterfly

5

European hedgehog

Red-sided garter snake

Daubenton's bat **7**

7 DAILY TORPOR

Some smaller animals, such as hummingbirds and bats, take time out on a daily basis. Hummingbirds keep their body temperature constant during the day. At night, when they rest, their body temperature falls, allowing them to save energy. Bats follow the same strategy except that they show torpor during the day and warm up at night when hunting for insects.

Chipmunk eats large amounts of food before hibernating, storing some in its winter burrow

6 DIAPAUSE

Insects, such as butterflies, go through various stages—egg to larva to pupa to adult—during their development. Stages can be delayed to give the insect the best chance of survival. This is called diapause. If a cabbage white butterfly lays eggs in late summer, development stops at the pupa stage over winter and starts up again in the spring.

Chipmunk

5 HIBERNATION

Mammals are endothermic (warm-blooded) and they need to eat regularly to maintain their body temperature. In winter, small mammals such as marmots, hedgehogs, chipmunks, and bats find this difficult because there is little food and they lose heat easily. To survive, they find shelter and go into hibernation, during which their body temperature and heart- and breathing rates fall dramatically.

Hard shell protects snail as it estivates

Giant land snails

ARCTIC

① RED CROSSBILL

Found in the northern forests of North America and Europe, red crossbills eat conifer seeds. In years when seeds are in short supply, a mass movement, or irruption, occurs as crossbills fly south in search of food.

NORTH AMERICA

② GRAY WHALE

Each spring and fall, gray whales migrate between summer feeding grounds in the Arctic and winter lagoons off Baja California, Mexico, where the females give birth.

③ SPINY LOBSTER

Adult Caribbean spiny lobsters live in coral reefs but in the fall they migrate to deeper waters to avoid colder conditions. Unusually, they travel together and in single file until they reach open water.

④ EUROPEAN EEL

After starting life in the western Atlantic Ocean, young eels migrate east to European rivers, a journey that can take three years. After many years there they migrate back to their birthplace to breed.

SOUTH AMERICA

⑤ GREEN TURTLE

Every three years or so, these marine reptiles take a break from feeding on seagrasses off the coast of Brazil and make the 2,500-mile (4,000-km) round trip to Ascension Island in the south Atlantic to mate and breed.

MIGRATION

While many animals never leave their habitats, others regularly migrate (move from one habitat to another) in order to avoid excessive heat or cold, to find food, or to breed. The journeys can be short, like those of the European toad, but sometimes the distances covered are immense. Migration often coincides with the changing seasons, but for some, such as the eel, it spans a lifetime.

7 ALPINE IBEX

Strong jumpers and surefooted climbers, these agile mountain goats live at high altitudes in summer but move to lower areas during the cold winter months when food is scarce.

8 COMMON SWIFT

These superb fliers spend the winter in Africa, feeding on insects that they catch on the wing. In April they fly north to Europe to breed during the summer, before returning to Africa in the fall.

10 EUROPEAN TOAD

As adults, European toads spend most of their time on land. But every year, when they emerge from their winter hibernation, they follow the same route back to the ponds where they hatched in order to breed.

9 BLUE WILDEBEEST

In the biggest mammal migration on Earth some 1.5 million wildebeest, a type of antelope, follow a triangular route across the African savanna in search of water and fresh grazing. On the way, many wildebeest fall prey to cheetahs, hyenas, crocodiles, and other predators.

6 ARCTIC TERN

This seabird migrates an incredible 25,000 miles (40,000 km) each year. Arctic terns breed in the Arctic during the long summer days. As fall approaches, they make the epic journey to the Antarctic, where the southern summer is just beginning.

11 BOGONG MOTH

Common in southern Australia, bogong moths escape the intense summer heat by flying by the millions to the Australian Alps. Here they roost in crevices and caves. In the cooler fall, they migrate to inland pastures to lay their eggs.

233

ANTARCTIC ICEFISH ▶

In addition to having "antifreeze" proteins to stop it from freezing, the Antarctic icefish also has thin, transparent blood that circulates easily in the cold.

Polar cod

COLD WATER ▶

Because fish are ectothermic (cold-blooded), the temperature of their insides matches that of their surroundings. So, in icy Arctic waters fish should freeze to death. Yet fish such as the arctic cod can survive the cold. They have "antifreeze" proteins that prevent ice crystals from forming so their blood and other body fluids stay liquid.

LIFE IN THE EXTREME

Wherever there is warmth, water, and plenty of food, animals will prosper. The same is not true of baking dry deserts, the dark depths of the oceans, or the icy-cold Arctic and Antarctic, where the harsh conditions would kill most animals. However, some hardy animals can survive in these places. They are adapted to life in the extreme by, for example, having no need to drink water, being resistant to the enormous pressure in the deep ocean, or by being well insulated against biting cold.

◀ UNDER PRESSURE

Deep in the ocean, animals must tolerate pressures that would crush a human. Sperm whales, which survive dives to depths of 10,000 ft (3,000 m), have a flexible rib cage that allows their lungs to collapse. In the dark ocean depths, deep-sea fish such as the gulper eel produce light to lure prey, and have large mouths to grab it.

Gulper eel

Sperm whale

White crab

Eelpout

Tubeworm

HYDROTHERMAL VENT ▶

Hydrothermal vents are openings in the deep ocean, hydrothermal water erupts. In the deep ocean, very hot, mineral-rich water erupts. In the deep ocean, very hot, mineral-rich water erupts. In the deep which very hot, mineral-rich water erupts. In the deep which very hot, mineral-rich through which very hot, mineral-rich water and use it to through which can tolerate the harsh conditions harvest In the deep ocean, hydrothermal water erupts. through which can tolerate the harsh conditions in vent water and use it to Bacteria that feed tubeworms such as eelpouts. energy from the feed tubeworms such as eelpouts. make sugars that feed animals are eaten by predators such as these animals are eaten by predators such as

Arctic fox

Emperor penguins

Wood frog

Desert jerboa

Camel

COLD ON LAND ▲
The arctic fox's thick coat and insulating body fat enable it to withstand temperatures as low as –40°F (–40°C). Similar conditions are tolerated in the Antarctic by male emperor penguins as they huddle together, incubating eggs. During bitterly cold Canadian winters, wood frogs freeze solid then thaw out the following spring.

DESERT HEAT ▶
Some animals thrive in the scorching heat in the desert jerboa does the daytime heat in of waterless deserts. The desert jerboa does not drink, shelters from the night to feed on a burrow, and emerges and can go seeds from which it gets the moisture and is Camels tolerate high temperatures and water is without water for weeks, then when water is available, make up the loss in minutes.

DESERT PUPFISH ▲
Found in the desert springs of southwest North America, this small fish is very tolerant of harsh conditions. It can survive in water that is six times saltier than the sea and as hot as 113°F (45°C).

PARTNERSHIPS

Day-to-day survival is a tough proposition for most animals. Some improve their chances by forging partnerships with other creatures. Symbiosis, the term that describes all such relationships, comes in various forms, including mutualism and commensalism. Mutualism is a partnership that benefits both partners. Commensal relationships, like that of the pearlfish and sea cucumber, have only one beneficiary.

Ant protects aphids from enemies

Buffalo tolerates oxpecker's presence

Oxpecker eats irritating parasites

Aphid sucks sap from plants

▲ OXPECKER AND BUFFALO
Oxpeckers are birds that live in the African savanna and have a close relationship with buffalo, rhino, and other big mammals. Perching on their partner, they dig out ticks and other irritating parasites. The oxpecker gets food, while its partner gets relief.

ANTS AND APHIDS ▲
Some aphids and ants have a mutually beneficial relationship. Aphids are insects that suck sugar-rich sap from plant stems. Excess sap, called honeydew, oozes from their rear ends and is harvested by ants to drink. In turn, ants protect aphids from predators, such as ladybugs.

Anemone's tentacles

Clownfish among tentacles

◄ CLOWNFISH AND SEA ANEMONE
Most animals that stray into the stinging tentacles of sea anemones are paralyzed and then eaten. Not so the clownfish, which appears to be immune. It lives close to the anemone, retreating between the tentacles should danger threaten. In turn, it may lure prey for its host to eat.

◀ PEARLFISH AND SEA CUCUMBER
The eel-like pearlfish spends its days protected inside the sea cucumber. At nightfall, it exits through its host's anus to feed. In the morning, it waits for the anus to open, then swims back in.

Pearlfish emerges from sea cucumber's anus

Sea cucumber lives on the seabed

Fly provides a free ride

CLEANER SHRIMP AND MORAY EEL ▼
This cleaner shrimp should be a tasty snack for a moray eel, or any of its other "client" fish. Yet the shrimp remains unharmed as it removes irritating parasites from the predator's skin, earning itself a meal.

Cleaner shrimp removes parasites

Pseudoscorpion uses pincers to latch on

▲ PSEUDOSCORPION AND INSECT
Tiny, clawed arachnids, pseudoscorpions employ a unique means of transportation to find new places to feed. They use their pincers to hang on to a handy fly, beetle, wasp, or other big insect, as they are flown to a new location. Only the pseudoscorpion benefits, but their host is not harmed.

Moray eel remains still

Dugong is not hurt by the remora

Remora attaches to host

REMORA AND PARTNER ▶
Commensalism is well illustrated by tropical remora fish. They use a suckerlike pad on top of their heads to attach to sharks, turtles, or marine mammals called dugongs. The remora gets free transportation, while its partner neither gains nor loses anything.

Thin paper wall made from chewed wood

Worker returns from foraging with food

COLONIES

Across the animal kingdom there are many examples of animals living together in social groups or colonies. The closest knit and most organized colonies are found in the group of insects that includes ants, bees, and wasps. Individuals within these insect societies belong to specific castes or classes, each with their own tasks, such as food gathering or rearing young. A wasp colony like this one is dominated by its queen.

❶ WASP CASTES

For most of its life the nest contains only two castes, the larger queen and her smaller workers. The queen lays eggs and controls the colony. Her workers have various tasks, including building and repairing the nest, foraging for food and feeding larvae, and defending the nest from intruders. In late summer larger larvae develop into males and new queens, which fly from the nest and mate. The males soon die, but the young queens seek shelter and hibernate. The old colony dies and its nest is now empty.

❸ NEST

A wasps' nest is cut away here to show its structure. In spring, a solitary queen starts to build the nest, mixing chewed wood fibers with saliva to make a papery substance. When the first workers hatch, they continue the process of building the central comb of cells which will house more eggs. As spring turns to summer the multistory nest, built from the top downward, is completed.

❷ QUEEN WASP

When a young queen emerges in the spring from hibernation, last fall's mating means she is ready to lay fertilized eggs. First, she finds a nest site and constructs a small comb of paper cells in which she lays her eggs. When they hatch, the sterile female workers continue the work of building the nest while their queen lays more eggs. The queen releases chemicals called pheromones to prevent her workers from becoming queens, and to control their behavior so they perform their various tasks.

❹ CELLS

These hexagonal (six-sided) chambers are remarkable examples of animal architecture. Although, like the rest of the nest, they are made of paper, their shape makes them enormously strong. The hexagonal shape also means that a lot of cells can be packed into the small space inside the nest. For the queen and her workers, knowing how to build the nest and its cells is instinctive.

❺ LARVAE

In each cell the queen lays one egg that hatches into a larva or grub. The larva grows rapidly as it is fed on a diet of chewed-up caterpillars and other insects brought to the nest by workers. When it is fully grown the larva spins a silken cap to close its cell, and becomes a pupa. After a few days, a worker wasp emerges from the cell, ready to take on its duties.

PARASITES

In parasitic partnerships one animal, a parasite, exploits the other, the host, in order to obtain food, shelter, or to reproduce. Endoparasites, such as flukes and tapeworms, live inside their hosts, while ectoparasites, such as lice, ticks, and mites, live outside. Other types of parasite include parasitoid wasps and brood parasites, like cuckoos.

HEADLICE ▶

Seen here magnified and in false color, headlice are wingless insects that live on human hair. They grip the hair shafts with their front legs to stop them from being dislodged by combing or washing. When they descend on to the scalp, they use their mouthparts to pierce skin and suck blood, causing itching in the human host.

▲ CUCKOO

The female common cuckoo is a brood parasite that tricks another bird into raising her offspring. She lays one egg in the host bird's nest. After hatching, the young cuckoo pushes the host's eggs out of the nest. Now the center of attention, it grows rapidly.

◀ PARASITOID

A parasitoid is an animal, typically a wasp, that lays its eggs on or in a living host. The host provides food for larvae when they hatch, and dies in the process. Here wasp larvae are emerging from a dead caterpillar.

▲ BOTFLY LARVAE

The botfly lays its eggs on the skin of mammals. The eggs hatch into larvae that burrow under the skin and grow until they resemble large maggots (above). They then push their way back to the surface and fall to the ground to form a pupa that will develop into an adult fly.

LAMPREY ▶

This jawless fish is an ectoparasite of trout, salmon, and other fish. It uses its suckerlike mouth and rows of small, pointed teeth to clamp onto the side of its host. The lamprey's rasping tongue wears a hole through the skin, then sucks out blood and tissues.

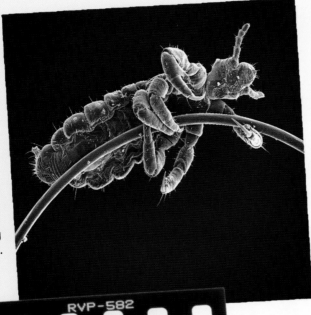

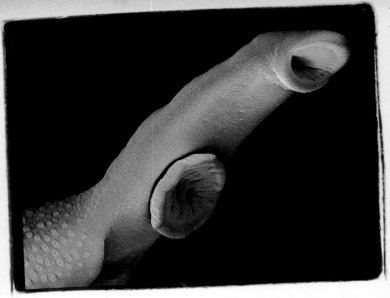

◀ SCHISTOSOME FLUKE

This highly specialized flatworm lives in the blood vessels that surround the human bladder or intestines. Male and female worms live together, held in place by the male's suckers (left). Together, they produce millions of eggs that may pass out of the body to infect new hosts.

ISOPOD ▶

Some members of this group of crustaceans are ectoparasites of fish. They attach to and erode the skin around the eyes, mouth, or gills of their host, and feed on blood and tissues. Isopod parasites make the fish less streamlined so it swims less efficiently. Other isopods are not truly parasitic and feed on discarded food scraps.

▲ TICK ON FROG

This blood feeder pierces the skin of its host, in this case a frog, using its hooked mouthparts. These hold the tick firmly in place for hours or days as it fills up with blood, swelling greatly as it does so. Fully engorged, the tick falls off its host and digests its meal.

TAPEWORM ▶

Hooks and suckers anchor the scolex (head) of this tapeworm to the intestine of its host, in this case a cat. The ribbonlike flatworm can grow to more than 33 ft (10 m) in length. It has no mouth, but absorbs food from the host's intestine through its surface.

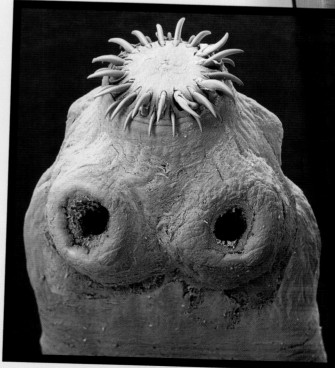

◀ MITES

Like ticks, mites are relatives of spiders. Some are free-living, but many are parasites of both invertebrates and vertebrates. This mass of parasitic mites carried on the back of a beetle is sucking out its tissues.

ALIEN SPECIES

Animals that live together in a particular habitat have evolved in ways that ensure an overall balance of numbers. However, if alien species are introduced accidentally or deliberately to a habitat, that balance can be destroyed. If the invasive species has no natural predators and a good supply of food, it will multiply uncontrollably and may cause native species to disappear. The five examples below are among the world's worst invasive alien species.

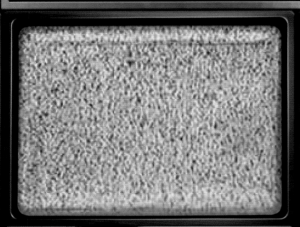

▲ STOAT
This small but ferocious predator was imported into New Zealand in the late 1880s to control rabbits, another introduced species. But these active hunters also eat eggs and chicks and have had a devastating effect on native bird species, most notably the kiwi.

▲ CHINESE MITTEN CRAB
Named for its furry claws, this native of China arrived in Europe and the US on ships. It lives in fresh water and breeds at an incredible rate. Mitten crabs will eat nearly anything—disrupting communities of native animals—and cause erosion by digging burrows in riverbanks.

▲ CANE TOAD
This large South American toad was introduced to Australia in 1935 as a pest controller. Their skin produces predator-killing poisons, making them hazardous to inquisitive family pets. Since they eat everything, from snakes and frogs to mammals, they have caused the decline of many native species.

▲ RABBIT
Rabbits were introduced to Australia in 1859. Only 24 were released but they multiplied so rapidly that soon there were millions. Rabbits outcompete native plant-eaters for food, making some extinct. By removing ground cover they allow soil to blow away and cause serious erosion. They are difficult to control, even with fences.

▲ ROSY WOLF SNAIL
This predatory snail was introduced to Tahiti and nearby islands in the 1970s to control another introduced species, the giant African land snail. But instead of targeting its intended prey, the rosy wolf snail attacked native snail species. Most of the native snails are now extinct and those that remain are endangered.

NEW VARIETIES

In the natural world, species change over time in a process called evolution. Evolution works through natural selection, with animals best adapted to a particular habitat more likely to survive long enough to breed and pass on their features to new generations than those that are less well adapted. For thousands of years, humans have used artificial selection (selective breeding) to produce new varieties of domesticated (tamed) animals for their own use. Genetic modification is the latest form of human interference.

African wildcat

Pet cat

Breeding has produced a flattened face

Aurochs

Gray wolf

▲ CATS
When agriculture developed in the Middle East and Egypt more than 8,000 years ago, harvested crops had to be stored. These stores were devastated by rodents such as rats and mice. Farmers domesticated wild cats to kill the rodents. Later, selective breeding produced the varieties of cat breeds seen today.

Chihuahua

Domesticated cockerel

Junglefowl

▲ DOGS
From Great Danes to Chihuahuas, all breeds of dogs are descended from wolves. Wolves were the first animals to be domesticated, about 13,000 years ago. Initially they were used for hunting, but, later, selective breeding was used to produce a variety of working dogs and pets.

▲ CHICKENS
The junglefowl found today in the forests of southeast Asia is the bird from which domestic chickens originated about 8,000 years ago. People tamed these birds to obtain both eggs and meat as food, then bred them to create new varieties.

Hereford bull

◀ CATTLE

Various types of wild cattle, including European aurochs, were first domesticated 10,000 years ago. Cattle are used for milk, meat, and leather. More recent selective breeding has produced some breeds that excel at milk production, and others that are primarily farmed for meat.

Wild boar

▼ GLOWING MICE

Genetic modification involves taking specific genes (instructions for a particular characteristic) from one organism and introducing them into another. For example, a jellyfish gene introduced into mice makes them glow. Scientists hope these genetic-engineering techniques will aid research into human diseases.

Mice glow green under blue or ultraviolet light

Young farm pigs

▲ PIGS

Over thousands of years, pigs have been domesticated in different places around the world at least seven times, probably because wild boar are very adaptable and are easy to look after. Selective breeding has produced animals that are less hairy and less aggressive than their wild boar ancestors. Domestic pigs are used mainly for meat, but some dwarf breeds are popular as pets.

Glossary

ABDOMEN
The part of an animal's body that contains reproductive and digestive organs. It forms the rear part of the body of insects, crustaceans, and arachnids.

ACCRETION
The process by which small particles cling together to make larger objects, including planets and asteroids.

ALGAE
Plantlike protists that can make food using solar energy. Most are single-celled, but they include seaweeds.

ALLOY
An artificial mixture of two different metals.

AMPHIBIAN
An ectothermic (cold-blooded) vertebrate, such as a frog or newt, that lives partly in water and partly on land.

ANNELID
A type of worm, such as an earthworm, with a soft, rounded body made up of segments.

ANTARCTICA
The continent around the South Pole that is covered by ice sheets.

ANTENNA (PLURAL: ANTENNAE)
A long sensory structure, or feeler, on the head of insects, crustaceans, and some other arthropods.

ANTICYCLONE
A high-pressure weather system in which sinking cool air creates cloudless skies.

ARACHNID
An arthropod with four pairs of legs, such as a spider or scorpion.

ARCTIC
The region around the North Pole, and a word that describes animals that live there.

ARTERY
A blood vessel that carries oxygen-rich blood from the heart to an animal's tissues.

ARTHROPOD
An invertebrate, such as an insect, crustacean, or arachnid, that has a hard body case and jointed legs.

ASTEROID
A relatively small, irregular rocky body orbiting the Sun.

ATMOSPHERE
The layers of gas that surround the Earth, retained by gravity.

ATOM
The smallest particle of an element such as iron. Compound substances, such as water, have more than one kind of atom.

BACTERIA
A group of simple, single-celled, microscopic organisms, the most abundant on Earth.

BIOSPHERE
The web of life that exists on or near the Earth's surface.

BIRD
An endothermic (warm-blooded) vertebrate, such as an eagle, that has a beak, feathers, wings, and can fly.

CALCIUM CARBONATE
A white, solid mineral salt that forms or reinforces the shells of mollusks and the cuticle of crustaceans.

CALDERA
A giant crater formed when a volcano collapses into its magma chamber after this has been emptied by an eruption.

CAMOUFLAGE
The way in which an animal uses its shape and/or color to blend in with its surroundings.

CARAPACE
Hard covering that protects the head and thorax of crustaceans such as lobsters and crabs.

CARBOHYDRATE
A substance, such as sugar or starch, that is made of carbon, hydrogen, and oxygen by a living organism, such as a plant.

CARBON DIOXIDE
A waste gas released by an animal as a result of cell respiration (energy release). It forms a very small fraction of the atmosphere. Living things, such as plants, use it to make carbohydrate food.

CARNIVORE
Specifically, a member of an order of mammals, including cats and wolves, that eats mainly meat. Also, any animal that is a meat-eater.

CARTILAGE
A tough, flexible tissue that makes up the skeleton of cartilaginous fish, such as sharks, and forms part of the skeletons of other vertebrates.

CELL
One of the many tiny living units that together make up an animal's body. Other living things, such as bacteria and plants, are constructed from one or many cells.

CEPHALOPOD
A type of mollusk, such as an octopus, that has a distinct head with large eyes and tentacles with suckers.

CEPHALOTHORAX
The front section of the body of spiders and other arachnids to which four pairs of legs are attached.

CHORDATE
A member of a group of animals that includes vertebrates, such as fish and reptiles.

CIRQUE
A craterlike depression near a mountain peak, carved out by ice building up to feed a glacier.

CLIMATE
The average weather of any region and its typical seasonal weather pattern.

COMET
An orbiting body made of ice and dust. Some comets pass close to the Sun at rare intervals, and their radiation makes them stream long tails.

COMPOUND
A substance containing two or more elements, formed by a chemical reaction that bonds their atoms together.

COMPOUND EYE
A type of eye, found in insects and crustaceans, that is made up of many small units.

CONDENSE
To change from a gas to a liquid.

CONTINENTAL SHELF
The submerged fringe of a continent, forming the relatively shallow floor of a coastal sea.

CONVECTION
Circulating currents in gases or liquids, such as air and water, and even hot, mobile rock, driven by differences in temperature.

CRUSTACEAN
An arthropod, such as a crab or shrimp, that has two pairs of antennae and several pairs of jointed legs.

CRYSTAL
A gemlike structure that may form when a liquid becomes a solid. Its shape is determined by the arrangement of its atoms.

CUTICLE
The hard, protective outer layer (exoskeleton) of arthropods such as insects and crustaceans.

CYANOBACTERIA
Bacteria that can use solar energy to make sugar from carbon dioxide and water.

CYCLONE
A weather system with clouds, rain, and strong winds caused by air swirling into a region of rising warm, moist air.

DEPRESSION
Another word for a cyclone.

DROUGHT
A long period with no rain.

ECHINODERM
A marine invertebrate, such as a starfish or sea urchin, with an internal skeleton and a body divided into five equal parts.

ECHOLOCATION
The use of reflected sounds, employed by animals such as dolphins and bats, to locate objects, especially food.

ECOSYSTEM
A community of interacting living organisms and their environment, such as a tropical forest or a coral reef.

ECTOTHERMIC
Describes an animal, such as a frog or snake, whose internal temperature varies with that of its surroundings.

ELEMENT
A substance that is made up of just one type of atom.

ENDOTHERMIC
Describes an animal, such as a duck or a rabbit, whose internal temperature remains the same regardless of the external temperature.

ENERGY
The capacity to perform work, required for all life functions including growth and movement.

ENZYME
A substance that speeds up chemical reactions—including the break down of food molecules during digestion—inside animals and other living organisms.

EQUATOR
An imaginary line drawn around the Earth halfway between the North and South poles, which divides it into northern and southern hemispheres.

EROSION
Wearing away, usually of rock, by natural forces such as flowing water or ocean waves breaking on the shore.

EVAPORATE
To turn from a liquid into a gas or vapor.

EVAPORITE
A solid such as salt that is left behind when a liquid solution, such as saltwater, evaporates.

EVOLUTION
The process by which species change over many generations, thereby giving rise to new species.

EXOSKELETON
The hard outer covering of animals such as insects and crustaceans.

EXTINCTION
The permanent disappearance of a particular species of animal or other living organism.

FAULT
A fracture in rock, where the rock on one side of the fracture has moved relative to the rock on the other side.

FERTILIZER
A mixture of plant nutrients used to promote plant growth.

FISH
A general name used to describe several groups of vertebrates, including sharks and bony fish, that live in water and have streamlined bodies with fins.

FJORD
A deep coastal valley eroded by a glacier that is now flooded by the sea.

FOOD CHAIN
A pathway that links together selected species within a habitat to show what eats what.

FOSSIL
The remains or traces of a living thing that have been preserved, usually in stony form and in sedimentary rock.

GALAXY
A vast mass consisting of many millions of stars in space, often circulating around a central nucleus.

GENE
One of the instructions, stored inside cells, required to build and operate an animal's body, and which is passed on from parents to offspring.

GILL
A structure, found in fish and other aquatic animals, used for taking in oxygen and releasing carbon dioxide under water.

GLACIER
A mass of ice formed from compacted snow that may flow slowly downhill.

GONAD
An organ, such as the testis or ovary, that produces sex cells used in reproduction.

GRAVITY
The attractive force between objects in space. The greater the mass of the object, the more gravity it has.

GREENHOUSE EFFECT
The way certain gases in the atmosphere absorb heat radiated from Earth, warm up, and keep the planet warmer than it would otherwise be.

HABITAT
The natural home of a species of animal or other living organism.

HERBIVORE
An animal, such as a cow, that eats only plants.

HIBERNATION
A state of deep sleep used by some smaller mammals to survive cold winters when food is scarce.

HOTSPOT
A zone of volcanic activity caused by a stationary plume of heat beneath Earth's crust. Where the crust is moving, the hotspot creates chains of volcanoes.

HYDROTHERMAL VENT
An eruption of very hot, mineral-rich water from the ocean floor, normally from a volcanically active midocean ridge.

IGNEOUS
A rock that has been formed by the cooling of molten magma or volcanic lava. Most igneous rocks are composed of interlocking crystals and are very hard.

INSECT
An arthropod, such as a beetle or butterfly, with three pairs of legs, usually two pairs of wings, and a body divided into three parts.

INSECTIVORE
An animal, such as an anteater, that feeds on insects. Also a member of an order of mammals that includes moles and hedgehogs.

INVERTEBRATE
An animal, such as an insect or an earthworm, that does not have a backbone.

KRILL
A shrimplike crustacean that forms the main food source of baleen whales.

LARVA (PLURAL: LARVAE)
A young animal, such as a caterpillar, that undergoes metamorphosis to become an adult, such as a butterfly.

LAVA
Molten rock that erupts from a volcano.

LIMESTONE
A rock made of calcite (lime) that is easily dissolved by slightly acid rainwater. Most limestones are formed from the skeletons of marine organisms.

LUNG
A structure, found in mammals and air-breathing animals, used for taking in oxygen and releasing carbon dioxide.

MAGMA
Molten rock that lies within or beneath Earth's crust.

MAMMAL
An endothermic (warm-blooded) vertebrate, such as a lion or bat, that has hair or fur and feeds its young on milk.

MANTLE
The deep layer of hot rock that lies between Earth's crust and the core. It forms 84 percent of the volume of the planet.

MARITIME CLIMATE
A climate influenced by a nearby ocean. Typically, it has mild winters, cool summers, and regular rainfall throughout the year.

METAMORPHISM
In geology, a process that turns one type of rock into another, usually involving intense heat, pressure, or both.

METAMORPHOSIS
A change that happens to the body of certain animals, including amphibians and many insects, as they mature into adults.

METEOR
A fragment of space rock or ice that plunges through the atmosphere and burns up as a "shooting star."

METEORITE
A fragment of space rock that survives its passage through the atmosphere and hits the ground.

MICROORGANISM
A living thing that can only be seen under a microscope.

MIDLATITUDES
The regions of the world that lie between the polar regions and the tropics and have temperate, seasonal climates.

MIGRATION
A journey undertaken by an animal, often on a seasonal basis, from one habitat to another in order to find food and/or breed.

MINERAL
A natural solid composed of one or more elements in fixed proportions, usually with a distinctive crystal structure

MOLECULE
Smallest particle of a substance that can exist without breaking up the substance into the elements from which it is made. Each molecule is formed from atoms of those elements.

MOLLUSK
A soft-bodied invertebrate, such as a snail, mussel, or squid, that is typically protected by a hard shell.

MONSOON
A seasonal change of wind that affects the weather, especially in tropical regions, where it results in wet and dry seasons.

MORAINE
A mass of rock debris carried by a glacier, or piled up at its end.

MUCUS
A thick, slippery fluid secreted by animals for lubrication and protection.

MUSCLE
An animal tissue that can contract (get shorter) in order to pull and create movement.

NATURAL SELECTION
The process whereby organisms that are better adapted to their surroundings survive longer and therefore have time to produce more offspring. It is the driving force of evolution.

NECTAR
A sugary liquid produced by flowers to attract animals, such as butterflies, that pollinate them.

NERVE
A bundle of long, specialized cells that rapidly relay signals from one part of an animal's body to another.

NOMADIC
Moving constantly in search of food or other resources, but with no fixed route.

NOCTURNAL
Describes an animal that is active at night, but inactive by day.

NORTHERN HEMISPHERE
The half of the Earth that is north of the equator.

NUCLEAR FUSION
Fusing the atoms of two elements to create a heavier element.

NUTRIENT
A substance taken in by an animal in its food that is needed for normal functioning.

NYMPH
A stage in the life cycle of certain insects. Nymphs look like smaller, wingless versions of adult insects.

ORBIT
The path taken by a body in space that is traveling around a larger body, such as the Sun.

ORGAN
A structure, such as the heart or an eye, that is made of two or more types of tissues and plays a specific role in keeping an animal alive.

ORGANIC
Technically, a substance that is based on the element carbon, but usually meaning something that is—or was once—alive.

ORGANISM
An individual living thing, such as an animal or a plant.

OMNIVORE
An animal that eats both plant and animal foods.

OXYGEN
A gas taken in by an animal that is used up during cell respiration (energy release).

PARASITE
An organism that lives inside or on the body of another species, and exists at the expense of its host.

PASTURE
Grassland used to feed animals, such as sheep and cattle.

PEAT
The compacted remains of plants that have not yet decayed, because waterlogging has led to the exclusion of oxygen, which is vital to the decaying of organisms.

PERMAFROST
Permanently frozen ground that covers vast areas of the Arctic.

PESTICIDE
A chemical used to kill the insects, fungi, and weeds that would otherwise reduce farm productivity.

PHEROMONE
A chemical "message" that is released by an animal, which has an effect on other members of its own species.

PHOTOSYNTHESIS
The process by which plants and plantlike plankton use sunlight energy to combine carbon dioxide and water to make food.

PHYTOPLANKTON
Drifting, microscopic, single-celled aquatic organisms that make their food using a process called photosynthesis.

PLANET
A large body made of rock and/or gas that orbits a star, but is not big enough to generate its own light by nuclear fusion.

PLANKTON
A term describing the mass of tiny, mostly microscopic animals (zooplankton) and plantlike protists (phytoplankton) that is found floating in both the sea and in fresh water.

PLATEAU
A broad area of land that lies at high altitude.

PLATE TECTONICS
The dynamic process in which the large plates that form the crust of Earth are constantly moving together or apart.

POLLINATOR
An animal such as a butterfly that, while visiting flowers to feed, transfers pollen from one flower to the next, enabling them to reproduce.

POLLUTION
Anything added to the natural environment that upsets the balance of nature.

PREDATOR
An animal, such as a lion, that hunts and eats other live animals, which are known as its prey.

PREY
An animal that is killed and eaten by another animal, the predator.

PRODUCER
An organism, such as a plant, that makes its own food using sunlight energy, and provides nutrients and energy for the animals that eat it.

PROTEIN
One of a group of substances made by an animal's cells that are essential for life and that include enzymes and the structural proteins found in hair and spiders' silk.

PROTIST
An aquatic or terrestrial organism that usually consists of a single, complex cell, such as the diatoms that drift in the ocean, but also including seaweeds. Protists comprise one of the five kingdoms of life.

PUPA (PLURAL: PUPAE)
The resting stage in the life cycle of many insects, including beetles and wasps, during which they change from a larva into an adult, with a complete change, or metamorphosis, in their body shape.

REPTILE
An ectothermic (cold-blooded) vertebrate, such as a crocodile or a snake, that has a scaly waterproof skin and lays its eggs on land.

RESERVOIR
A natural or artificial store of liquid, usually water.

RIFT
A widening crack in rocks or Earth's crust, caused by the rocks pulling apart.

RIFT VALLEY
A region where the Earth's crust has dropped into the gap formed by the crust pulling apart.

SAVANNA
A grassland habitat with few or widely spaced trees, found in the hotter, tropical regions of the world, most notably in parts of Africa.

SCAVENGER
Animal that feeds on the remains of dead animals and other scraps.

SEDIMENT
Solid particles, such as stones, sand, and mud that have been transported by water, wind, ice, or gravity, and have settled, usually in a layer.

SEDIMENTARY ROCK
Rock formed from compressed and hardened sand, mud, or other sediments.

SILICA
A compound of silicon and oxygen that is an important component of most rocks, and the main ingredient used for making glass.

SPECIES
A group of organisms consisting of similar individuals that can breed together.

STERILE
Describes an animal that is unable to reproduce.

STRATA
Layers of sedimentary rock.

SUBDUCTION ZONE
A region where one tectonic plate of the Earth's crust dives beneath another, creating an ocean trench, which causes earthquakes, and generates the lava that erupts from volcanoes.

SUPERHEAT
To heat a liquid, such as water, under pressure, so it gets hotter than its boiling point under normal atmospheric pressure.

SYMBIOSIS
A close relationship between members of two different species that can be either mutually beneficial or one-sided.

SYSTEM
A set of linked organs inside an animal's body that perform a specific function or functions.

TADPOLE
The larva of amphibians.

TEMPERATE
A climate that is neither very hot nor very cold, or a region that has such a climate.

TERRITORY
An area claimed and defended by an animal in order to protect sources or food or water, to mate, or to bring up young.

THORAX
The central body region of an insect, which is combined with the head in arachnids and crustaceans. An alternative name for the chest of a vertebrate animal.

TRANSFORM FAULT
A plate boundary between two slabs of Earth's crust where they slide sideways relative to each other.

TRIBUTARY
A stream that flows into a river, or a small glacier that flows into a bigger one.

TROPICS
The hot regions to the north and south of the equator, lying between the Tropic of Cancer and the Tropic of Capricorn.

TROPOSPHERE
The lowest layer of the Earth's atmosphere.

TSUNAMI
A fast-moving and powerful ocean wave generated by an earthquake on the ocean floor, or by the collapse of an oceanic volcano.

TUNDRA
The cold, largely barren, treeless landscape that lies on the fringes of the polar ice sheets.

ULTRAVIOLET RADIATION
A form of light that can damage living tissue. It is invisible to humans, but not to some other animals, such as insects.

UNGULATE
A mammal, such as a horse or pig, that has toes tipped with a hard hoof.

UNIVERSE
The entirety of space, including all the galaxies.

VEIN
A blood vessel that carries oxygen-poor blood from the tissues toward an animal's heart.

VENOM
A poisonous substance released by an animal (a venomous animal), such as a rattlesnake, in its bite or sting in order to immobilize or kill prey or enemies.

VERTEBRATE
An animal, such as a fish, amphibian, reptile, bird, or mammal, that has a backbone.

VISCOUS
Refers to a fluid that is sticky and thick, like glue or syrup.

WATER VAPOR
The invisible gas that forms when energized water molecules escape into the air.

ZOOPLANKTON
Animals that mainly drift in the water, although some may also swim actively.abdomen

Index

Acknowledgments

DK would like to thank:
Kieran Macdonald and Charlotte Webb for proofreading; Steven Carton for editorial assistance; Chris Bernstein and Jackie Brind for the index; Fran Vargo for additional picture research; Dave King for photography; KJA-artists.com for illustration; Richard Ferguson for paper engineering; Robert J. Lang for the origami animals; Simon Mumford for cartography; and the Zoology Library of the Natural History Museum, London, for access to the collection there.

The publisher would like to thank the following for their kind permission to reproduce their photographs:

Key: a–above; b–below/bottom; c–center; f–far; l–left; r–right; t–top

Jacket images Dorling Kindersley: Natural History Museum, London/Frank Greenaway, (ftr, butterfly); Weymouth Sea Life Centre/Frank Greenaway (cb, octopus); Whipsnade Zoo, Bedfordshire/Dave King (ra, baby rhinoceros). Dreamtime: Visceral Images/John J. Henderson (ftr, Arctic Fox). Fotolia: Dundanim (c, Planet Earth); Giuliano 2022 (tl, rhinoceros beetle). Rough Guides: Greg Ward (cr, rock formation)

4 Corbis: Yann Arthus-Bertrand (r); zefa/Frank Krahmer (bl). Landov: UPI Photo (tl). **5** Corbis: Yann Arthus-Bertrand (l); epa/Ed Oudenaarden (r). **8-9** Landov: UPI Photo. **10-11** NASA: JPL-Caltech. **12** Corbis: Denis Scott (r). NASA: JPL (cl) (cr). Science Photo Library: Californian Association for Research in Astronomy (l). **12-13** NASA: SOHO (c). **13** NASA: JPL (cl) (cr) (r); USGS (l). 12 NASA: JPL (bc) (br) (tr). Science Photo Library: Royal Observatory, Edinburgh/AAO (l). **14-15** Corbis: Jonathan Blair. **15** NASA: Hubble Space Telescope (tr). The Natural History Museum, London: (bc) (br). Science Photo Library: Manfred Kage (cr); Walter Pacholka/Astropics (tl). **16** Corbis: Bettmann (tc). NASA: (bl) (br). Science Photo Library: RIA Novosti (tl). **16-17** NASA. **17** Corbis. NASA: (bl) (bc) (1/c) (2/c) (3/c) (4/c). Science Photo Library: John Sanford (t). **18** iStockphoto.com: Claude Dagenais (bl); Snezana Negovanovic (b). Science Photo Library: Bonnier Publications/Henning Dalhoff (tr); Mark Garlick (bc). **18-19** iStockphoto.com: Branko Miokovic. **19** iStockphoto.com: Nicholas Belton (tr); Onur Döngel (ca); Alisa Foytik (br); Igor Terekhov (bl). Science Photo Library: Mark Garlick (c). **20** iStockphoto.com: Angelo Gilardelli (b/background); Linda Steward (b). NASA: (t). The Natural History Museum, London: (cr). Photolibrary: Animals Animals/Breck P. Kent (c). Science Photo Library: Joyce Photographics (cl). **21** DK Images: © Satellite Imagemap Copyright 1996-2003 Planetary Visions (tc). **23** iStockphoto.com: Jon Helgason (t). **25** Alamy Images: Lyroky (t). **26** Corbis: Gallo Images/Roger De La Harpe (bl); Didrik Johnck; NASA (cl). FLPA: Terry Whittaker (br). **27** Alamy Images: Ian Paterson (c). Photolibrary: Imagestate/Randa Bishop (cl); Stefan Mokrzecki (b). **28** James Jackson, Department of Earth Sciences, University of Cambridge: (t). Marli Miller/Department of Geological Sciences, University of Oregon: (br). Science Photo Library: W. K. Fletcher (cl). **28-29** Getty Images: AFP. **29** Alamy Images: Images of Africa Photobank/David Keith Jones (tl). FLPA: Imagebroker/Konrad Wothe (tr). Science Photo Library: Dr. Ken MacDonald (b). **30** Corbis: Comet/Lloyd Cluff (bl). Science Photo Library: Gary Hincks (cr). **30-31** iStockphoto.com: Beacon Hill Photography. **31** Corbis: George Hall (tr); Lucid Images/Mark Downey (tl); Sygma/Xinhua (br); Michael S. Yamashita (bl). **32** Alamy Images: Mark Lewis (t). DK Images: Andy Crawford/Donks Models - modelmaker (br). iStockphoto.com: Floortje (bl). Science Photo Library: US Geological Survey (cr). **32-33** iStockphoto.com: MBPhoto. **33** Alamy Images: Roger Coulam (crb); Zach Holmes (c). Getty Images: Science Faction/G. Brad Lewis (bc). NASA: Aster (t). **34** Alamy Images: INTERFOTO Pressebildagentur (cr). Getty Images: Photographer's Choice/Francesco Ruggeri (b); Stone/G. Brad Lewis (cl).

34-35 Science Photo Library: Stephen & Donna O'Meara. **35** Corbis: Comet/Gary Braasch (cl); NASA/Roger Ressmeyer (br); Sean Sexton Collection (cr); Sygma/Pierre Vauthey (c). **36** Alamy Images: David Muenker (bl); WoodyStock (tr). Corbis: Frans Lanting (br). **37** Alamy Images: James Kubrick (tr); David Muenker (tl). Corbis: Ralph White (br). Photolibrary: age fotostock/Juan Carlos Munoz (bl). **38-39** Corbis: zefa/Frank Krahmer. **40** Alamy Images: Jack Clark Collection/Phil Degginger (3). The Natural History Museum, London: (6). **41** Alamy Images: GC Minerals (7). Dreamstime.com: Lightprints (tl). The Natural History Museum, London: (8) (9). Science Photo Library: Mark. A. Schneider (10). **42** Alamy Images: WILDLIFE GmbH (10/t). Corbis: Visuals Unlimited (8/l). Dreamstime.com: Araminta (1/r); Egis (4/l); Elnur (9/b); Fordphotouk (5/b); Galdzer (2/r); Holligan78 (8/r); Mhryciw (3/l); Ptaxa (6/b). The Natural History Museum, London: (4/r). Science Photo Library: Jean-Claude Revy, ISM (1/l); Ben Johnson (2/l) (3/r) (6/t). **42-43** Alamy Images: Mira. **43** Corbis: Visuals Unlimited (11/l). Dreamstime.com: Bernjuer (7/l); Brent Hathaway (11/r). Science Photo Library: Arnold Fisher (7/r). **44-45** Alamy Images: Hemis/Emilio Suetone. **46** Alamy Images: David Muenker (bl). Photolibrary: Imagestate/Gavin Hellier (cr). **46-47** www.dinodia.com: (t). **47** Graeme Peacock, www.graeme-peacock.com: (b). Photolibrary: JTB Photo (tr). **48** Dreamstime.com: Milosluz (bc). FLPA: Mark Newman (br). Getty Images: Image Bank/Karin Slade (bl). Photolibrary: Jon Arnold Travel/James Montgomery (t). Science Photo Library: Fletcher & Baylis (cb). **49** Corbis: Visions of America/Joseph Sohm (cla). Dreamstime.com: Dannyphoto80 (br/goggles); Dingelstad (bl/gloves); Christopher Dodge (bc/tools). FLPA: Imagebroker/Thomas Lammeyer (cra). Getty Images: Image Bank/David Sanger (clb). Photolibrary: Robert Harding Travel/James Emmerson (tl). **50** Alamy Images: nagelestock.com (tl); Robert Harding Picture Library Ltd./Ellen Rooney (br). USGS: (bl). **50-51** ESA: (c). iStockphoto.com: Valeria Titova. **51** FLPA: David Hosking (bl). Photolibrary: Robert Harding Travel/Tony Waltham (tl). stevebloom.com: (tr). **52** Tony Waltham Geophotos: (1) (2) (3) (4) (5). **53** Tony Waltham Geophotos: (6) (7) (8). **54** Corbis: Annie Griffiths Belt (tl). iStockphoto.com: pixonaut (t/background). The Natural History Museum, London: (bl). Science Photo Library: Lawrence Lawry (crb). **55** Camera Press: Gamma/Benali Remi (3). Science Photo Library: Tom McHugh (6); MSF/Javier Trueba (4); Smithsonian Institute (5). **56** Alamy Images: Wild Places Photography/Chris Howes (bc). Corbis: Louie Psihoyos (bc/inset); Scott T. Smith (br). Science Photo Library: Martin Bond (bl). **56-57** FLPA: Nicholas & Sherry Lu Aldridge. **57** Dreamstime.com: Joe Gough (bc/inset); Pancaketom (t/inset). Science Photo Library: Martin Bond (bl) (br); W.K. Fletcher (bc). **58** DK Images: Colin Keates/courtesy of the Natural History Museum, London (br). iStockphoto.com: mikeuk (bl). **58-59** The Natural History Museum, London: (c). **59** Science Photo Library: Jean-Claude Revy, ISM (bl). **60** Alamy Images: Danita Delimont (ftl). Dreamstime.com: Christopher Ewing (bc). Science Photo Library: Simon Fraser (tr); Edward Kinsman (cr); Michael Szoenyi (tl). **60-61** DK Images/Colin Keates/courtesy of the Natural History Museum (c). **61** Dreamstime.com: Homestudiofoto (tl); Picturephoto (tr). Science Photo Library: Joyce Photographics (cr) (ca); Doug Martin (br). **62** Alamy Images: blickwinkel/Schmidbauer (cr); blickwinkel/Schmidbauer (3). Dreamstime.com: Dusty Cline (3/worms). iStockphoto.com: Marcin Pawinski (cr); Csaba Zsarnowszky (bl). Photolibrary: Animals Animals/Doug Wechsler (b); Animals Animals/Doug Wechsler (2). Tony Waltham Geophotos: (cl) (1). **63** iStockphoto.com: Richard Goerg (r). Photolibrary: OSF/Iain Sarjeant (cr); OSF/Iain Sarjeant (5). Tony Waltham Geophotos: (bl) (br) (4) (6). **64-65** Corbis: Yann Arthus-Bertrand. **66** iStockphoto.com: Donna Poole (cl). Science Photo Library: Biosym Technologies/Clive Freeman (tr) (cra) (crb); ESA/DLR/FU Berlin/G. Neukum (bl). **66-67** Dreamstime.com: Martin Green. **67** Alamy Images: bobo (cb); JLImages (bc). Science Photo Library: (tr); John Mead (tl); Claire Ting (br). **70** Alamy Images: Leslie Garland Picture Library/Alan Curtis (b). Getty Images: Photonica/Kai Wiechmann (t). Photolibrary: age fotostock/Andoni Canela (c).

71 Alamy Images: Guy Edwardes Photography (t); NASA (br). Corbis: Ashley Cooper (c). iStockphoto.com: techno. **72** NASA (tl). Corbis: Comet/Dale Spartas (cr); Roger Ressmeyer (bl). **72-73** Corbis: Atlantide Phototravel/ Stefano Amantini. **73** Corbis: Torleif Svensson (cl). naturepl.com: Jeremy Walker (cr). **74** FLPA: Mark Newman (4). iStockphoto.com: Ryan Kelly (bc). **74-75** Alamy Images: Jupiterimages/Ablestock (b). **75** Alamy Images: John C. Doornkamp (1); Volvox Inc/Tsuneo Nakamura (5). Corbis: Tom Bean (2). FLPA: Minden Pictures/Colin Monteath (6); Malcolm Schuyl (7). iStockphoto.com: Andy Hwang (t). Photolibrary: Robert Harding Travel/Dominic Harcourt Webster (3). **76** Alamy Images: Leslie Garland Picture Library/Vincent Lowe (1/inset); Chuck Pefley (1). Corbis: JAI/Jon Arnold (2/inset); zefa/Juergen Becker (2). Photolibrary: Index Stock Imagery/Eric Kamp (3). Science Photo Library: Kaj R. Svensson (3/inset). **77** Alamy Images: Jeremy Inglis (6/inset); Wolfgang Kaehler (5/inset); Stan Pritchard (4/inset). Corbis: William Whitehurst (4). Photolibrary: Index Stock Imagery/Martin Paul Ltd. Inc. (5); Index Stock Imagery/Eric Kamp (6). **78** Corbis: zefa/José Fuste Raga (1). FLPA: Minden Pictures/Jim Brandenburg (2). Photolibrary: Index Stock Imagery/Craig J. Brown (3). **78-79** Alamy Images: Arco Images GmbH (t); David Cheshire. **79** Alamy Images: Arco Images GmbH (6); Kuttig-Travel (5); Nicholas Pitt (4). **80** Alamy Images: Anthony Baker (tc). Corbis: Arne Hodalic (tr); George Steinmetz (tl). Dreamstime.com: Jorge Folha (bc). iStockphoto.com: Jacqueline Hunkele (br). **81** Alamy Images: Wild Places Photography/Chris Howes (br/inset). Corbis: Macduff Everton (tr); Hans Strand (tc). Getty Images: Dorling Kindersley/Stephen Oliver (br). iStockphoto.com: Tina Rencelj (bl). **82** Alamy Images: Steve Allen Travel Photography (2). Corbis: Roger Ressmeyer (1). National Geographic Stock: Medford Taylor (bl). **82-83** Corbis: Image Source. **83** Alamy Images: Design Pics Inc/Carson Ganci (5); Stephen Frink Collection/Masa Ushioda (3); Stock Connection Distribution/Tom Tracy (6). **84** Alamy Images: John Morgan (3). Corbis: Lawson Wood (2). iStockphoto.com: Ryan Burke (tr). Science Photo Library: Karsten Schneider (1). **84-85** iStockphoto.com: bravobravo (background). **85** Alamy Images: Peter L. Hardy (6); Buddy Mays (5); Peter Titmuss (4). Corbis: NASA/Roger Ressmeyer (7). iStockphoto.com: appleuzr (tl); Philip Barker (cb); Ryan Burke (bl); Brandon Laufenberg (br). **86** Corbis: Tiziana and Gianni Baldizzone (cr). Dreamstime.com: David Hughes (bl). iStockphoto.com: DSGpro (cb). Science Photo Library: NASA (cl). **86-87** Alamy Images: moodboard. **87** Alamy Images: blickwinkel/Laule (tc); BrazilPhotos.com/Patricia Belo (bc). Science Photo Library: Dr. Jeremy Burgess (bl). **88** Corbis: Brand X/The Stocktrek Corp (2); Ecoscene/Richard Glover (3). Science Photo Library: AGSTOCKUSA/Mike Boyatt (4); Claude Nuridsany & Marie Perennou (5). **89** Alamy Images: Pablo Paul (bl/inset). Dreamstime.com: Drx (br); Pyewackett (bl). Science Photo Library: Eurelios/Karim Agabi (cr). **90** Dreamstime.com: Marc Dietrich (ca) (crb); Barbara Helgason (tl); Beata Wojciechowska (clb). Photolibrary: Animals Animals/Stephen Ingram (crb/inset). Science Photo Library: Sally McCrae Kuyper (clb/inset) (ca/inset); Pekka Parviainen (tl/inset). **90-91** Dreamstime.com: Mark Emge (t); Sebastian Kaulitzki (b). iStockphoto.com: David H. Lewis (bc). **91** Dreamstime.com: Marc Dietrich (br); Barbara Helgason (tl) (c) (tr). Science Photo Library: Gustoimages (tl/inset); Stephen J. Krasemann (tr/inset); John Mead (br/inset); David Parker (c/inset). **92** Corbis: Tim Wright (br). Dreamstime.com: Jon Helgason (bl). Science Photo Library: Keith Kent (bl/inset); Jim Reed (tr). **92-93** Science Photo Library: Reed Timmer. **93** Corbis: epa/Skip Bolen (cl); Reuters/Mia Shanley (tr). Dreamstime.com: Ann piaia (br); Solarseven (cr). Science Photo Library: NOAA (tl). **94** Alamy Images: ICP-Pano (5). Corbis: Godong/Michel Gounot (3). FLPA: Minden Pictures/Michael & Patricia Fogden (2). iStockphoto.com: Jakub Semeniuk (bl). **94-95** iStockphoto.com: Luca di Filippo (bc); fotosav. **95** Alamy Images: Gavin Hellier (6); Robert Harding Picture Library Ltd./Tony Waltham (7). Corbis: Robert Harding World Imagery/John Henry Claude Wilson (4). iStockphoto.com: Robert Payne (br). Photolibrary: Picture Press/Thorsten Milse (8).

96-97 Corbis: Yann Arthus-Bertrand. **98** FLPA: Imagebroker/Alessandra Sarti (10); Minden Pictures/Norbert Wu (8). Science Photo Library: Alexis Rosenfeld (7); Peter Scoones (9). **98-99** Alamy Images: Marvin Dembinsky Photo Associates. **99** Science Photo Library: Michael Abbey (6); Christian Jegou Publiphoto Diffusion (11); Eye of Science (3); Steve Gschmeissner (5); Laboratory of Molecular Biology/Dr. A. Lesk (2); Friedrich Saurer (12); Claire Ting (4). **100** Alamy Images: Andrew Darrington (bc); Scenics & Science (c). Ardea: Jean Paul Ferrero (crb). FLPA: Ron Austing (bl); Imagebroker/Alessandra Sarti (clb). Photolibrary: Flirt Collection/Chase Swift (br). Science Photo Library: Jeff Lepore (cla); David Scharf (tr). **101** Alamy Images: Martin Harvey (b); Robert Harding Picture Library Ltd./Jack Jackson (br/inset b). Ardea: David Dixon (clb); Jean Michel Labat (br/inset crb); Duncan Usher (bl). Dreamstime.com: Sara Robinson (br). FLPA: Imagebroker/Andreas Rose (br/inset t); Panda Photo (br/inset cra). Science Photo Library: Dee Breger (tl); A.B. Dowsett (tr); Eurelios/Philippe Plailly (cra); Steve Gschmeissner (cla) (ca); Maximilian Stock Ltd. (tc). **102** Alamy Images: digitalunderwater.com (7); Stephen Frink Collection/Masa Ushioda (6). Ardea: Roy Glen (1); Valerie Taylor (4). Corbis: Visuals Unlimited (1/tl). Dreamstime.com: Eline Spek (r). FLPA: Gerard Lacz (3); D. P. Wilson (1/r). Science Photo Library: Steve Gschmeissner (1/bl); Andrew Syred (2). **10** Ardea: Pat Morris (15). Corbis: Reuters/NOAA (14). FLPA: Minden Pictures/Bruce Robison (11); Minden Pictures/Norbert Wu (12). naturepl.com: Doug Perrine (5); David Shale (9) (10) (13). **104** Ardea: Auscape/Dr. David Wachenfeld (bc) (crb); Francois Gohier (2); Jean Michel Labat (cra); Ken Lucas (cb); D. Parer & E. Parer-Cook (1); Gavin Parsons (tl) (bl) (br) (tr); Valerie Taylor (3). **105** Ardea: Kurt Amsler (bc) (crb); Auscape/Dr. David Wachenfeld (6); D. Parer & E. Parer-Cook (cr); Valerie Taylor (t) (bl) (br) (c). **106** Alamy Images: M. A. Battilana (bl); Konrad Zelazowski (cl). FLPA: David Hosking (cra). Photolibrary: OSF/Richard Packwood (crb). **106-107** FLPA: Minden Pictures/Tim Fitzharris. **107** Alamy Images: Mike Kipling Photography (cr). Ardea: B. Moose Peterson (br). Corbis: Momatiuk - Eastcott (clb). Dreamstime.com: Nathalie Speliers Ufermann (cla). Science Photo Library: Jim Edds (tr). **108** Alamy Images: Arco Images GmbH/F. Scholz; Redmond Durrell (tc). FLPA: David Hosking (bl); Jo Halpin Jones (cr); Minden Pictures/Pete Oxford (tl). **109** FLPA: Elliott Neep (br); Bob Gibbons; Tony Hamblin (tr); Minden Pictures/Gerry Ellis (tl); Minden Pictures/Katherine Feng (cb); Martin B. Withers (bl). **110** Corbis: zefa/Schmitz-Söhnigen (c). FLPA: David Hosking (br); Winfried Wisniewski. **110-111** iStockphoto.com: Patricia Hofmeester (c). **111** FLPA: Andrew Bailey (tr); Elliott Neep (cr); David Hosking (tl); Imagebroker/Alessandra Sarti (bl, x); Minden Pictures/Tui de Roy (br). **112** Alamy Images: Kevin Schafer (br). FLPA: S. & D. & K. Maslowski (bl); Minden Pictures/Tim Fitzharris; Minden Pictures/Tui de Roy (cl). **113** Alamy Images: Martin Harvey (cb); Jon Arnold Images Ltd./Jon Arnold (cr); Thomas Lehne. FLPA: Frans Lanting (tc); Minden Pictures/Michael & Patricia Fogden (bc); Ariadne Van Zandbergen (cl). **114-115** Corbis: epa/Ed Oudenaarden. **115** Corbis: Sygma/Herve Collart (1). FLPA: Minden Pictures/Pete Oxford (2). Photolibrary: Robin Smith (3). **116-117** Corbis: Denis Felix (b). **117** Alamy Images: Richard Cooke (4); Trip (6). Corbis: Louie Psihoyos (5). Dreamstime.com: Astroid (tr); Andrew Kazmierski (tl). iStockphoto.com: Dieter K. Henke (bc); studiovancaspel (br). **118** Corbis: Gary Braasch (1); H. David Seawell (2). Getty Images: Aurora/Robert Caputo (3/l). Photolibrary: Robert Harding Travel/Sybil Sassoon (4). **118-19** Corbis: Brand X/Andersen Ross. **119** Alamy Images: INSADCO Photography/Willfried Gredler (8); Trip (5). Photolibrary: Imagestate RM/Stephen New (7). Still Pictures: Argus/Peter Frischmuth (6). **120** Alamy Images: Martin Jenkinson (t); Transtock Inc/Steve Crise (b). Corbis: epa/Hapag-Lloyd (l); zefa/Roland Gerth (r). **120-121** Corbis: Justin Guariglia. **121** Alamy Images: David R. Frazier Photolibrary, Inc (tr). Corbis: Ron Chapple (tl); Comet/Jean-Pierre Lescourret (b). **122** Alamy Images: nagelestock.com (2). Corbis: Yann Arthus-Bertrand (6); Hemis/Hervé Hughes (1); Sergio Pitamitz (5). **122-123** Alamy Images: Jon Arnold Images Ltd./